THE DOBERMAN OWNERS'
MEDICAL MANUAL

THE DOBERMAN OWNERS' MEDICAL MANUAL

Robert M. Brown, D.V.M.

Breed Manual Publications
3370 Jackson Drive
Jackson, WI 53037

Copyright © 1986 by Robert M. Brown, D.V.M.
First Printing 1986
Printed in the United States of America
Cover Illustration by James J. J. Cabay
Typeset by Kruepke Printing, West Bend, Wisconsin
Printing by Miller Press, Racine, Wisconsin

LIBRARY of CONGRESS CATALOGING IN PUBLICATION DATA
Brown, Robert M. 1940
The Doberman Owners' Medical Manual
1, Dogs, 2, Veterinary Medicine. I Title
Library of Congress Catalog Card Number 86-71340
ISBN 0-938681-00-1 Softcover

Preface

The purpose of THE DOBERMAN OWNERS' MEDICAL MANUAL is to serve as a ready reference for medical information about the Doberman Pinscher. While 'THE MANUAL' is not designed as an owner's home remedy guide for 'DO-IT-YOURSELF' treatment, its contents will enhance your understanding of conditions which are common or are hereditary in the Doberman Pinscher. Medical information regarding conditions and situations which occur in other breeds of dogs is also included. This book will become a valuable reference guide to help you to understand a specific condition that your veterinarian might diagnose.

The 'MEDICAL MANUAL' is categorized by body systems: gastrointestinal, cardiopulmonary, skin and related structures, musculoskeletal, blood and blood forming organs, neurological, urogenital, endocrine (hormone), and sensory - eyes, ears and nose. Poisoning, nutritional management and supplementation, anesthesia and surgery are part of the reference section. Within each system, topics appear in alphabetical order with cross referencing to ease in finding them. All italicized words can be found in the index where they are listed by page numbers for more complete information in that particular area of interest.

As the author, I am actively soliciting from my readers any information related to Doberman specific conditions not mentioned in 'THE MANUAL.' Your comments on 'THE MANUAL' are welcomed by both the author and the publisher as we endeavor to improve and update the information in each edition. We are sure that you will enjoy using 'THE MANUAL.' Be sure to keep it in a readily accessible place for a quick reference.

RMB

TABLE OF CONTENTS

Chapter 1

ANESTHESIA AND SURGERY

AMERICAN COLLEGE OF VETERINARY SURGEONS (ACVS):

The ACVS, established in 1970, is recognized as an organization for the advancement of the art and science of veterinary surgery. Presently, the over 250 members are regarded as experts in veterinary surgery. While most members are employed by Veterinary Colleges, some members are employed in private practices and see surgery cases on a referral basis. Their level of surgical expertise is much greater than that of the general veterinary practitioner.

ANESTHESIA, DRUG COMBINATIONS AFFECTING:

The usage of some drugs just prior to or during surgical procedures may complicate recovery from anesthesia. If the antibiotic *chloramphenicol* is given to a dog under barbiturate anesthesia, a recovery period up to two times normal length will result. A good safety precaution is the removal of flea collars 24 to 48 hours before barbiturate anesthesia. Some of the *insecticides* impregnated in *flea collars* potentiate the activity of injectable anesthetics. The drug *epinephrine* should not be used with the inhalation anesthetic *halothane* because halothane predisposes the heart muscle to ventricular fibrillation resulting in *heart failure*. When in doubt, remove all drugs from the dog's body at least 24 hours before any anesthetic is given.

ANESTHESIA, DRUGS USED IN:

Acepromazine maleate (Promace®) is a tranquilizer commonly used prior to surgery. It is also used as a sole source to restrain a patient for procedures such as radiography and various lab tests or to facilitate the administration of certain medications. The quieting effects may last for 4 to 8 hours and cause the third eyelids to come across the eyes. Because acepromazine maleate is a *phenothiazine type tranquilizer*, it should never be used to treat *seizures* associated with *chlorinated hydrocarbon poisoning*.

Atropine sulfate is used in combination with preanesthetic drugs like *Innovar-Vet®* and *Rompun®* to dry up secretions and slow down the GI tract. It blocks the slowing of the heart affect and helps to block potential *laryngospasms* on *intubation* with an endotracheal catheter.

Benzocaine is a *topical anesthetic* used on mucous membranes.

Bio-tal® is an ultra-short-acting anesthetic. Refer to *Thiamylal sodium*.

Brevital® is a short-acting anesthetic. Refer to *Methohexital*.

Cetacaine® is a *topical anesthetic* combination of *benzocaine* and *tetracaine* that will deaden mucous membranes when applied by swab or spray. It 'freezes' the larynx to help prevent laryngospasms during endotracheal intubation. Refer to *INTUBATION, ENDOTRACHEAL* and *Tetracaine*.

Demerol® is a narcotic preanesthetic agent. Refer to *Meperidine*.

Diazepam (Valium®) is the drug of choice in controlling severe, violent, recurring *epileptic seizures*. Given intravenously, the procedure must be repeated because the effects wear off. Diazepam as an oral sedative in dogs is not very effective.

Enflurane (Ethrane®) is a volatile inhalant anesthetic agent. When combined with oxygen, *general anesthesia* is produced which requires special equipment for its use.

Ethrane® is a volatile *general anesthetic agent*. Refer to *Enflurane*.

Fentanyl: Refer to *Innovar-Vet®* .

Fluothane® is a volatile *general anesthetic agent.* Refer to *Halothane*.

Glycopyrrolate (Robinul-V®) is a preanesthetic agent used in place of atropine to reduce salivary and tracheal secretions. This drug should not be used in pregnant bitches.

Halothane (Fluothane®) is a commonly used *inhalant general anesthetic* agent. Special equipment carries it to the patient in oxygen. Halothane can sometimes cause *liver damage* or sensitize the heart muscle to *epinephrine*. While dogs recovery from halothane anesthesia is rapid, it produces poor muscle relaxation. Because of halothane's volatile nature, anesthesia can be induced with a face mask.

Innovar-Vet® , the trade name for a combination of the two drugs fentanyl and droperidol, is used to produce neuroleptanalgesia (depression and numbness to pain). Some breeds react adversely to the use of Innovar-Vet® (Silky Terriers, for instance). Others have a 24 to 36 hour recovery time from a low dose. Because there is little fetal depression, this drug is commonly used in *cesarean sections. Atropine* is routinely given with Innovar-Vet® to minimize the sting on intramuscular injection and to dry up secretions.

Ketamine hydrochloride (Vetalar® , **Ketaset®**) is a dissociative type of injectable anesthetic approved for use in humans and felines but not in canines. A small percentage of canine patients have *seizures* under the influence of this drug. Ketamine, however, is used on dogs with the owner's consent. Because it stimulates rather than depresses the cardiac system, it can be very valuable in old dogs. The drug is given either intramuscularly or intravenously at a much reduced dosage. Usual anesthetic monitoring signs cannot be used with this type of anesthesia because of its dissociative nature. Ketamine hydrochloride is ideal for short procedures and as restraint for radiography.

Ketaset® : Refer to *Ketamine hydrochloride.*

Lidocaine hydrochloride (Xylocaine®) is a drug used to 'freeze' an area of the body causing *local anesthesia*. The drug is injected under the skin or in the region of a nerve resulting in 45 to 60 minutes of anesthesia. Lidocaine is injected intravenously in the treatment of certain heart irregularities.

Meperidine (Demerol®) is a controlled substance used to numb the response to pain. By depressing the cardiopulmonary system, it greatly reduces the amount of *barbiturate anesthesia* needed to produce unconsciousness.

Methohexital (Brevital®) is a barbiturate classified as an ultra-short-acting anesthetic. This drug is given intravenously either alone or in combination. Barbiturates do not produce good *analgesia* (freedom from pain). The ultra-short anesthesia lasts from 5 to 15 minutes.

Methoxyflurane (Metofane®) is a volatile liquid that is used to produce anesthesia when combined with oxygen and then delivered through a special machine. The degree of muscle relaxation is excellent during anesthesia. This inhalant agent should not be used in dogs with kidney impairment where the surgery is expected to last over two hours. *Analgesia* after removal from the anesthetic machine may last up to 30 minutes. Recovery from methoxyflurane is longer than for *halothane*

Metofane® : Refer to *Methoxyflurane.*

Morphine hydrochloride is a controlled substance used as a preanesthetic agent, as a pain killer, or as an *emetic* (vomit inducer). This narcotic is not commonly used in modern veterinary practices because of the high potential for abuse. Better drugs are available for the same job.

Nitrous oxide, also known as *laughing gas* or *giggle gas,* is used with oxygen and some other volatile anesthetic agent to produce gaseous *general anesthesia*. Because this gas cannot produce deep anesthesia by itself, nitrous oxide is generally used with other anesthetics to allow a smaller amount of the volatile anesthesia to be used, especially in high risk patients. Because nitrous oxide is rapidly excreted by the lungs, a patient must be maintained on pure oxygen for 5 to 10 minutes following usage of nitrous oxide. Nitrous oxide should not be used in intestinal surgery.

Ophthaine® : Refer to *Proparacaine hydrochloride.*

Pentobarbital sodium (Nembutal®), a short-acting injectable anesthetic agent, has effects lasting 30 to 90 minutes. Deep anesthesia causes respiratory and cardiac depression and may also depress kidney function. Pentobarbital should not be used in *cesarean sections* because of extreme neonatal puppy depression. High concentrations of this drug are often used for euthanasia of dogs.

Promace® : Refer to *Acepromazine maleate.*

Proparacaine hydrochloride (Ophthaine®) is used as a *local anesthetic* by topical administration in either the nose, ear, or eye. When applied to the eye, proparacaine hydrochloride does not sting. Rapid onset of anesthetic activity will last approximately 15 minutes.

Robinul-V® : Refer to *Glycopyrrolate.*

Rompun® : Refer to *Xylazine.*

Surital® : Refer to *Thiamylal sodium.*

Tetracaine hydrochloride (Pontocaine®) is an anesthetic limited to topical usage in a powder for skin application or in a 0.5% solution for usage in the eye. On application, it stings the cornea of the eye without slowing down *corneal ulcer* healing.

Thiamylal sodium (Surital® , **Bio-tal®**) is an ultra-short, injectable *anesthetic* agent used for very short procedures such as radiography or wound suturing, or as an agent to allow *tracheal intubation.* Surgical anesthesia lasts from 5 to 15 minutes.

Xylazine (Rompun®) is a non-narcotic sedative and *analgesic* (pain killer) that produces good muscle relaxation creating a sleeplike state lasting 30 minutes. Rompun® , however, causes severe slowing of the heart rate and, rarely, a *heart block* with severe respiratory depression. *Atropine sulfate* is given with xylazine to reduce the side effects on the heart. Xylazine is commonly used as a preanesthetic and as a stimulus for measuring *growth hormone levels.* A dog under the influence of xylazine can still bite!

Xylocaine® : **Refer to** *Lidocaine hydrochloride.*

ANESTHESIA, TYPES OF:

Anesthesias are classified by the area of the body undergoing anesthesia. The four classes of anesthesia include local, regional, topical, and general.

Local anesthesia is the loss of feeling to one part of the body. A drug like *lidocaine hydrochloride* is injected into the area where a nerve supplying the specific part is located. The resulting anesthesia lasts from 45 to 60 minutes. The removal of small tumors and wound suturing is done under local anesthesia.

Regional anesthesia is the loss of sensation to a larger area of the body. The most common form is *epidural anesthesia* or 'spinal' anesthesia. In this procedure, a drug like *lidocaine* is injected into the epidural space around the spinal cord. The region behind (or below) the level of the anesthesia is then deadened. The procedure is useful in anal area surgeries and in *cesarean sections* since the newborn pups are not depressed. The thorax and head must be kept elevated above the level of the anesthesia injection. If the liquid anesthesia gravitates toward the head, respiratory paralysis and death will occur. This form of anesthesia requires a veterinarian who is very familiar with its usage and adept at the art of its administration.

Topical anesthesia is the loss of sensation to an area of the body surface - either skin, mucous membrane, eye, or ear. Drugs such a *Cetacaine®* , *tetracaine,* or *proparacaine* are applied directly to the body surface. Within a few minutes, superficial nerves have lost sensation. This anesthesia is useful in the treatment of some painful skin problems, in the control of pain associated with *corneal (eye) ulcers,* and in the removal of *foreign bodies from the external ear canal.*

General anesthesia or the loss of sensation or awareness to the entire body, is classified into *injectable anesthesia* and *inhalant anesthesia.* A single injectable anesthetic, usually a form of barbituric acid, may create an anesthetic state ranging from five minutes to several hours. These drugs are transformed and excreted through the liver and kidneys. Hence, normal liver and kidney activity is necessary for the safe use of these drugs for anesthesia. Inhalation anesthesia is accomplished by using a volatile liquid that easily forms a gas in the presence of oxygen which causes loss of sensation to the body when inhaled. The most common volatile anesthetic agents are *methoxyflurane* and *halothane. Two very new anesthetics that are not yet widely used in veterinary medicine are enflurane* and *isoflurane.* All of these agents have advantages and disadvantages. The veterinarian must decide how best to utilize them.

ANESTHESIA RECOVERY:

Anesthesia recovery is the process of recovering and the time involved in that recovery from general anesthesia. This period varies with the kind of anesthesia used, the size and age of the dog, and the individual idiosyncrasies of the patient. Some recoveries are rather violent or stormy. These are lessened by placing the dog in a recovery situation with as little stimuli as possible (e.g. a darkened, quiet environment). The period of freedom from pain on emergence from anesthesia also varies with the kind of anesthesia used and indirectly affects the recovery phase. Generally, injectable anesthetics like *thiamylal sodium* or *sodium pentobarbital* produce longer and more active anesthetic recovery periods than do gas anesthetics like *halothane* or *Metofane®* . Metofane® recovery will take longer than halothane recovery.

DRUG COMBINATIONS AFFECTING ANESTHESIA:
Refer to *ANESTHESIA, DRUG COMBINATIONS AFFECTING.*

DRUGS USED IN ANESTHESIA:
Refer to *ANESTHESIA, DRUGS USED IN.*

ENDOTRACHEAL INTUBATION:
Refer to *INTUBATION, ENDOTRACHEAL.*

GENERAL ANESTHESIA:
Refer to *ANESTHESIA, TYPES OF.*

HEALING, WOUND:

Wounds vary in characteristics as well as differing in location, shape, depth, and degree of infection. The healing process consists of four stages: 1) the inflammation stage, 2) the debridement stage, 3) the repair stage, and 4) the maturation stage. All of these stages overlap so no exact time period for each one exists. Simple tissues, such as connective tissue and fat, heal quickly. Complex tissues, such as the skin and nerves, take much longer. Most simple wounds reach the repair stage of healing by the third to the fifth day after the trauma. The healing phase goes on for over three weeks with the healing wound becoming stronger daily. By three weeks, the wound matures and gains strength. The complete healing process may take years.

Many factors affect wound healing. Wounds heal more slowly in older dogs. Obese dog tissues don't hold sutures well. *Anemia* and *anti-inflammatory drugs* (such as *aspirin*) slow healing. *Steroid* medication or steroids released by the body during stress also slow the healing process. Use of *vitamin A* and bandaging speed up healing. *Insulin* is very important to wound healing which explains why *diabetic dogs* have lengthened wound healing times. Factors such as temperature, movement of the wound, and radiation affect the rate of healing. Wounds heal side to side and not end to end so the length of a wound is not important.

INTUBATION, ENDOTRACHEAL:

When *inhalant anesthetics* are used for *general anesthesia,* an endotracheal tube is usually placed in the trachea (windpipe) to facilitate the administration of the anesthetic-oxygen mixture. The correct placement of a plastic, silicon, or rubber tube adds safety to the anesthetic procedure. Placement of the endotracheal tube insures that if the patient vomits, none will enter the respiratory system. The larynx (voice box) is kept open, eliminating the chance of a *laryngospasm* (muscular closing of the larynx cartilage not allowing air to enter the lungs). The endotracheal tube is necessary if surgery is to be done on the thorax (lungs or heart) because artificial respirations are maintained while the chest cavity is open. Occasionally after the endotracheal tube is removed, hoarseness or coughing is present for a few days but will clear up without medication as the irritation abates. Some endotracheal tubes have cuffs (balloons that blow up to improve the snug fit within the trachea) while others fit snugly without cuffs. The later type allows a small amount of anesthesia gas to escape around the tube when the dog exhales.

LOCAL ANESTHESIA:

Refer to *ANESTHESIA, TYPES OF.*

REGIONAL ANESTHESIA:

Refer to *ANESTHESIA, TYPES OF.*

SECOND OPINIONS PRIOR TO SURGERY:

Refer to *SURGERY, SECOND OPINIONS PRIOR TO.*

SEDATION:

Sedation is a mild degree of central nervous system depression in which the dog is awake but calm. Sedative drugs are used to treat thunderstorm fears and to help in the performance of procedures such as radiography, anal sac expression, or blood sample collection.

STERILE SURGERY:

Refer to *SURGERY, STERILE.*

STRESS, SURGICAL:

Stress is initiated by both the surgical procedure and the anesthetic used. The body tries to cope with a stressful situation by increasing the secretion of *adrenal corticosteroid hormones* and *epinephrine*. In small amounts, these chemical secretions protect the body from the stresses of the procedure. However, in individuals that do not have normal immune systems or normal adrenal gland function, surgical stress is a very serious problem.

SURGERY, SECOND OPINIONS PRIOR TO:

The use of second opinions is much more common today than ten years ago. You have a right to inquire about the expectations of the surgery, the complications anticipated, the cost of the procedure, and the number of similar procedures your veterinarian has done. While some emergencies do not lend themselves to seeking second opinions, many procedures can be postponed until a second opinion verifies that the procedure will benefit the patient. You do not need a second opinion in the following circumstances: when the procedure is routine, when you have a long standing relationship with the veterinarian and he has referred you to specialists in the past, when the situation is a life-threatening emergency, or when you completely trust the veterinarian.

SURGERY, STERILE:

Absolute sterile surgery eliminates the need for antibacterial agents after the body has been invaded. To achieve sterility, a number of precautions must be taken. All of the surgical instruments and a drape for the area of surgery must be sterilized. Sterilization is accomplished by using high temperature and high pressure as in an autoclave (similar to a pressure cooker), by using a gas like ethylene oxide, or by immersing instruments in an antibacterial solution. The surgical site must be properly prepared by removing the hair (when possible), scrubbing the area with a germicidal soap, and then saturating it with cotton soaked in a germicide like Betadine® or Nolvasan®. The surgeon must prepare for surgery by thoroughly scrubbing his arms and fingers with a germicidal soap, and by wearing a sterile cap, a mask, gloves, and a gown or scrub suit. Everything used in the surgical procedure must be sterile including the *suture* material and the absorbent gauze sponges. If the entire procedure is carried out with meticulous care, sterile surgery will result.

SURGICAL COMPLICATIONS:

Any time an operation is done and anesthesia of some kind is used, surgical complications are a possibility. Fortunately, new anesthetics, new surgical techniques, and skillful surgeons keep complications to a minimum. If the surgical patient is monitored using visual, tactile, or electrical equipment, complications from cardiac and respiratory depression are greatly lessened. In surgery where some question about cardiac function and output is present, routine use of intravenous fluids to maintain cardiovascular pressure greatly reduces *shock syndromes* both during and after the procedure. Strict asepsis (sterility) and judicious use of antibiotics before, during, and after some surgical procedures (e.g. bowel surgery, bone and joint surgery) greatly reduces post-surgical complications from infection. On rare occasions, post-surgical blood clots (emboli) enter the blood circulation causing fatal results several days after the completion of surgery. If the possibility of this kind of problem occurring is anticipated, drugs are used to reduce intravascular clotting. The opposite complication is post-operative hemorrhage from poor surgical technique, from a lack of hemostasis (blood clotting) due to the kind of tissue operated on, or from a clotting defect (e.g. *Von Willebrand's Disease* or *hypothyroidism).*

SURGICAL STRESS:

Refer to *STRESS, SURGICAL.*

SUTURES:

Suture material can be generally classified as absorbable or non-absorbable. The presence of body fluids and chemicals causes the suture material of the absorbable type to eventually break down and disappear. The non-absorbable suture is not chemically destroyed by the body and should last for an indefinite period. Different suture materials are necessary for different jobs. For instance, cat gut suture, which is absorbed, is useful in the tying of severed blood vessels, urogenital surgery, and gastrointestinal surgery. However, cat gut is not used on the skin or nerve tissue. The two common types of absorbable suture are surgical gut from the submucosal layer of sheep intestines, not cat, and polyglycolic acid, a synthetic absorbable type. Non-absorbable types of sutures are metals like stainless steel and tantalum, natural sutures like silk and cotton, and synthetic types like nylon-braided polyester fiber and polyethylene. Every suture type has its advantages and disadvantages. The veterinary surgeon will use the type and size best suited for the procedure.

TOPICAL ANESTHESIA:

Refer to *ANESTHESIA, TYPES OF.*

TRANQUILIZERS:

Tranquilizers alter the apprehensive disposition of animals that are being prepared for surgery or are exhibiting fear from the unknown, such as thunderstorms. Premedicating surgical patients insures a more stable induction to anesthesia and less excitatory phases on recovery from general anesthesia. The use of these drugs may also help in radiography procedures and sample collecting for lab procedures. In rare instances, patients react to the normal dose of tranquilizer by remaining under its influence for 48 to 72 hours. Extreme drug sensitivity should be mentioned to the veterinarian so that future dosage levels can be adjusted.

TYPES OF ANESTHESIA:

Refer to *ANESTHESIA, TYPES OF.*

WOUND HEALING:

Refer to *HEALING, WOUND.*

Chapter 2

BLOOD AND
BLOOD FORMING ORGANS

SPLEEN AND BONE MARROW

ANEMIA:

The lack of red blood cells is defined as a condition in which the blood is deficient either in hemoglobin within the red blood cell, or in the number of red blood cells, or both. Clinical signs associated with anemia are weakness, loss of consciousness, and pale tongue, gums and lips. The causes of anemia are many and varied, requiring some lab testing.Tests commonly done are hematocrit (packed cell volume), hemoglobin level, mean corpuscular volume (MCV), mean corpuscular hemoglobin (MCH), mean corpuscular hemoglobin concentration (MCHC), reticulocyte count, erythrocyte sedimentation rate (ESR), *bone marrow biopsy, kidney tests, thyroid test, fecal examination, autoimmune tests (Coombs, ANA, LE Prep)*, and serum iron.

The three general classes of anemia are: 1) less than normal red cell production in response to anemia, 2) increased red cell production but with fewer reaching the circulatory system (rare in dogs), and 3) anemia due to blood loss or blood cell destruction. Treatment for anemia is directed toward eliminating the underlying cause and replacing the lost red blood cells by transfusion when necessary. Hereditary hemolytic anemias have been found in several breeds of dogs. The Beagle and Basenji have an RBC deficiency of the pyruvate kinase enzyme. A shortened RBC life span occurs in the Alaskan Malamute with short-limbed dwarfism. To date, neither of these forms of anemia have been found in the Doberman.

BACTERICIDAL DEFECT IN DOBERMANS, NEUTROPHIL:

Refer to *NEUTROPHIL BACTERICIDAL DEFECT IN DOBERMANS.*

BIOPSY, BONE MARROW:

A bone marrow biopsy provides information on the kinds and numbers of cells present in the bone marrow. In dogs, the most common site for the biopsy of marrow material is the iliac crest (hip bone). Few dangers exist from performing a bone marrow biopsy. The knowledge gained, however, provides important information. Sedation and *local anesthetic* infiltration of the subcutis and the area around the bone is necessary. Sterile technique is important. Biopsies done at three or four day intervals allow the evaluation of the production and maturation of cell types.

BLEEDING DISORDERS:

Hemorrhage can result from a local lesion such as a damaged blood vessel that allows blood to escape. It can also be due to a defect in the general clotting mechanism in the body. Three functions are necessary for clotting to occur. In the vascular function, injury to a blood vessel causes a local reflex which contributes to the reduction of blood loss. During the platelet function, the platelet cell components within the bloodstream are attracted to the site of bleeding where they release their contents contributing to the plugging of the site in the blood vessel where blood is being lost. Coagulation is the stimulation of a systemic effect by which various factors associated with clotting are released and activated to help clotting occur. Defects in any of these three mechanisms lead to blood loss. The wide ranging causes of defects follow: lack of bone marrow activity, cancer involving the bone marrow, lack of platelets for various reasons, *vitamin deficiency*, severe *liver disease*, poisons like *warfarin*, and numerous inherited coagulation defects. In the Doberman Pinscher, *Von Willebrand's Disease (VWD)* is the most important *inherited coagulation disorder*.

Treatment of bleeding disorders involves identifying the source when possible and eliminating the cause. Usually whole blood transfusions are needed. Determining the blood type is necessary because multiple transfusions are required throughout the life of a dog with an inherited coagulation defect. If *vitamin K deficiencies* or *warfarin poisoning* are present, replacement of vitamin K orally or by injection is needed. If a life long coagulation defect is discovered, the dog's environment must be modified to minimize chances of accidental injury causing serious bleeding problems. The elimination of all parasites, both inside and out, is important. An owner must feed the dog a soft diet and eliminate bones that might irritate the gums or GI tract. Padded housing surrounded by a smooth wire fence is preferable. Being very careful with the use of modified live vaccines and drugs like aspirin or *Banamine*® which affect blood coagulation is also part of the life long management of this blood dyscrasia.

BLOOD TRANSFUSION:

Refer to *TRANSFUSION, BLOOD.*

BLOOD TYPES:

A number of blood types and factors that affect the compatibility of one dog's blood to another have been identified. Some confusion exists in the naming of these antigens. They have been assigned letter names A, B, C, etc. and numbers 1, 2, 3, etc. The A antigen is the most important in the alphabetical nomenclature. Canine erythrocyte antigens (CEA) 1, 2, and 7 are the most important in the numerical system. Eight numerical antigens have been identified. CEA-1 and CEA-2 are thought to be inherited through a dominant gene. The most desirable blood types for donor dogs are negative CEA-1, CEA-2, and CEA-7 or A negative typing.

BONE MARROW:

All of the cell types in the blood stream are produced by the bone marrow of most bones in the dog's body. The cell types include leukocytes (white blood cells), erythrocytes (red blood cells), and thrombocytes (platelets). Various stages in the development or maturation of these cell types are seen on smears of bone marrow material. Abnormalities observed in bone marrow cells give important answers about causes of anemia, leukemia, and some coagulation disorders.

BONE MARROW BIOPSY:

Refer to *BIOPSY, BONE MARROW*.

CHRISTMAS DISEASE:

Refer to *COAGULATION DISORDERS, INHERITED*.

COAGULATION DISORDERS, INHERITED:

Eight inherited coagulation disorders have been found in dogs. While other breeds are mentioned, all of these disorders can occur in the Doberman Pinscher. The most common disorder in all breeds is **Factor VIII Deficiency** *(hemophilia A* or *classic hemophilia)*. Because it is a sex-linked chromosome problem, males are primarily involved. However, females are asymptomatic carriers. Much variation is seen in the degree of hemorrhage. Normal numbers of blood platelets are present. **Factor IX Deficiency** *(hemophilia B* or *Christmas disease)*, is a rare sex-linked clotting disorder. The following breeds of dogs have been most frequently diagnosed with this disorder: Cairn Terriers, Black and Tan Coonhounds, St. Bernards, French Bulldogs, Old English Sheepdogs, Malamutes, and Cocker Spaniels. Only sophisticated laboratory tests will distinguish Christmas disease from classic hemophilia. A minor coagulation defect, **Factor VII Deficiency**, has been observed most frequently in Malamutes and Beagles. Coupled with the Factor VII bleeding disorder is an increased susceptibility to generalized *demodectic mange*. Cocker Spaniels also have a **Factor X Deficiency** that is inherited as an incomplete dominant gene. In young animals, bleeding exacerbations are usually more serious than in adults. **Deficiency of Factor XI** is most commonly found in Great Pyrenees and English Springer Spaniels. Again, an incomplete dominant gene is the means of genetic transmission. **Factor XII Deficiency** is of minor importance not having been observed in dogs. A **deficiency** of the **prothrombin complex** has been described in the Boxer breed and Fibrinogen deficiency occurs in the St. Bernard and Collie but both can occur in the Doberman.

The most important clotting defect in the Doberman Pinscher is **Von Willebrand's Disease (VWD)**. According to some estimates, as high as 65% of Dobermans are affected to some degree with this condition. The disease consists of a Factor VIII deficiency and also a platelet function defect. A protein necessary for normal platelet function and Factor VIII activity is missing from Dobermans affected by the disease. Von Willebrand's Disease is inherited as an autosomal incomplete dominant gene. While the incidence of the disease is high, the mortality rate is rather low. Bleeding tendencies lessen with age. Some Dobes have both *VWD* and *hypothyroidism*. Treating the hypothyroidism controls the VWD bleeding. However, since the ears are cropped at a young age, VWD is a significant disease. Screening for VWD is now possible. Specially prepared samples of plasma are frozen and sent to Dr. W. Jean Dodds, Division of Laboratories and Research, New York State Department of Health, Empire State Plaza, Albany, New York 12201. Recently, an in-office rapid screening test has been marketed. Information on the *Lyaglutin 8 V test* kit can be obtained from Hemochek Corporation, P.O. Box 15028, Gainesville, Florida 32604. In office VWD screening should be compared to results on VWD testing media developed by Dr. Dodds' laboratory. Since the disease diminishes with age, screening every Doberman puppy at 8 weeks of age or before ear cropping would be beneficial. Treatment of VWD involves replacing the defective blood elements (platelet function factor and Factor VIII). Transfusion with fresh-frozen plasma will replace the Factor VIII material The platelet function defect can be corrected temporarily by a transfusion of whole blood.

COMPLETE BLOOD COUNT (CBC):

A complete blood count is made from a small quantity of whole blood. The component parts of a CBC are packed cell volume (PCV or hematocrit), WBC (white blood cell count), and a differential cell determination. Blood cell counts determine the amount or number of red and white blood cells. The kind and morphology of white cells, platelets, and red cells are determined from the differential part of the count. The counts can be determined by hand or with the aid of a Coulter counter in a lab.

DEFICIENCY, FACTOR VIII:

Refer to *COAGULATION DISORDERS, INHERITED* and *VON WILLEBRAND'S DISEASE*.

FACTOR VIII DEFICIENCY:

Refer to *COAGULATION DISORDERS, INHERITED* and *VON WILLEBRAND'S DISEASE.*

HEMOPHILIA, CLASSIC:

Refer to *COAGULATION DISORDERS, INHERITED.*

LEUKOCYTOSIS:

Leukocytosis is an increase in the number of circulation white blood cells. The five different kinds of white blood cells are *neutrophils,* eosinophils, basophils, lymphocytes, and *monocytes.* The increase in white cell numbers may be in any one or all of the types. The knowledge of which kind of cell increased and its degree of change reveals important information.

LEUKOPENIA:

A decrease in the number of white blood cells in the blood is called leukopenia. The kind and amount of decrease provides important information in determining the cause and treatment of disease processes.

LYAGLUTIN 8 V TEST KIT:

Refer to *COAGULATION DISORDERS, INHERITED.*

NEUTROPHIL BACTERICIDAL DEFECT IN DOBERMANS:

Recently an immune deficiency related to the neutrophil type of white blood cell has been found in a family of Doberman Pinschers. Clinically, young puppies about three weeks of age developed chronic nasal infections and pneumonias. The immune globulin system was normal. The white blood cells also exhibited normal abilities to attract and engulf *Staphylococcus bacteria.* However, a serious deficiency was found in the ability of the white blood cells to kill the bacteria once in contact with it.

Bone marrow transplants might be helpful. Otherwise, the prognosis is guarded, at best, since long term bactericidal antibiotic therapy would be necessary to control the continual serious infections resulting from this defect. The neutrophil bactericidal disease may have a hereditary basis.

POISONING, WARFARIN:

The most common kind of acquired blood coagulation disorder is caused by warfarin poisoning. Warfarin and related compounds (diphacinone and pindone) are the active ingredients in most rodent poisons. The action mechanism of warfarin inhibits the production of *vitamin K* dependent factors (VII, II, X, IX) in the liver causing clotting defects. The signs of bleeding range from slight to severe, with fatal consequences. The antidote is vitamin

K and any other support needed to restore normal vascular function. Refer to WARFARIN POISONING in Chapter 9 for further discussion.

POLYCYTHEMIA:

Polycythemia, the opposite of anemia, is an increase in the number of red blood cells, either due to a physiological reaction or a disease process.

RED BLOOD CELLS (RBC):

The red blood cell carries oxygen in the form of hemoglobin to all of the body tissues. These cells are primarily produced in the *bone marrow* but are also produced in the *spleen* when enough red cells to provide for normal oxygen needs are not present. The stimulation of red blood cell production is influenced by a number of factors: *hormones (sex, thyroid, adrenal, pituitary)*, nutrition *(iron, copper, cobalt, vitamins)*, and the hormone erythropoietin that regulates the production of erythrocytes (RBC's).

SPLEEN:

The spleen is a large ductless organ, closely associated with the stomach, lying along the greater curvature of the stomach. The spleen may undergo torsion (twisting) during the acute *gastric dilatation (bloat) syndrome* further complicating the seriousness of that condition. Its function is most closely related to the destruction of red blood cells although it is able to store red blood cells and release them into the circulation during times of stress. The spleen is the primary site of the *hemangiosarcoma* tumor. Life without a spleen can be relatively normal. Reasons to remove a spleen surgically include tumors, trauma to the spleen, and gastric torsion (twisting) of the blood vessels to the spleen associated with *gastric torsion* or *volvulus*.

TESTS TO EVALUATE CLOTTING DEFECTS:

Since there are many and varied clotting defects, the utilization of rather sophisticated tests is necessary to elaborate the exact cause. A list of tests necessary to diagnose these defects includes partial thromboplastin time (PTT), activated partial thromboplastin time (APTT), activated coagulation time (ACT), Lee White clotting time, one-stage prothrombin time, PF3 release test, *autoimmune panel - Coombs Test, LE Prep, antinuclear antibody test (ANA)*, and the Von Willebrand's disease testing from Dr. Dodds' laboratory. The toenail cutting bleeding time test is the most valuable test in veterinary offices.

TRANSFUSION, BLOOD:

From time to time, canine blood transfusions are necessary. They should be considered when the red blood cell volume is greatly decreased. A decrease occurs rapidly in traumatic blood loss or gradually where blood cell production is not adequate. A transfusion is necessary when the total packed red blood cell volume is less than 15%. A single transfusion can be done without crossmatching or worry of a reaction. However, if the potential for multiple transfusions exists, the donor and recipient should be crossmatched to ensure compatibility.

At least eight different factors exist in a dog's blood. Three of these are important in transfusion reactions: Canine erythrocyte antigen or CEA-1, CEA-2, and to some degree CEA-7. Ideally, permanent canine blood donors should be CEA-1, CEA-2, and CEA-7 negative. Dogs can donate blood as frequently as every 7 to 10 days, but an interval of 14 to 21 days is probably best if long term collection is anticipated.

VITAMIN K DEFICIENCY:

Vitamin K is essential for proper clotting of the blood. Deficiencies in vitamin K occur in diseases that cause bile duct obstruction, in diseases where food is not absorbed properly, or in cases where antibiotics have been administered for long periods of time decreasing the bacterial synthesis of this vitamin. Vitamin K is necessary for the production of clotting Factors II, VII, IX, and X in the liver. Supplemental vitamin K is given orally three times daily or by injection as needed until bleeding tendencies cease. The most active form of vitamin K is K1 or phytonadione (Aquamephyton®). Response to this form of therapy is evident in 30 to 60 minutes as witnessed by a decrease in hemorrhage.

VON WILLEBRAND'S DISEASE (VWD):

Refer to COAGULATION DISORDERS, INHERITED.

WARFARIN POISONING:

Refer to POISONING, WARFARIN and Chapter 9, WARFARIN POISONING.

WHITE BLOOD CELL (WBC):

Five different cells circulating in the bloodstream are classified as white blood cells (leukocytes). All of these cells have specific functions in the body. Neutrophils function in the body defense system by engulfing and destroying foreign substances like bacteria. Eosinophils are increased in inflammatory reactions caused by parasitic infestations, allergies, and respiratory diseases. Basophils, very rare in circulating blood, play a role in the maintenance of the inflammatory reaction. Monocytes are important cells in the immune response and in engulfing those particles larger than the neutrophil is capable of handling. Increased numbers of monocytes are seen in systemic fungal infections and in chronic infections. Two types of lymphocytes, T and B cells, are very important in the development of immunity. These cells have diverse origins and promote different types of immunity.

Chapter 3

CARDIOPULMONARY SYSTEM

HEART, LUNGS, AND RELATED STRUCTURES

CANCER, LUNG:

Primary lung tumors, the tumors that occur originally in the lung, are uncommon in dogs. Most of these tumors are malignant with a poor prognosis. Dogs past the age of ten years are likely to be affected by this type of cancer. Two forms of *adenocarcinoma* are the most common lung cancers. *Squamous cell carcinoma* of the lung also occurs metastasizing (spreading) very early.

Malignant tumors of other parts of the body commonly spread to the lungs. These tumors may reach the lungs by the blood stream, through the lymph system, or from extension from adjacent tissue. Sometimes tumors from other parts of the body are removed many months before the lungs become involved, indicating that small tumor seeds were still present in the body after to removal.

The common clinical signs of both primary lung cancer and metastatic tumors are *coughing* and *dyspnea*. The severity of the signs depends on the magnitude of the tumor involvement and the degree of mechanical blockage of the airway. The diagnosis of these forms of lung disease is usually made with a physical diagnosis and chest radiographs.

The usual forms of cancer therapy, chemotherapy, surgery, and radiation therapy are generally not done in canine lung tumors. However, if some type of treatment is desired, ask your veterinarian to refer you to a veterinary oncologist for the available options. In most cases of lung cancer, the prognosis is grave.

CARDIOMYOPATHY, CONGESTIVE:

The cause of congestive cardiomyopathy is unknown. Cardiomyopathy results in severe degenerative changes in the heart muscle drastically

27

affecting the ability of the heart to pump blood through the body. A sudden severe congestive heart failure syndrome is first seen. Clinically, left, right, or generalized heart failure can be observed. The heart beats very rapidly, up to 250 times per minute. Sometimes, changes in the kidney and liver result from cardiomyopathy. In a number of these cases, the dog is also drastically *hypothyroid*. The significance of concurrent hypothyroidism is not yet clear.

Most commonly, congestive cardiomyopathy is found in young to middle-aged dogs of either sex. The prognosis is guarded to poor because the life expectancy varies from days to years. Treatment involves the use of low salt diets (Refer to *HEART DIET* and **H/D** in Chapter 8.), oral diuretics, and digoxin to slow the heart's electrical conduction. These patients should be carefully examined by your veterinarian every one to three months.

CARDIOMYOPATHY, DOBERMAN:

A very serious degenerative heart condition occurs in some lines of Doberman Pinschers. Most Dobes are between four and six years of age when affected by Doberman cardiomyopathy, with a high percentage being males. A very gradual onset produces the early signs as subtle as a slight cough or weight loss. As the degenerative heart condition progresses, the number of serious clinical signs increases. Fluid accumulation in the lungs and abdomen is common. Very rapid, irregular heart beats are heard. Periodic loss of consciousness may occur. Radiographs and *ECG* findings are consistent with a diagnosis of severe myocardial degeneration. Usually the left ventricle is the most severely affected area of the heart muscle area.

Treatment must be designed to meet the needs of the individual dog. Procainamide orally or *lidocaine* intravenously are used to control the irregular rapid heart beats. Affected Dobermans must be kept quiet, avoiding stress in any form. Sometimes oxygen therapy is necessary. Digoxin is used to increase myocardial efficiency, but overall, the prognosis is only fair to poor. Some dogs die within days while others may 'exist' for months. Presently the cause is not known.

CARDIOMYOPATHY, HYPERTROPHIC:

Hypertrophic cardiomyopathy affects the left ventricle of the heart and occasionally the muscular wall (septum) between the left and right ventricle. The size of the cardiac muscle increases greatly causing the heart muscle to become very inflexible. Many times no clinical signs are seen. The only indication may be sudden death, especially while the dog is under *general anesthesia*. Sometimes *ECG* tracings show abnormal thickening in the ventricular heart muscle. Radiographs also indicate cardiac enlargement especially involving the left side. Treatment can be attempted if the condition is diagnosed. However, use of digoxin is contraindicated and the prognosis is poor. Verapamil® and propranolol might help in treating the disease.

CAVAL SYNDROME:
Refer to *HEARTWORM DISEASE.*

CHEMODECTOMA:
Refer to *TUMOR, HEART BASE.*

COUGH:
A cough is a reflex action that originates somewhere in the respiratory system. A partial list of causes includes throat irritation, postnasal drip, swollen lymph nodes, tumors, tracheal (windpipe) collapse, infections of the windpipe (Refer to *TRACHEOBRONCHITIS.*), *heartworm disease*, and *pulmonary edema* from left side *heart failure.* A complete medical history is important when determining the exact cause of a cough. Unless the reason is as obvious as *kennel cough* or in toy breeds, *collapsed trachea*, certain tests are necessary to define the problem. A minimum data base would include a *heartworm test*, CBC, fecal exam, thoracic radiographs, and serum tests. If necessary, more extensive tests like bronchography, pulmonary function tests, *ECG*, and radioisotope lung scanning can be performed by specialists or at large hospital facilities.

DIPETALONEMA RECONDITUM:
Refer to *HEARTWORM DISEASE.*

DIROFILARIA IMMITIS:
Refer to *HEARTWORM DISEASE.*

DISCHARGE, NASAL:
Nasal discharge can involve one or both nostrils. The length of time the discharge has been present classifies it as either acute or chronic. The discharge appears either clear, cloudy, or bloody in nature. The color of the discharge helps to identify the cause. Clear discharges are caused by allergies, viral infections, or sometimes foreign particles like dust. Cloudy or pus discharges are a result of infections, foreign bodies in the nasal cavity, or cancer. Bloody nasal discharges *(epistaxis)* can be due to infection, trauma, *clotting disorders*, or some types of cancer.

Cancer or foreign bodies are more likely causes if the discharge is from only one nostril. A bilateral discharge can come from anywhere in the respiratory system. Causes include clotting disorders, generalized infections, and cancers involving both sides of the nasal septum.

To diagnose the cause of a nasal discharge, a number of tests can be performed including radiographs, a *complete blood count*, *chem-panel* series of tests, and even a clotting deficiency profile. Once the diagnosis is made, treatment can be directed toward eliminating the cause through surgery, antibiotics, or other means of therapy.

DYSPLASIA, MITRAL VALVE:

Mitral valve dysplasia is a common *congenital heart defect* seen most frequently in medium-sized to large-sized dogs, especially Great Danes and German Shepherds. The heart murmur is very loud on the lower left chest area. The upper left heart chamber (atrium), as well as the lower left chamber (ventricle) enlarge as the disease progresses. Treatment is symptomatic for progressive heart failure disease. The prognosis is fair to poor.

DYSPLASIA, TRICUSPID VALVE:

Predominantly, medium to giant breed males are affected by the *congenital heart disease*, tricuspid valve dysplasia. The right side of the heart (atrium and ventricle) becomes enlarged enabling a loud, harsh heart murmur to be heard about mid-thorax. Thoracic radiographs show enlargement of the right side of the heart. Electrocardiography will verify the involvement. Control of congenital heart failure is very difficult and not very effective.

DYSPNEA:

By definition, dyspnea is difficult or labored breathing. Determining in which phase breathing difficulty occurs - breathing in, breathing out, or all of the time - is important in identifying the cause. Some breeds of dogs with short noses (brachycephalic breeds) commonly have a difficult time with both *inspiration* (breathing in) and *expiration* (breathing out). In general, inspiratory dyspnea occurs in diseases of the upper respiratory system, with fluid accumulation in the thoracic cavity, or with blockage of the trachea. If the breathing difficulty is related to expiration, the problem may involve the lungs. The causes of both inspiratory and expiratory difficulty are chronic bronchitis, *heart disease*, and the presence of tumors in the chest cavity.

EDEMA, PULMONARY:

An accumulation of fluid in the lungs is called pulmonary edema. This fluid build up occurs in the lung tissue or in the terminal spaces of the respiratory apparatus. The common clinical signs include *dyspnea, cyanosis*, abnormal lung sounds, and *coughing*. Common causes of edema are insect bite hypersensitivity, drug hypersensitivity, chronic heart failure syndrome, trauma, water in lungs from drowning, and electrical shock.

Therapy for pulmonary edema includes cage rest, oxygen therapy, use of diuretics to remove interstitial fluid, appropriate cardiac therapy if the heart is involved, bronchodilation, and the insertion of an *endotracheal catheter* (tube). With early treatment, pulmonary edema has a good prognosis.

ENDOCARDITIS:

Endocarditis is a serious systemic disease caused by common bacteria that infect the valves of the heart or inner lining of the heart wall. The most common kinds of bacteria causing this condition are *Staphylococcus,Streptococcus* and several gram negative bacteria including *Escherichia coli* and *Pseudomonas aeruginosa*. Male dogs over four years of age that have had surgery, IV catheters, immunosuppressive (cortisone) therapy, or antibiotic therapy are predisposed to develop endocarditis. The clinical signs are many and diverse. Because the heart is involved, murmurs may be detected or the heart rate may increase. Occasionally signs of *congestive heart failure* are observed as the heart muscle fails and increases in size. A number of signs not related to the heart are seen with endocarditis including chills (fever), lameness, stiffness, depression, and *seizures*.

Proving the presence of bacteria that cause endocarditis is very difficult. Multiple cultures from blood or other body fluids are needed. *Echocardiography* is extremely useful in helping to define the problem. The equipment, however, is not readily available to most general veterinary practitioners so the testing must be done at university settings or veterinary cardiologist specialty practices.

Therapy includes very high doses of antibiotics for extended periods of time - at least 5 or 6 weeks. Generally, the initial antibiotics are given by injection or by a combination of injection and oral administration. Sometimes additional supportive therapy is needed. Frequent reexamination is necessary to insure complete elimination of the causative organism.

FLAIL CHEST:

The flail chest or flail segment is a life-threatening problem that results from a car accident or a large dog grabbing a small dog over the chest. In this condition, one or more ribs are broken in two or more places allowing the chest wall to move in and out to a great degree. On *inspiration*, the fractured segment of the chest is sucked in, creating trauma for the lungs and other thoracic structures. On *expiration*, the lungs are blown out against the fractured segment causing further trauma (hemorrhage and lacerations) to the lungs.

Clinically, a section of the chest wall moves in and out in an exaggerated manner. The dog experiences much pain and a great deal of *dyspnea*. Temporary stability may be gained by having the dog lie with the fractured ribs DOWN. Immediate veterinary attention is essential. The fracture must be stabilized and any lung contusions treated. Many times, *local anesthesia* is used to stabilize the fracture. However, if bone pins or wires are needed to mend the flail segment, *general anesthesia* is necessary in addition to positive ventilation from a respirator.

FUNGI, SYSTEMIC:

Blastomycosis, a systemic fungal disease caused by *Blastomyces dermatitis*, is naturally found in the eastern United States, especially the areas drained by river systems. While blastomycosis initially infects the lungs, other tissues of the skin, bones, and eyes are soon affected. Dogs cannot spread the disease to other dogs or humans. Thoracic radiographs, direct smears from skin, and serological tests for increased blastomycosis titer are used for diagnostic purposes. Currently, the only approved treatment is amphotericin B (Fungizone® , Solvay), a drug that can produce fatal kidney toxicity. Renal function must be constantly evaluated during the six to eight weeks necessary to treat the condition. If bones are involved, the length of treatment is considerably longer.

Recently, a new antifungal drug, ketoconazole (Nizoral® from Janssen Pharmaceutical), has shown promise in the treatment of systemic fungal diseases in dogs. When administered orally, the drug appears to be much less toxic than amphotericin B. Although no standard dosage has been established, a range of 10 to 30 mg. per kilogram three times daily for two to six months is effective. Because ketoconazole is rather expensive, a definitive diagnosis should be made before treatment is initiated.

Coccidioidomycosis *(Valley Fever)* is a systemic fungus disease that occurs in the southwest United States, Mexico, and Central America. Valley Fever is not a contagious disease. The fungus is found in dry, dusty soils, and dogs become infected when they dig in the dirt. Doberman Pinschers are more susceptible to this fungus than most other breeds.

Two clinical forms of the disease are recognized. While the *pulmonic form* causes coughing and respiratory distress, the *disseminated* form affects the bones and other body tissues. Dogs with the disseminated form have fevers up to 106º F., weight loss, decreased appetite, and diarrhea. Affected long bones commonly appear swollen or thickened. In rare cases, the neurological system is affected, causing *lack of coordination*. The prognosis is guarded to poor, depending on the degree of involvement and amount of dissemination to bone tissue. If treatment is attempted, the same drugs are used as for blastomycosis therapy.

Cryptococcosis is a systemic fungal disease that affects the lungs, central nervous system, skin, or eyes. This disease, which is not contagious, is spread by pigeon and other bird droppings. The clinical signs are extremely variable. Many times respiratory signs are not apparent. When the central nervous system and eyes are involved, more dramatic symptoms appear. The prognosis is guarded to poor depending on the degree of involvement. The use of amphotericin B or ketoconazole could be attempted.

Histoplasmosis is a noncontagious systemic fungus disease caused by Histoplasma capsulatum. It is common in the area of the United States east of the Mississippi River, especially several areas in the Ohio River Valley. The fungal spores are found in soil contaminated with bird droppings. The clinical forms of the disease which occur in dogs are the *pulmonary form* and the *intestinal form*. Dogs with advanced cases of this disease have high fevers, intractable diarrheas and a very emaciated appearance. Dogs also experience *dyspnea* and *coughing* with lung involvement. Again, the prognosis is guarded to poor. The treatment is similar to other systemic fungi.

Aspergillosis is a fungal disease that is classified with the other fungal diseases even though it is confined to the upper respiratory tract. A *mucus nasal discharge* out of one or both nostrils, sneezing, and snorting are signs associated with this condition. Very few dogs will show signs of systemic disease involvement such as loss of appetite and depression. No nasal swelling is apparent. The diagnosis of aspergillosis is made with a *fungal culture* (one week is necessary for growth) or a serological serum test. A specific serum test for aspergillosis can be run by the Clinical Immunology Laboratory, Veterinary Hospital of the University of Pennsylvania, 3850 Spruce Street, Philadelphia, PA 19104. A 3 ml. serum sample is required.

Four types of therapy are available for aspergillosis: 1) the use of povidone - iodine (1:10) or thiabendazole nasal flushes, 2) systemic therapy with thiabendazole 20 mg./kg./day or ketoconazole 10 mg./kg. daily for six weeks, 3) in dogs with nasal turbinate bone involvement, surgical debridement of the diseased bone and flushing with thiabendazole is necessary, and 4) use of immune stimulants. Appropriate therapy over a period of time may justify a fair to good prognosis.

HEART 'ATTACK':

Refer to *HEART FAILURE.*

HEART BASE TUMOR:

Refer to *TUMOR, HEART BASE.*

HEART BLOCK, AV:

The letters AV represent the atrial (upper) and ventricular (lower) compartments of the heart. Normally, electrical impulses are carried from the atria through the heart muscle walls down into the ventricle. In this manner, the heart muscle contracts and pumps blood. An AV heart block is a disruption of the electrical impulse so that rhythmic sequential contractions fail to occur some or all of the time.

Three degrees of AV heart blocks are recognized. *First degree blocks* occur in *cardiomyopathy* from the use of drugs like digitalis and *xylazine* and from the administration of the anticancer drug Adriamycin® . *Second degree heart blocks* occur normally in some dogs and also in cardiomyopathy patients. Complete blockages of the electrical impulses or *third degree heart blocks*, occur in cardiomyopathy, cancer, and infections involving the inner lining of the heart (Refer to *ENDOCARDITIS.*).

AV heart block is first treated with a drug like atropine. If the problem is not resolved or becomes chronic, the patient may be a candidate for a pacemaker to maintain proper cardiac electrical impulses.

HEART DISEASE, CONGENITAL:

Congenital heart disease is an abnormality of the heart present at birth. At least eight separate conditions are considered to be congenital in nature, a number of which are hereditary. All of these conditions have one thing in common, the presence of a *heart murmur*. However, many normal puppies, prior to reaching six months of age, may also have an *innocent* or *functional heart murmur*. Therefore, if a murmur is detected in a young dog, a veterinary cardiologist should examine the puppy thoroughly to determine whether the murmur is normal or abnormal. Most general veterinary practitioners do not possess the skills necessary to differentiate between these two conditions. The following is a list of eight congenital heart problems:

1) Atrial septal defect (ASD)	Rare
2) *Mitral Valve Dysplasia*	More males
3) *Patent Ductus Arteriosus* (PDA)	More females, hereditary
4) Pulmonic Stenosis	Hereditary
5) *Subaortic Stenosis*	Hereditary
6) *Tetralogy of Fallot*	Hereditary
7) *Tricuspid Valve Dysplasia*	More Males
8) *Ventricular Septal Defect* (VSD)	May correct itself by one year of age

HEART FAILURE:

Heart failure or *'heart attack'* may occur very suddenly or over a period of time. In the sudden cases, no cardinal signs of heart disease are seen. A disruption in the electrical impulses carried through the heart muscle is known as a *heart block* which causes heart failure. A sudden lack of blood to the arteries supplying the heart muscle is also a cause. Chronic heart failure is due to partial *heart blocks* or diminished heart muscle blood supply.

If heart failure occurs over a period of time, cardinal signs of heart disease such as coughing, fluid in the chest and/or abdomen, loss of consciousness, bluish tongue color, and easy fatigue are seen. Prompt treatment may delay death from chronic heart failure. In the case of *heartworm* disease, treatment can be curative.

HEART MURMUR:

A heart murmur is heard during a normally quiet period of the heart contraction cycle. These vibrations provide information about the cause and location of heart lesions. Heart murmurs are classified by the time that they occur in the cycle, by the loudness of the murmur, by the place on the chest wall where they are most plainly heard, and by their intensity.

Generally, heart murmurs are classified as *functional* and *organic*. *Functional murmurs* may or may not be due to a disease process. *Innocent murmurs* are classified as a functional type with no underlying disease cause. *Organic murmurs* are always due to some form of heart disease occurring continually during both the contraction phase and the relaxation phase of the cardiac cycle. The use of murmur determination is important in the identification of various cardiac diseases, especially in young animals where congenital heart problems are suspected.

HEART MURMUR, INNOCENT:

In a puppy less than six months of age, an innocent murmur is not an abnormal sound when all other associated tests (ECG and thoracic radiographs) are normal. The murmur is early-to-mid-systolic in the contraction cycle and very short in duration. These functional murmurs require no treatment or further diagnosis.

HEARTWORM DISEASE:

Canine heartworm disease is caused by a filarial worm called *Dirofilaria immitis.* One of several varieties of mosquitoes is necessary for completion of the heartworm life cycle. The heartworm has an affinity for the right side of the dog's cardiovascular system (posterior vena cava, right ventricle, and pulmonary artery). The earliest sign of heartworm disease is a soft cough. In advanced heartworm disease, the clinical signs are those of *heart failure.*

Caval syndrome is a very advanced form in which the accumulation of worms is so great that death occurs rapidly. Both male and female heartworms exist making the presence of their offspring (microfilaria) in the bloodstream the basis for many heartworm tests.

Another filarial worm affects dogs in the United States. *Dipetalonema reconditum* is a parasite that exists asymptomatically under the skin producing microfilaria offspring. Expert clinicians can microscopically differentiate between Dirofilaria and Dipetalonema microfilaria.

A condition called **Occult Heartworm Disease** exists in a small percentage of heartworm cases. In these cases, no circulating microfilaria exist. The diagnosis of this form of heartworm disease must be made from immunological blood tests, radiography, and clinical signs. A dog not receiving heartworm preventive medication, living in a region with a high incidence of heartworm disease, and showing signs of heartworm disease should undergo the above tests. Heartworm preventive drugs are given only after the dog has had a negative blood test, since the presence of both microfilaria and preventive medication in the blood stream causes a fatal shock-like syndrome. Currently, the only approved preventive medication is *diethylcarbamazine citrate (DEC).* However, within the next few years, the method of heartworm prevention will probably change drastically if ivermectin is approved by the government for use in dogs. A monthly preventive dose of ivermectin effectively controls heartworm reproduction. A toxic reaction, however, has been observed in collies and collie-type breeds given ivermectin.

Dogs that have heartworm infections are treated by intravenous injections of an *arsenical drug* which kills the adult worms. While drugs like levamisole have some effect on adult worms, the only highly effective approved treatment for adult heartworms is arsenic. After arsenical therapy, dogs must be kept very quiet for five to six weeks to minimize the chance of a fatal pulmonary embolism from elevated blood pressure depositing dying worms in the lungs.

After the first phase of therapy, a drug is given to remove microfilaria from the blood stream. Currently, Dizan® (dithiazanine iodide) is the only approved drug. However, ivermectin and levamisole are also used with the disclaimer that they are not approved for this purpose.

After two weekly heartworm tests indicate heartworm free status, preventive medication is started. In the northern United States, preventive medication is given from four weeks prior to the start of the mosquito season until six or eight weeks after the mosquito season ends. In more temperate areas, dogs are given the preventive medication all year long. Heartworm preventive medication does not cause reproductive infertility or tumor proliferation.

Because the heartworm carrying mosquito does not usually travel more than a mile from its breeding grounds, clusters of the disease occur in small areas. Thus, heartworm preventive medication becomes absolutely mandatory in some areas and less critical in others.

HERNIA, DIAPHRAGMATIC:

The diaphragm is a fibrous and muscular sheet of tissue that separates the abdomen and its organs from the chest cavity with its heart and lungs. Any abnormal opening in this tissue sheet is termed a diaphragmatic hernia. Two types of hernia exist - a congenital form which is present at birth and a traumatic form that occurs after an accident. Until misplaced organs penetrate the opening or openings in the diaphragm, no clinical signs are evident. Difficult breathing is the most common clinical sign. Many dogs with this condition prefer to sit or elevate their front quarters in some manner, apparently making breathing easier. A number of chemical changes occur in the body depending on the degree of respiratory embarrassment and the amount of shock present. An X-ray of the junction of the thorax and abdomen will show that the diaphragmatic line cannot be visualized in its entirety. Occasionally, a barium sulfate swallow is needed to outline GI organs in the thoracic cavity. Surgical correction by someone with a high level of surgical and anesthesia expertise is the only effective treatment.

KENNEL COUGH:

Refer to *TRACHEOBRONCHITIS*.

LUNG CANCER:

Refer to *CANCER, LUNG*.

MYOCARDITIS, PARVO INFECTION:

When parvovirus surfaced as a new disease in 1978, the virus affected not only the gastrointestinal tract and lymphatic tissue, but also the cardiac muscle cells of newborn puppies. Puppies infected with parvovirus before birth or shortly after parturition have an affinity for the development of viral myocarditis. Parvovirus affects rapidly growing cells from four to eight weeks of age making puppy heart muscle cells a perfect target.

Because of the overwhelming nature of this viral infection, clinical signs are frequently not seen. If present, signs include difficult breathing, depression, crying, and convulsive movements shortly before death. On veterinary examination, the affected pups have *tachycardia* (rapid heart beat), *heart murmurs*, an irregular heart beat, and pink fluid coming from the nose and mouth. Often entire litters are affected. An increased incidence of infection occurs in the Doberman Pinscher and Rottweiler breeds. After heart damage, the prognosis for long term survival is poor. Even those puppies that show temporary improvement have severely damaged heart muscle cells and ultimately undergo *congestive heart failure* by six months of age.

A definite diagnosis of parvovirus myocarditis is made on necropsy (autopsy) when the pathologist finds viral inclusion bodies in the nuclei of the involved heart muscle cells. Serum analysis then supports presumptive evidence that parvovirus has caused the problem. At the present time, affected puppies and those that survive the initial parvovirus attack are treated symptomatically.

OBSTRUCTION, TRACHEAL:

Tracheal obstruction can result from the accidental ingestion of a large foreign object like a rubber ball. The object becomes lodged at the tracheal-laryngeal junction, totally occluding the windpipe. The dog turns blue immediately and may panic as it attempts to breath. A person only has a five minute period at act before irreversible brain damage occurs. Rapid attempts to remove the ball or object through the mouth should be limited to three or four minutes. Insertion of a sharp object into the median tracheal membrane below the larynx and positioning an <u>empty</u> ball-point pen case into the trachea may allow enough air to be exchanged to reach proper veterinary care.

Another form of tracheal obstruction occurs if the cartilaginous rings that support the trachea collapse when the dog breathes in. While most severe in toy breeds and English Bulldogs, collapse can occur in any dog with weak cartilage.

In cases of severe respiratory disease, the trachea becomes completely plugged with thick mucus causing extreme *dyspnea*. The best means of removing thick occluding secretions is with aerosol therapy and the use of expectorants.

OCCULT HEARTWORM DISEASE:
Refer to HEARTWORM DISEASE.

PACEMAKER:

Pacemakers can add years to the lives of dogs with certain heart problems. Some of the heart problems managed by pacemakers include various types of *heart blocks*, sinus bradycardia, bradycardia-tachycardia syndrome, and sinus arrest.

Pacemakers have been used in dogs for over twenty years but have not been realistic due to the high cost of the equipment. However, some companies (Medtronic Corporation of Minneapolis, MN) and some foundations now make old or obsolete equipment available for dog usage. Costs of equipment vary with the complexity of the unit. Those designated VOO and AOO are not programmable making them less expensive than the programmable varieties designated DVI and DDD. At this time, probably only twenty to thirty pacemaker implant operations are done yearly in dogs. Many of these dogs are not good surgical risks so care must be taken with the anesthesia.

Almost as important as the surgical technique is the follow-up care. Weekly checks for the first month are necessary, then monthly exams for six months should be anticipated. The pacemaker battery should last from 16 to 24 months after which a replacement is necessary.

PATENT DUCTUS ARTERIOSIS (PDA):

The most common *congenital heart defect* is a patent ductus arteriosis (PDA). Found to be hereditary in some breeds of dogs, PDA is twice as common in females as in males. A very characteristic 'machinery' murmur is audible about halfway up the left side of the thorax, making an accurate diagnosis possible with the stethoscope. Should doubt remain, the use of radiographs, ECG's, and echocardiography result in a definitive diagnosis. A skilled surgeon with proper anesthesia and ventilator equipment is needed to correct PDA. The prognosis after surgery is good to excellent.

PNEUMONIA:

Pneumonia, by definition, is inflammation of the lungs. Both infectious and noninfectious causes occur. The clinical signs are fever, *coughing, dyspnea*, and sometimes spitting up blood.

Infectious pneumonia is caused by bacteria like *Pseudomonas, Bordetella, Klebsiella, Staphylococcus,* and *Streptococcus*, as well as systemic fungi like *blastomycosis, histoplasmosis,* and *coccidioidomycosis*, or by the protozoan parasite *Toxoplasma gondii.* Causes of noninfectious pneumonias are allergy, aspiration of vomitus following surgery, and certain swallowing problems.

The exact causes of pneumonia should be ascertained so that proper therapy can be initiated. Aggressive antibacterial therapy is necessary to eliminate bacterial pneumonia before it has done permanent damage to the lungs. Blood counts, serum titers, radiography, and *bacterial* and *fungal cultures* are necessary to determine the cause of pneumonia. Early diagnosis improves the prognosis. With the exception of *aspiration pneumonia*, most have a good prognosis when proper, aggressive therapy is used.

PNEUMOTHORAX:

Air in the pleural cavity is called pneumothorax. Classification is made by where the air came from and the cause of the injury. For example, air may enter the pleural cavity in the chest from a penetrating external wound or from a tear internally in the tissues associated with the lungs. Pneumothorax also occurs as a result of rib fractures.

The major clinical sign associated with pneumothorax is *dyspnea* with fewer than normal breathing sounds. Radiographs, especially standing side views, will confirm the tentative diagnosis. The primary goal in treating pneumothorax is to reestablish negative pressure in the thoracic cavity. Since pneumothorax occurs frequently after thoracic trauma, other subtle traumatic changes may exist. Some of these changes are a ruptured esophagus and cardiac tamponade, a condition where the sac around the heart fills with fluid inhibiting heart function.

PULMONARY EDEMA:

Refer to *EDEMA, PULMONARY.*

RESPIRATORY DIFFICULTY, SIGNS OF:

A number of signs of respiratory difficulty can be observed without any special equipment. Valuable information can be gathered for the veterinary clinician as he evaluates the case. In all cases of respiratory difficulty, the dog shows signs of *dyspnea*.

Examination of the mucous membranes, gums, and tongue may show *cyanosis*, a bluish discoloration to the membranes caused by a lack of oxygen in the blood. An obstruction, *pulmonary edema* where fluid has replaced oxygen in the lung air spaces, or a collapsed lung are causes. The pale color of the membranes can be caused by severe anemia, shock, or a decreased heart output. In some instances, the membranes take on a brownish cast from the presence of *methemoglobin* in the blood which prevents oxygen from reaching the body tissues. Some kinds of poisons and drug intoxications can cause this phenomena.

A patient in great respiratory difficulty shows an extreme level of anxiety with a tendency to panic on handling or manipulation. One should watch the pattern of breathing to determine where the greatest difficulty arises - on *inspiration* (breathing in) or on *expiration* (breathing out).

A dog's body temperature may give a clue to the cause of respiratory difficulty. In cases of overheating, the respiratory rate is extremely rapid and inefficient. Extreme shock and low body temperatures also cause respiratory depression. Normal respiratory rates are between 8 and 25 breaths per minute.

SNEEZE:

The reflex action of sneezing occurs because of irritation to the fine hairs (cilia) that line the nasal passage. Nasal discharge is often present in conjunction with sneezing. The causes of sneezing include infection, *allergies,* foreign bodies, *parasites*, tumors, and *osteomyelitis.* Radiographs, blood tests, and cultures are necessary to determine the cause. Treatment is directed at eliminating the irritation.

SUBAORTIC STENOSIS:

Subaortic stenosis is a serious *congenital heart defect* hereditary in breeds like the Golden Retriever and Newfoundland. Other working and sporting dogs are also predisposed. After a dog reaches six months of age, one might see radiographic evidence of a dilated aorta. The *electrocardiogram* pattern is normal or only slightly altered. A relatively loud *heart murmur* is present about halfway up the thorax on both the left and right sides. Subaortic stenosis has no treatment other than what would be attempted for left side heart failure. Because very few clinical signs exist, subaortic stenosis is most commonly diagnosed on autopsy after a young dog has collapsed and died suddenly.

TETRALOGY OF FALLOT:

The tetralogy of Fallot is a hereditary *congenital heart disease* found in several breeds of dogs, especially Keeshonden and English Bulldogs. A loud systolic *heart murmur* is detected. Actually, four cardiovascular abnormalities are found on autopsy. Radiographs show right heart enlargement and malposition of the aorta. *Electrocardiogram* patterns indicate right ventricle enlargement. Affected dogs fatigue easily, 'turn blue,' and have a rapid heart beat. No form of treatment is effective although the use of beta blockers like Propranolol HCl (Inderal® from Ayerst Labs) might extend the life of these affected dogs.

TRACHEOBRONCHITIS (KENNEL COUGH):

Infectious tracheobronchitis *(kennel cough)* is a highly contagious respiratory disease of dogs caused by a combination of etiological agents. While *mycoplasma* and a number of viruses and bacteria have been incriminated in the disease, the most important etiological agents are *canine parainfluenza virus (CP1), CAV-2 virus,* and the bacteria Bordetella bronchiseptica.

These agents are used in various vaccines against the disease. The bacterial agent has been utilized as an intranasal vaccine. Since maternal antibodies do not interfere, intranasal administration of this vaccine may be done as early as two weeks of age. Yearly booster inoculations are recommended. Conventional vaccination with other 'kennel cough' vaccines is generally undertaken on the same schedule as distemper and hepatitis. While yearly booster vaccinations are adequate with distemper and hepatitis, the duration of parainfluenza vaccine immunity is only six months.

Dogs exposed to others in kennels, dog shows, and field trials are at higher risk than those that are not exposed to outside environmental challenges. Transmission occurs through respiratory droplets or aerosol spread from the cough of an infected dog. The cough is a very dry, hacking cough that can be elicited by gentle pressure on the trachea just beneath the larynx.

Treatment with a wide spectrum antibiotic like *chloramphenicol* for ten days is effective. The use of antitussives minimizes the cough irritation to the tracheal and laryngeal membranes. Sometimes butter or honey are used to coat the pharyngeal membranes as an aid in soothing the throat. Chronic tracheobronchitis cases lead to pneumonia. Because kennel cough is a very contagious disease, dogs with coughs should be well segregated from healthy animals.

TUMOR, HEART BASE:

A tumor that invades the base of the heart near the aorta is called a **chemodectoma**. Heart base tumors are found almost exclusively in short nosed breeds of dogs. Unfortunately, surgical removal is not realistic since the tumor attacks vital structures. Therefore, treatment is symptomatic as signs of heart failure develop. Chemotherapy does not help, therefore the prognosis is poor.

VALLEY FEVER:

Refer to *FUNGI, SYSTEMIC.*

VENTRICULAR SEPTAL DEFECT (VSD):

Ventricular septal defect is caused by the failure of normal fetal shunts (holes) in the wall of the heart to close at birth. Clinically, harsh heart murmur sounds are present well forward on the thoracic wall, especially on the right side. Small septal defects close over during the first year of life. Thoracic radiographs show enlarged ventricles. Large openings in the wall of the heart record on the *electrocardiogram* as left ventricular enlargements. An adept cardiac surgeon with the proper equipment can repair ventricular septal defects.

Chapter 4

ENDOCRINE SYSTEM

HORMONES - ADRENAL GLANDS, THYROID GLAND, PITUITARY GLAND, SEX HORMONES

ACROMEGALY:

A chronic hormone condition produced by an excess of growth hormone, acromegaly causes an overgrowth of bony structures and soft tissue in adult dogs. Affected dogs show signs of fatigue, increased frequency of urination and water consumption, increased space between teeth, and a tendency toward development of *diabetes*. When occurring in an unspayed bitch, an *ovariohysterectomy* will help resolve the condition.

ACTH-DEXAMETHASONE SUPPRESSION TEST:

This timed test is the most common test done to determine the origin of high resting cortisol (cortisone) levels in the body. In normal animals, *ACTH* is a hormone that should stimulate the adrenal gland to produce cortisone. When given in a measured amount, a predictable rise of cortisone in the blood should occur. Two hours after *dexamethasone* (a potent form of cortisone) is given, ACTH gel administration should have a predictable depressing affect on ACTH production in the pituitary gland. By measuring the change in the blood cortisol level, the veterinarian learns if a suspected cortisone production problem is in the pituitary gland, the adrenal gland, or is idiopathic.

ADDISON'S DISEASE (HYPOADRENOCORTICISM):

Addison's disease (*hypoadrenocorticism*) is a disease in which the adrenal gland is not producing adequate amounts of adrenal hormones. *Glucocorticoids*, *mineralocorticoids*, or both are deficient. When the causes of Addison's disease are classified as primary, over 90% of the adrenal gland has been destroyed or replaced with tumor cells. Causes of primary hypoadrenocorticism include *autoimmune destruction of adrenal tissue*, tumors of the adrenal gland, granulomatous lesions of the adrenal gland, hemorrhage in the adrenal gland as a result of certain diseases (*distemper, pyometra*), vascular clots in adrenal blood vessels, and Lysodren® administration.

A secondary form occurs when the ACTH hormone from the pituitary gland fails to stimulate the adrenal gland to produce corticosteroid hormones. The most common cause of secondary hypoadrenocorticism is prolonged administration of cortisone by pill or injection. This indirectly causes atrophy (shrinkage) of the adrenal gland. To a small degree, tumors involving the pituitary gland may decrease ACTH production.

The clinical signs of Addison's disease include depression, lack of appetite, vomiting and/or diarrhea with abdominal pain, and hypotensive shock with weakness and shivering. Primary Addison's disease causes depression of serum sodium levels and elevation of serum potassium levels. Other serum chemical abnormalities exist to varying degrees. Kidney function is diminished due to decreased blood flow through the kidneys. A very slow heart beat, a weak pulse, and normal to subnormal temperatures are observed. The most valuable lab test is a *CBC* (complete blood count) in which the *eosinophil cells* occur in higher than normal numbers. Signs of Addison's disease are related to stressful incidents like boarding, showing, training, and surgery.

Treatment is designed to bring the serum electrolytes (*sodium* and *potassium*) into balance, reverse the shock signs, reestablish kidney function, and then replace the *mineralocorticoids* and *glucocorticoids* that are not being made in the adrenal gland. Cortisone replacement is accomplished in one of three ways: 1) give fludrocortisone (Florinef®) once daily for life, 2) give desoxycorticosterone pivalate (Doca®) ("Percorten® acetate") intramuscularly every 25 to 30 days, or 3) have a desoxycorticosterone pivalate (Doca®) ('Percorten® pellet') implanted every 8 to 12 months. These methods will control the condition after the kidney and other body needs have become normal. In addition, salt should be added daily to the diet. If periods of stress are anticipated, the additional administration of glucocorticoids is necessary to prevent exacerbations of the disease.

ALDOSTERONE:

Refer to *HORMONES.*

ALOPECIA, BILATERAL SYMMETRICAL:

Equal hair loss on both the left and right sides of the body is termed bilateral symmetrical alopecia. Hair loss in this pattern is characteristic of hormone disorders.

ANESTRUS:

Anestrus is the time in a bitch's heat cycle when the body is making a transition into the next cycle. During this 1 to 8 month period, sex hormones are at a low level in the bloodstream.

AZIUM® (DEXAMETHASONE):

Refer to *CORTISONE.*

BETAMETHASONE:

Refer to *CORTISONE.*

BETASONE® (BETAMETHASONE):

Refer to *CORTISONE.*

CALCINOSIS CUTIS:

Calcinosis cutis is a rare skin condition resulting from calcium salts in the skin which form solid mineral deposits. This occurs most frequently as a result of hyperglucocorticoidism (too much cortisone) from whatever source. Most cases are seen in large breeds, especially German Shepherds. If the excess levels of cortisone are removed from the body, the calcinosis cutis resolves itself in 2 to 6 months. Surgical excision is the treatment of choice if calcinosis cutis is present without excess cortisone.

CHEQUE® (MIBOLERONE):

Refer to *DRUGS, HEAT ALTERING.*

CORTISONE:

The cortisone secreted by the adrenal glands is very important in the homeostasis of all body tissues. The secretion of two *glucocorticoids*, cortisol and corticosterone, is regulated by two other hormones, ACTH and corticotropin-releasing factor (CRF). These hormones are produced by the anterior portion of the pituitary gland and the hypothalamus, an organ in the base of the brain. The amount of natural glucocorticoid activity is highest during the hours of greatest activity and stress. *Diurnal rhythm* is important in the principle of medicating with glucocorticoids. Less suppression of the adrenal gland occurs if cortisone medications are given during hours of greatest adrenal activity. In the dog, these are the morning hours.

Glucocorticoids have a profound effect on the metabolism of *glucose*, *protein*, and *lipids* (fats). Increasing glucose levels in the blood stream are formed from non-sugar sources. Glucocorticoid activity is anti-insulin in nature since tissue utilization of sugar (glucose) is decreased resulting in more sugar being stored in the liver. Regulation of diabetic dogs who also receive glucocorticoid drugs is thus more difficult. Glucocorticoids break down proteins causing muscles to atrophy and skin to become thinner. Fat metabolism is affected with fat abnormally accumulating in the liver. Virtually all of the body organs and cells are affected by glucocorticoids. A partial list of body tissues and the effect cortisone has on them follows:

BONE - antagonizes *Vitamin D* presence and accelerates bone resorption

CARDIOVASCULAR SYSTEM - increases blood pressure

CENTRAL NERVOUS SYSTEM - euphoria and behavioral changes result and *seizure* threshold lowers

GASTROINTESTINAL TRACT - decreases absorption of *iron* and *calcium* and increases absorption of *fats*

HEMATOPOIETIC SYSTEM (BLOOD CELL SYSTEM) - shrinks lymphoid tissues, decreases numbers of eosinophils, lymphocytes, and monocytes in the blood stream, decreases clotting time, increases number of *RBC's, platelets,* and *neutrophils* in the blood stream

KIDNEYS - increases water and salt retention, increases calcium and potassium excretion

REPRODUCTIVE SYSTEM - may induce birth in later pregnancy; in early pregnancy causes *birth defects*

SKELETAL MUSCLE - causes weakness and atrophy when given in excess

SKIN - excess causes thinning of skin

Because of the listed effects on most organ systems in the body, prolonged or excessive use of glucocorticoids contributes to the following degenerative changes in the dog:

1) *CENTRAL NERVOUS SYSTEM*: nervousness, mood alteration

2) *DERMATOLOGIC: calcinosis cutis,* allergy to cortisone

3) *DIGESTIVE SYSTEM*: *pancreatitis*, GI tract ulceration, and *liver disease*

4) *ENDOCRINE (HORMONE): Cushing's Disease (hyperadrenocorticism), diabetes mellitus*

5) *METABOLIC EFFECTS:* general tissue breakdown, increases blood sugar, and growth retardation occurs

6) *MUSCULOSKELETAL SYSTEM:* muscle wasting and weakness, osteoporosis

7) *OCULAR SYSTEM: cataract* development

Over the years in the search for a better glucocorticoid drug, many different kinds of steroids have become available. All have certain assets and drawbacks. The following list includes some of the most common glucocorticoids with their relative anti-inflammatory potency and duration of action. Trade names appear in parentheses.

GLUCOCORTICOIDS	POTENCY	DURATION OF ACTION
SHORT-ACTING:		
Hydrocortisone	1	less than 12 hours
INTERMEDIATE-ACTING:		
Prednisone	3.5	12 to 36 hours
Prednisolone	4	12 to 36 hours
Methylprednisolone (Medrol®)	5	12 to 36 hours
Triamcinolone (Vetalog®)	5	12 to 36 hours
Flumethasone (Flucort®)	7.8	12 to 36 hours
LONG ACTING:		
Betamethasone (Betasone®)	25	over 48 hours
Dexamethasone (Azium®)	30	over 48 hours

The longer the duration of action, the greater the chance of suppressing normal adrenal gland function. One must trade off the increased anti-inflammatory potency for the longer or shorter duration of action. Glucocorticoid drugs can be administered orally, intravenously, intramuscularly, and subcutaneously. If the cortisone therapy is anticipated to last for some time or is at a high dosage, ALTERNATE DAY THERAPY should be attempted. In alternate day treatment, the calculated dose is doubled and given every other day in the morning, decreasing the chance of adrenal gland suppression.

If a glucocorticoid drug is used longer than one week, the drug dosage must be lessened daily before discontinuing the medication completely. For example, if your Doberman Pinscher was receiving 10 mg. of prednisolone once daily over a period of weeks, reduce the daily dosage to 5 mg. for 7 days, then cut that dosage to 2.5 mg. for 14 days, going to the alternate day administration of 2.5 mg. for 29 additional days before ceasing usage of the drug. The longer the dog has been on glucocorticoids, the longer the tapering period should continue before stopping completely.

CUSHING'S DISEASE (HYPERADRENOCORTICISM):

Cushing's Syndrome or Cushing's Disease is an increase in the amount of corticosteroids in the body. Cushing's can be caused by the secretion of too much ACTH hormone by the pituitary gland in the brain which in turn causes the adrenal glands to produce too much cortisol for normal needs. Excessive amounts of cortisol can also be produced naturally by hyperplasia (increase in size) of the adrenal gland and by the presence of adrenal gland tumors. Iatrogenic hyperadrenocorticism is produced when glucocorticoid drugs are administered over a long period of time.

The signs of Cushing's Syndrome are variable with the most common being polyuria (increased urination), polydipsia (increased water consumption), pendulous abdomen, enlarged liver, hair loss, weakness and depression, increased appetite, muscle weakness, obesity, increased panting, and hyperpigmentation. In a small number of cases, calcinosis cutis is observed.

The lab tests utilized in diagnosing this condition are a CBC (complete blood count), urinalysis, serum chemistries for liver function, and an *ACTH stimulation test*. If the clinical signs and preliminary testing are highly suspicious of Cushing's, use of the high dose dexamethasone suppression test or the combination *ACTH-dexamethasone suppression test* is needed to help determine the origin of the excess cortisone.

Treatment of Cushing's Syndrome is directed toward removing the excessive cortisone from the body. If an adrenal gland tumor is found, surgical removal of the affected adrenal gland is the treatment of choice. Because adrenal gland removal is very delicate surgery, an expert surgeon is required as is extra care in the monitoring of blood cortisol levels during and immediately after surgery. About 50% of adrenal tumors are malignant resulting in a poor prognosis. Therefore, euthanasia should be considered. If the cortisol excess is from a pituitary lesion causing an increase in the amount of circulating ACTH, surgical removal of the pituitary gland or of both adrenal glands could relieve the problem. Again, a very accomplished surgeon is required.

The most common drug therapy used to decrease cortisol production is Lysodren® (Op-DDD or mitotane) which causes the adrenal gland to atrophy. After the initial dose of Lysodren® atrophies the adrenal gland tissue, a lower maintenance level of the medication follows for life. Periodic blood tests are necessary to determine if the patient is developing any toxicity to Lysodren® .

CYTOBIN® :

Refer to *TRIIODOTHYRONINE*.

DEFICIENCY, GROWTH HORMONE:

Two clinical syndromes are recognized when the level of growth hormone secretion from the pituitary gland is insufficient. The first syndrome is *dwarfism*. Because of a recessive gene, the affected puppy will not grow to full size. Affected puppies appear normal up to three months of age. The difference between litter mates becomes apparent later as the growth hormone deficient puppy stays small and retains a puppy hair coat. *Growth hormone stimulation tests* with *xylazine* or *clonidine* are used to identify this condition. Samples must be tested at either the University of Pennsylvania or the University of Tennessee clinical endocrinology labs.

The other form of growth hormone deficiency, more aptly called *growth hormone responsive*, is a *pattern baldness*. The baldness occurs in some small breeds due to a deficiency of growth hormone. In the secondary form, a deficiency of thyroid hormone affects growth hormone production and regulation. Growth hormone for treatment of these deficiencies is in short supply. Genetically engineered growth hormone should available within two years for veterinary use. Several breeds are more predisposed to growth hormone deficiencies: German Shepherd Dogs, Karelian Bear-dogs, Chow Chows, Pomeranians, Keeshonden, and Toy and Miniature Poodles.

DEXAMETHASONE:

Refer to *CORTISONE.*

DIABETES INSIPIDUS:

Diabetes insipidus is caused by a malfunction involving the posterior part of the pituitary gland. The *antidiuretic hormone (ADH)* is not produced in the pituitary gland nor released for use by the kidneys to promote water conservation. Characterized by consumption of large quantities of water *(polydipsia)* and frequent urination of very dilute urine *(polyuria)*, the cause can rarely be determined. If the condition is severe, dogs frequently vomit from the large amounts of water consumed, lose weight from reduced food intake, and exhibit *convulsions* and *incoordination*. A urine specific gravity measurement equivalent to that of water (1.001 to 1.005) is necessary to prove diabetes insipidus. Also, evidence must indicate that urine cannot be concentrated by withholding water but can be concentrated by giving antidiuretic hormone. Treatment is directed toward supplying ADH. The hormone is given as a long acting injection, repeated as water consumption starts to increase, usually in 1 1/2 to 3 days. As a liquid, Desmopressin acetate (APDDV®) can be dropped into the nasal passage every eight hours.

The conjunctival sac of the eye is also used for administration if dogs resist nasal administration. Any treatment will need to be maintained for the life of the dog.

DIABETES MELLITUS:

Diabetes mellitus *(sugar diabetes)* is caused by the lack of *insulin* necessary to control the amount of *blood glucose* present. Insulin is produced in the beta-cells of the *pancreas*. Normally, enough insulin is produced to keep the level of sugar below the point that allows passage through the kidneys into the urine.

Diabetes mellitus is diagnosed by finding sugar in the urine and by finding an elevated blood glucose level. Other blood test values may also be abnormal. The extent of the blood sugar elevation is related to the seriousness of the insulin deficiency and the length of time the dog has been diabetic.

Treatment of diabetes mellitus is accomplished by using injectable insulin to lower the blood sugar level. Oral hypoglycemic drugs are not predictable or particularly effective when used in dogs. Occasionally, one will find a dog that will respond to the oral medication, but very rarely. The most effective kind of insulin is NPH insulin which must be given daily. Because the drug's peak insulin activity is about nine hours after injection, a rigid time schedule for injections, feeding, and exercise must be maintained by the owner.

Heat cycle, pregnancy, cortisone administration, thyroid medication, and exercise all affect the amount of insulin needed.

Complicated diabetes occurs when the excess sugar level has been present for a long time. The general metabolism of the dog is altered, creating a condition called *diabetic ketoacidosis.* Hospitalization with very close scrutiny is necessary to bring the complicated form under control. The most common complication of the ketoacidosis form of diabetes is the inflammation of the pancreas creating a life threatening problem. The enzyme *amylase* is greatly elevated, making that test beneficial in determining the presence of *pancreatitis.*

The prognosis for simple diabetes is excellent providing the dog's feeding, exercise, and insulin administration are maintained on a predictable schedule. The habit of monitoring urine sugar even after the patient has been brought under control is important.

DIESTRUS:

Refer to *METESTRUS and HEAT CYCLE.*

DIETHYLSTILBESTROL:

Refer to *HORMONES, SEX.*

DRUGS, HEAT ALTERING:

Several drugs are used to eliminate, prevent, or control the heat cycle in the dog. Currently, two drugs are cleared by FDA for this purpose: **Ovaban®** *(megestrol acetate)* and **Cheque®** drops *(mibolerone).* Ovaban® given at the rate of 1 mg./lb. daily for 8 days, if started before the second day of heat is completed, will cause the bitch to go out of heat rapidly. An alternate dosage may be given at 1/4 mg./lb. daily for 32 days starting at least one week prior to the onset of proestrus.

If the *megestrol* acetate (Ovaban®) is given late in anestrus, heat will be postponed approximately five to six months. If the drug is started early or in the middle of anestrus, usually no postponement of the scheduled heat period occurs. Side effects from Ovaban® include increased appetite, weight gain, decreased activity, and rarely, milk production. Ovaban® is a progestational hormone used in the United States since 1975. Its use does not seem to affect subsequent fertility and heat cycling.

Cheque® or *mibolerone* is an androgenic (male) anabolic steroid that is approximately 95% effective in inhibiting the heat cycle. Cheque® must be started at least 30 days before *proestrus* bleeding is anticipated in order to be effective in preventing heat signs. The liquid medication is given daily for an indefinite period. Side effects include mild clitoral enlargement, vaginitis, and worsening of any already existing *seborrheic skin condition.* German Shepherd dogs and Shepherd mixes require a much higher dosage than other breeds. Use is not recommended in the Bedlington Terrier breed and only with periodic *liver tests* in the Doberman Pinscher.

A food containing mibolerone is to be marketed by Carnation Pet Foods. Having not yet received final FDA approval, it will not available commercially until some later date.

Two other drugs are occasionally used to suppress heat cycles. Testosterone, a male hormone, has been used but because of side effects is not recommended. Depo-Provera® , a long acting time-released progestational hormone used in human medicine, has also been used to keep bitches out of heat. Changes caused in the uterus may lead to pyometra. Further predisposition to mammary tumors and diabetes mellitus also occurs from Depo-Provera® usage. Depo-Provera® should not be used in the canine. For additional discussion of heat altering drugs, refer to Chapter 12 on the UROGENITAL SYSTEM.

ESTRADIOL:

Refer to *HORMONES, SEX.*

ESTROGEN:

Refer to *HORMONES, SEX.*

ESTROUS CYCLE:

The estrous cycle (heat cycle) is the entire process of *proestrus, estrus, metestrus (diestrus)* and *anestrus*. The entire process in most dogs takes approximately six months. However, in large breeds, an eight, ten or even twelve month cycle is normal. If hormonal imbalances are present, the cycle is shortened, lengthened, or non-existent.

ESTRUS:

That part of the estrous cycle *(heat cycle)* when the bitch is receptive to the male dog is termed estrus. It generally lasts 9 days, but varies from 3 to 21 days. During *"standing heat"* as estrus is commonly called, the bitch will lift her tail, will stand with her rear legs firmly planted, and upon stimulation, will lift her vulva. During estrus, the *estradiol hormone* level has peaked and is starting to decrease while the *progesterone hormone* level is rising. Also during this period, *luteinizing hormone (LH)* and *follicle stimulating hormone (FSH)* are interacting to bring about ovulation. Most of the time, ovulation occurs 1 to 3 days after the peak of LH activity.

FLUCORT® :

Refer to *FLUMETHASONE* and *CORTISONE.*

FLUMETHASONE:

Refer to *CORTISONE.*

FOLLICLE STIMULATING HORMONE (FSH):

Refer to *HORMONES, SEX.*

FSH:

Refer to *HORMONES, SEX.*

GLANDS, ADRENAL:

The paired glands located at the cranial end of each kidney are the adrenal glands. Necessary for the production of *glucocorticoid hormone,* mineralocorticoids *(aldosterone),* and sex hormones *(progesterones, estrogens,* and *androgens),* the adrenal glands are stimulated by the presence of *adrenocorticotrophic hormone (ACTH)* that is secreted by the pituitary gland. A dog can live without adrenal glands if the necessary hormones are supplied from an outside source.

GLANDS, THYROID:

The thyroid glands are small paired glands located toward the chest from the larynx (voice box) on either side of the trachea (windpipe). Thyroid hormones are important in the regulation of many body functions.

The four hormones or prohormones produced by the dog's thyroid gland are *thyroxine (T$_4$), triiodothyronine (T$_3$),* reverse T$_3$, and diiodothyronine (T$_2$). The more potent T$_3$ is secreted in preference to T$_4$. Triiodothyronine is the major metabolic hormone associated with the thyroid gland.

The secretion of too much thyroid hormone causes a condition known as *hyperthyroidism.* Clinically, panting, increased heart rate, and personality agitation are present. Hyperthyroidism is rare in dogs but is found with increased frequency in older cats. The Doberman Pinscher is more likely to develop hypothyroidism than are other breeds. Refer to **HYPOTHYROIDISM** in Chapter 11 on SKIN DISORDERS.

HEAT CYCLE:

Refer to *CYCLE, ESTROUS.*

HORMONE, FOLLICLE STIMULATING (FSH):

Refer to *HORMONES, SEX.*

HORMONE, LUTEINIZING (LH):

Refer to *HORMONES, SEX.*

HORMONES:

A hormone is a chemical substance produced or secreted by one endocrine organ which has an effect on another organ. The following list of endocrine organs either produce the hormones listed or are affected by the hormone listed:

- ADRENAL GLANDS produce glucocorticoids and mineralocorticoids (aldosterone)

- OVARY produces estrogen and progesterone and is affected by follicle stimulating hormone (FSH) and luteinizing hormone (LH)

- PANCREAS produces insulin (lowers blood sugar) and glucagon (raises blood sugar)

- PITUITARY GLAND produces adrenocorticotrophic hormone (ACTH), antidiuretic hormone, growth hormone, thyroid stimulating hormone (TSH or thyrotropin), thyrotropin releasing hormone (TRH), follicle stimulating hormone (FSH), and luteinizing hormone (LH)

- TESTES produce testosterone and are affected by follicle stimulating hormone (FSH) and luteinizing hormone (LH).

- THYROID GLANDS produce L-thyroxine (T_4), triiodothyronine (T_4), reverse and free T_4 and T_3.

HORMONES, SEX:

Sex hormones, important in the perpetuation of the species, must be produced in proper amounts and in proper sequence for conception to occur.

In the BITCH, the following hormones are part of her reproductive system. **Estrogen** is a class of hormones responsible for the physical signs of estrus (heat). The most active estrogen hormone, **17-B-estradiol**, peaks in late proestrus. **Diethylstilbestrol**, a synthetic female hormone, has been used in older spayed bitches to control urinary incontinence and to produce mesalliance (mismating) after a bitch is bred accidently. Prolonged or constant usage of **diethylstilbestrol (DES)** will cause bone marrow depression and contribute to the development of pyometra. **FSH (follicle stimulating hormone)**, a hormone produced in the anterior pituitary gland, is responsible for maturation of ovarian follicles in the bitch. The anestrus levels of FSH decrease during early proestrus. The decrease is followed by a peak level of FSH similar to that found in anestrus. **Luteinizing hormone (LH)**, also produced in the anterior pituitary gland, is responsible for stimulating ovulation 24 to 72 hours after the LH peak and for initiating a new follicular phase at proestrus. Another pituitary gland hormone, prolactin, is part of the hormone picture in the maintenance of normal pregnancy and mammary gland development. Progesterone hormone is necessary for maintenance of the pregnant uterus and the development of the mammary milk duct system. Progesterone increases to facilitate behavioral estrus (standing for breeding, 'flagging' the tail). About ten days after ovulation, progesterone levels peak helping to stimulate mammary glandular development and changing the uterine lining. Because levels in serum progesterone are identical in pregnant and unpregnant bitches, no advantage is gained in pregnancy diagnosis by measuring the level of this hormone in the dog. The *MALE DOG* produces **testosterone** from germinal cells in the testes. Testosterone is the hormone responsible for male behavior - leg lifting, territory marking, aggressiveness, larger size, and the development of male behavioral traits such as wandering and protecting his territory. **FSH,** also produced in the male, is thought to be the primary hormone stimulating sperm production. **LH** plays an important part in testosterone hormone production because of its action on the cells of Leydig in the testes.

HYPERADRENOCORTICISM:

Refer to *CUSHING'S DISEASE.*

HYPOADRENOCORTICISM:

Refer to *ADDISON'S DISEASE.*

HYPOTHYROIDISM:

The lack of either T_4 *(L-thyroxine),* T_3 *(triiodothyronine),* or thyroid stimulation by *thyrotropin (TSH - thyroid stimulating hormone)* causes clinical signs associated with hypothyroidism. The most common clinical signs are lethargy, mental depression, either obesity or weight loss, heat seeking, low body temperature, hair loss, *hyperpigmentation, seborrhea,* ear infections, muscle and joint weakness, slow heart beat, *infertility,* and several eye conditions. A number of breeds of dogs including the Doberman Pinscher show increased risk of developing hypothyroidism. The larger the breed of dog affected, the younger the age when signs are first observed.

One of the most common causes of hypothyroidism is *lymphocytic thyroiditis (Hashimoto's Disease)* in which the thyroid gland activity is destroyed by the production of auto-antibodies against itself. The other common type is atrophy and necrosis (death) of the thyroid gland functional tissue from unknown causes. Clinical lab findings associated with hypothyroidism are *anemia,* hypercholesterolemia (too much cholesterol in the blood), elevated *CPK enzyme test* (creatinine phosphokinase) in over half, possibly low or baseline T_3 and T_4 levels, and a lack of response to thyroid stimulating hormone.

Along with measuring baseline T_3 and T_4 levels by radioimmunoassay, a *thyroid stimulation* test should be done with TSH. History, clinical signs, and other lab tests help to substantiate the diagnosis of hypothyroidism.

Treatment is for life. In most cases, dogs will respond to T_4 *(L-thyroxine)* administration even though T_3 alone or T_3 and T_4 are low. Most failures in therapy are from using the wrong product such as desiccated thyroid or T_3, or from giving an inadequate amount of T_4. The correct dosage is 20 mg./kg.

(0.1 mg./10 pounds) two times per day. After response is achieved, the dosage may be lowered to a maintenance level in some dogs.

LUTEINIZING HORMONE (LH):

Refer to *HORMONES, SEX.*

L-THYROXINE (T_4):

The main secretory product of the thyroid gland is called L-thyroxine or T_4. In some non-thyroid illnesses, T_4 levels are depressed as a means of helping the body conserve calories and decreasing tissue breakdown processes. Synthetic L-thyroxine is the most widely utilized therapeutic form of thyroid medication. Evidence does not indicate that "name brand" forms of the medication are any more effective than some generic forms available at substantial savings. L-thyroxine tablets can either be given two times daily or a double dose once daily. Therapy should be continued for a minimum of three months before the clinical changes are evaluated. Dogs with concurrent heart problems should be started at lower amounts and increased gradually to therapeutic levels over a three or four week period. Dogs on L-thyroxine therapy require increased doses of *insulin for diabetes* and *anticonvulsant drugs to control epilepsy.*

MEGESTROL ACETATE:

Refer to *DRUGS, HEAT ALTERING.*

METESTRUS (DIESTRUS):

Metestrus begins with the refusal of the bitch to allow the stud dog to mate. At this point in the cycle, *progesterone hormone* levels increase for 15 days and then gradually diminish for the next 5 to 6 weeks. Your veterinarian can estimate more accurately when whelping is due by looking under the microscope for the disappearance of superficial vaginal epithelial cells rather than by noting breeding dates or behavior changes. The decline of superficial epithelial cells occurs at the onset of diestrus (metestrus).

MIBOLERONE:

Refer to *DRUGS, HEAT ALTERING.*

OVABAN® :

Refer to *DRUGS, HEAT ALTERING.*

PREDNISONE:

Refer to *CORTISONE.*

PREDNISOLONE:

Refer to *CORTISONE.*

PROESTRUS:

The period of the *estrous cycle* when the bitch is attractive to the male but will not stand for breeding is termed proestrus. Clinically, the bitch has a swollen, turgid vulva and passes various amounts of a thin bloody discharge. The average length of proestrus is 9 days but varies from 2 to 17 days. The level of *estradiol hormone* is very high during proestrus, decreasing one or two days before the end of the proestrus period.

PROLACTIN:

Refer to *HORMONES, SEX.*

SMEARS, VAGINAL:

Vaginal smears aid in determining the stage of the heat cycle. With multiple smears, evidence of estrus cycle progression can be charted. A complete discussion on the smear technique and the cytology present is found in Chapter 12 on the UROGENITAL SYSTEM.

STIMULATION TEST, GROWTH HORMONE:

The growth hormone stimulation blood test is used to determine if a frank growth hormone deficiency exists. To date, only the University of Pennsylvania and the University of Tennessee endocrinology labs perform the growth hormone stimulation test and then only infrequently. Before undertaking this test, the veterinarian should contact the lab of choice to ask for specific instructions. A baseline plasma sample is obtained after which either *xylazine (Rompun®*) at 100 to 300 micrograms/kilogram or *clonidine* at 10 to 30 micrograms/kilogram is given intravenously. A post-stimulation plasma sample is obtained after thirty minutes. This test is valuable in determining true growth hormone deficiencies but is both difficult and expensive to run.

STIMULATION TEST, TSH (THYROID STIMULATING HORMONE):

The TSH stimulation test is the most accurate assessment of thyroid gland dysfunction. Because the thyroid stimulating hormone used in the test is very expensive and is in limited supply, the procedure is costly.

The testing is simple. A pre-TSH blood sample is taken. Five to ten units of TSH are injected intravenously and a post-TSH injection sample is collected. The samples are tested for T_3, T_4, and reverse T_3. If the response is less than two times the baseline value or if the response fails to reach the normal level, the diagnosis of hypothyroidism is justified.

SUGAR DIABETES:

Refer to *DIABETES MELLITUS.*

TEST, T_3 - T_4:

The common symbols for a measure of thyroid activity are T_3 and T_4, most commonly measured by radioimmunoassay. A measurement of T_3 and T_4 is not enough to make the diagnosis of hypothyroidism if the values are borderline. Use of the TSH (thyroid stimulating hormone) stimulation test should be considered. T_3 is triiodothyronine. T_4 is L-thyroxine which is converted into T_3 for active use in the body. T_3, the more active form in the dog, is secreted preferentially by the thyroid gland. Most dogs can be medicated with either T_3 or T_4 if a deficiency exists. T_4 is given once or twice daily and is relatively inexpensive. T_3 (Cytobin® or triiodothyronine) is more expensive than T_4 and must be given three times a day.

TEST, THORN:

The Thorn test is a crude, easily performed adrenal gland measure that has been replaced by the radioimmunoassay test. Seven hours after giving a patient ten units of *ACTH* gel intramuscularly, the number of *eosinophils* in the circulating blood stream are counted. A normal response is a 70% reduction of eosinophils in the blood stream. A reduction of less than 70% is an indication of decreased adrenal gland function or *Addison's Disease.*

TESTOSTERONE:

Refer to *HORMONES, SEX.*

TRIAMCINOLONE:

Refer to *CORTISONE.*

TRIIODOTHYRONINE (T_3):

Triiodothyronine is the most active form of thyroid hormone secreted by the thyroid gland or produced by tissue degradation of T_4. The most potent and metabolically active form of thyroid hormone in the dog is T_3. A commercially available form of T_3, Cytobin® produced by Norden Laboratories, can be used to treat most thyroid deficiencies. However, its high cost and the fact that it must be given three times a day to be effective are drawbacks.

TUMOR, SERTOLI CELL:

The Sertoli cell tumor is a peculiar tumor of the canine testes. It normally occurs in only one testicle and is fairly common in undescended testes. Sertoli cell tumors produce *estrogen hormone* which causes feminine changes in the male dog. Clinically, *hair loss* is evident from both sides of the body, nipples enlarge, a pendulous prepuce is present. There may even be an attraction to other male dogs. If the cancerous testicle and normal appearing testes are removed early enough, an excellent prognosis is given. Long standing Sertoli cell tumors spread to nearby tissues producing high estrogen hormone concentrations which cause fatal *bone marrow depression*.

VAGINAL SMEARS:

Refer to *SMEARS, VAGINAL* and Chapter 12 on the *UROGENITAL SYSTEM.*

VETALOG® (TRIAMCINOLONE):

Refer to *CORTISONE.*

Chapter 5

GASTROINTESTINAL TRACT & RELATED ORGANS

TEETH, LIVER, PANCREAS, STOMACH, INTESTINE

ACHALASIA:

The term achalasia is a failure of the muscles of the gastrointestinal tract to relax. Two forms of the disease are recognized - *CRICOPHARYNGEAL ACHALASIA and ESOPHAGEAL ACHALASIA*. The cardinal sign, frequently recognized at weaning, is persistent vomiting immediately after ingesting solid food.

In CRICOPHARYNGEAL ACHALASIA the problem occurs at the location where the pharynx enters the esophagus. Constriction of throat muscles prevents swallowing. Surgical correction is possible by severing these muscles. Recovery is generally rapid and permanent. However, sometimes surgical scarring causes a constriction requiring additional surgery later in life.

ESOPHAGEAL ACHALASIA occurs in the muscle surrounding the esophagus at the entrance to the stomach. The cause is a lack of nerve innervation to the esophageal muscle which prevents normal *peristalsis*. Eventually the accumulation of food in the esophagus creates a *megaesophagus*. Both long term dietary management and surgery are required. Achalasia surgery should be performed by a highly skilled surgeon. Dietary management includes feeding the dog from a high platform which elevates his front feet. Gravity will then help carry the food into the stomach. Feeding a gruel mixture also helps in the long term management of achalasia. Because the disease is hereditary, carriers or affected dogs should not be used for breeding.

ALANINE AMINOTRANSFERASE (ALT):

Refer to *TESTS FOR GI, LIVER, AND PANCREATIC DISEASES, DIAGNOSTIC.*

AMMONIA TOLERANCE TEST:

Refer to *TESTS FOR GI, LIVER, AND PANCREATIC DISEASES, DIAGNOSTIC.*

AMYLASE:

Refer to *ENZYMES AND HORMONES, PANCREATIC.*

ANI, ATRESIA:

Atresia ani is a congenital anomaly where no anal orifice or opening is present. Diagnosis occurs at several weeks of age when the puppy whines and exhibits a progressively distended abdomen. Some of these anomalies lend themselves to simple surgical repair under *local anesthesia.* Others require general anesthesia and more heroic methods.

ANODONTIA:

In the standard for the breed of the Doberman Pinscher, missing teeth result in varying penalties ranging from a slight degree to the most serious penalty of disqualification. The absence of teeth from the dental arch, anodontia, has a genetic basis.

The most common *missing teeth* are the small molar teeth - those located most closely to the angle of the jaw. Normal Dobes have one large and one small molar on each side in the upper jaw and one large and two small molars on each side in the lower jaw. They should be erupted and in place by seven months of age. Any or all of the small molar teeth can be missing.

The second most common location for anodontia is the upper and lower premolar teeth where the small premolars are not present. The upper jaw has three small premolars and a large fourth premolar tooth. In the lower jaw, there are four premolars of increasing size between the "fang" and the large molar on each side. These should all be erupted and in place by seven months of age. Radiographs may determine the presence or absence in the jaw at six months of age. Occasionally, one or several incisors are missing from the six upper or lower teeth in the dental arch between the canine teeth.

ANOREXIA:

Anorexia is a term meaning loss of appetite for food. There are numerous causes. Refer to Chapter 8 on NUTRITION.

AORTIC ARCH, PERSISTENT RIGHT:

Persistent right aortic arch is a common congenital anomaly which causes a stricture of the esophagus and vomiting within ten minutes after eating solid food. A *barium swallow radiograph* will show dilation of the esophagus anterior to the base of the heart. A ligament or vessel remnant that does not disappear after birth is the reason for the digestive upset. A fibrous cord, the ligamentum arteriosum, connects from the left pulmonary artery to the descending aorta, completely encircling the esophagus not allowing the esophagus to dilate as food descends.

The only treatment is surgical involving open chest surgery. The procedure requires a higher degree of surgical expertise with additional ventilation equipment to assist breathing during the procedure. One of the complications from surgery is failure of the esophagus to dilate after the fibrous cord is severed, resulting in *aspiration pneumonia* and ultimately death. A second complication to the surgery is dilation of the esophagus posterior to the surgical site. The prognosis is poor if either complication occurs.

ASCARIDS (ROUNDWORMS):

Refer to *PARASITES, INTESTINAL.*

BIOPSY, COLONIC:

Refer to *TESTS FOR GI, LIVER, AND PANCREATIC DISEASES, DIAGNOSTIC* and *COLITIS.*

BLOAT:

By definition, bloat is the accumulation of gas in the stomach causing distention of the abdomen. Bloat occurring in a nursing puppy may be corrected by gentle abdominal massage. Administration of a carbonated beverage like 7-UP™ helps to stimulate burping. On the other hand, bloat in an adult deep-chested breed must be treated as a true emergency. Professional care must be found immediately! Additional information about simple bloat or gastric dilatation is found in the section on *GASTRIC DILATATION, GASTRIC TORSION, AND INTESTINAL VOLVULUS.*

BLOOD AMMONIA TEST:

Refer to *TESTS FOR GI, LIVER, AND PANCREATIC DISEASES, DIAGNOSTIC.*

"BLUE EYE:"

Refer to *HEPATITIS, INFECTIOUS CANINE.*

BROMSULPHALEIN® (BSP) RETENTION TEST:

Refer to *TESTS FOR GI, LIVER, AND PANCREATIC DISEASES, DIAGNOSTIC.*

CBC:

Refer to *TESTS FOR GI, LIVER, AND PANCREATIC DISEASES, DIAGNOSTIC.*

CESTODES:

Refer to *PARASITES, INTESTINAL.*

CIRRHOSIS:

Cirrhosis of the liver, the end result of chronic liver disease, is irreversible. The definition of cirrhosis is a diffuse process characterized by fibrosis (scarring) and conversion of normal liver cells into structurally abnormal nodules. Cirrhosis is caused by many different agents that affect the liver over a period of time.

The signs that are present in a dog with cirrhosis vary in intensity. They include *icterus* (jaundice), *ascites* (fluid accumulation in the abdomen), and *hepatic encephalopathy*. In hepatic encephalopathy, central nervous system signs like *circling*, head pressing, *convulsions*, and coma are present. Treatment of cirrhosis is generally supportive. Most important is maintenance of electrolyte and fluid balance, control of infections, and prevention of low blood sugar levels. The prognosis is poor.

COCCIDIOSIS:

Refer to *PARASITES, INTESTINAL.*

COLITIS:

Colitis is the inflammation of a portion of the large bowel (colon). Clinically, several characteristics separate large bowel disease from small bowel problems. Frequent attempts to defecate, straining, and the passage of red blood and mucous are signs of colitis. A diagnosis is made from these signs and a *colonic biopsy*. Colonoscopy may be necessary to observe the lining of the colon. The lining of the colon affected with chronic colitis is very friable. It bleeds easily resulting in areas of ulceration. Although the cause of colitis is not known, there may be an immune system relationship. Treatment with *sulfasalazine* (Azulfidine®) and an *appropriate diet* control the signs. Colitis is likely to recur throughout the life of the dog.

COLITIS, HISTIOCYTIC ULCERATIVE:

While histiocytic ulcerative colitis is more common in the Boxer breed, it can occur in any breed. A similar counterpart in man is called *Whipple's Disease*. It is usually observed before two years of age as a chronic hemorrhagic, mucoid diarrhea. Affected dogs do not run a fever and initially remain in good body weight. As the disease progresses, weight decreases and the hair coat becomes unthrifty. About 30% of the affected dogs exhibit some vomiting.

A definitive diagnosis is made from a *colonic biopsy* via a proctoscope. A radiograph after a *barium enema* is also useful. *Blood tests* and *fecal examinations* are commonly negative. The cause is unknown, although both environmental and hereditary factors have been incriminated. Under certain conditions, bacteria or viruses may play a part in the etiology. Treatment is continuous. One must think of control, not cure. Antibiotics and Azulfidine® provide reasonable control. *Cortisone* drugs should not be used due to the ulcerative nature of the disease unless there has been no response to antibacterial therapy.

CONTRAST MEDIA X-RAY STUDY:

Refer to *TESTS FOR GI, LIVER, AND PANCREATIC DISEASES, DIAGNOSTIC.*

COPPER TOXICOSIS IN DOBERMANS:

Evidence now shows that some Doberman Pinschers may have a biological defect in their ability to remove copper from the body. Copper toxicosis, now well-documented in the Bedlington Terrier, has a definite genetic basis. While little is known about this disease in the Doberman Pinscher, the following facts are presented. The condition occurs much more frequently in females than in males. Clinical signs of liver failure including weight loss, increased thirst, increased urination, abdominal fluid buildup, and yellow mucous membranes are typical. Biochemical alterations in the blood include greatly increased *SGPT*, greatly increased *alkaline phosphatase*, and decreased *serum* or *plasma protein* levels (especially albumin). Also refer to POISONING in Chapter 9.

Presently, the problem appears to be due to abnormal accumulations of copper in the liver which cause degenerative changes. First, subacute hepatitis occurs, followed by *chronic active hepatitis*, and finally *cirrhosis* of the liver. Most cases are not diagnosed until the Dobe is in liver failure. When the disease has progressed this far, therapy is of limited value. Increased therapeutic response is expected if dogs are treated early in the course of the disease before clinical signs are seen. When given over a three to four month period, D-penicillamine (Cuprimine®) at the rate of 250 mg. two times daily will lower body copper levels. Also, *low copper diets,* steroids, and ascorbic acid therapy help lower body copper levels. Studies have been conducted on Dobermans with this condition by Dr. Larry P. Thornburg of the University of Missouri Veterinary Pathology Department.

CORONAVIRUS:

Canine coronavirus produces a highly contagious disease of the gastrointestinal tract. The distribution of the disease is worldwide with an incidence of up to 30% in some areas. While the virus affects dogs of any age, it is particularly devastating to young puppies. The early clinical signs are a lack of appetite and depression followed by vomiting which may contain blood. The moderate to severe diarrhea that occurs is characterized by a yellow-orange color and foul odor. Dehydration, loss of weight, and death can occur. In some cases, the diarrhea phase may recur up to three weeks later. Treatment is supportive by maintaining fluid and electrolyte balance. Until recently, no vaccine existed. Currently, a killed virus vaccine has been marketed by Ft. Dodge Laboratories. Because the vaccine has only been available for a short time, its efficiency in the field is not known.

DEFICIENCY, CHRONIC PANCREATIC:

Chronic pancreatic deficiency is a relatively common form of food malassimilation that occurs most frequently in young German Shepherd dogs. It is thought to be hereditary through an autosomal recessive trait. The common clinical signs are progressive weight loss, an increase in stool volume, and a ravenous appetite. The affected dogs are active and alert but they may develop *pica* (depraved appetite).

Oral administration of deficient pancreatic enzymes is an effective treatment. However, three or four meals daily are necessary even with enzyme replacement, as this form of therapy is not efficient in digesting food. The two forms of enzyme replacement are powdered and tablet. The powdered form is better utilized. Also, feeding a diet that is low in fat and high in carbohydrates and quality protein is recommended. Treatment is necessary for life.

DEHYDRATION:

Refer to *VOMITING AND/OR DIARRHEA, SIGNS OF.*

DIABETES MELLITUS:

Diabetes mellitus is a disease of the beta-cells of the pancreas. Refer to the ENDOCRINE SYSTEM in Chapter 4 for further discussion.

DIARRHEA:

Diarrhea is the passage of soft or watery feces. The four methods by which the feces become soft or watery are: 1) greater fluid secretion from the gut than absorption due to increased permeability of the intestine, 2) increased movement or motility of the GI tract, 3) lack of absorption due to disease of the GI tract, and 4) excess secretion without changes in gut permeability. All are causes of diarrhea due to malabsorption of fluids. Diarrhea is also caused by maldigestion due to pancreas and/or bile duct diseases. The exact diagnosis of the cause of diarrhea requires careful study of the history of the case and utilization of specific lab tests. After a cause is determined, appropriate treatment is initiated.

DIMENHYDRINATE:

Refer to *MOTION SICKNESS, DRUGS USED FOR.*

DIPYLIDIUM TAPEWORM:
Refer to PARASITES, INTESTINAL.

DISTEMPER:
Distemper, a life threatening viral disease of dogs, causes severe diarrhea. Its presence today is not as ominous as in past decades due to the availability of good vaccines.

DRAMAMINE® (DIMENHYDRINATE):
Refer to MOTION SICKNESS, DRUGS USED FOR.

DYSPHAGIA:
Dysphagia is difficulty in swallowing due to diseases of the throat region that cause mechanical blockage, pain, or a nerve dysfunction.

ECHINOCOCCUS TAPEWORM:
Refer to PARASITES, INTESTINAL.

ELECTROLYTE IMBALANCE:
Refer to VOMITING AND/OR DIARRHEA, SIGNS OF.

ENCEPHALOPATHY, HEPATIC:
In hepatic encephalopathy, the liver fails to adequately detoxify waste products in the blood stream resulting in neurological signs. This problem occurs as a result of several abnormalities: acute liver failure, a deficiency in the urea cycle enzyme level in the liver, a congenital portal-systemic shunt (abnormal blood vessel distribution around instead of through the liver), and chronic liver damage causing the production of new blood vessels which bypass the liver.

The clinical signs actually occur because of an accumulation of toxic products either formed or ingested in the gastrointestinal tract. The congenital portal-systemic shunt occurs most commonly in young dogs.

The clinical signs are mostly neurological in nature. The affected dog may constantly pace or circle, become disoriented, develop behavior or personality changes, have seizures, or become comatose. Non-nervous system signs include stunted growth, lack of appetite, increased water consumption, increased urination, anesthesia intolerance, abdominal fluid buildup, vomiting, and diarrhea.

One test by itself will not diagnose hepatic encephalopathy. However, by utilizing combined test data, the diagnosis can be made. Combined test data eliminates the need for electroencephalogram and cerebrospinal fluid aspiration. The six most important tests and their results are as follows: 1) a *blood ammonia test* showing increased blood ammonia (an unreliable test to do unless a local lab or hospital is closer than 30 minutes away), 2) a urinalysis showing the presence of ammonium biurate crystals (these look like golden brown thorn apples), 3) a lower than normal *BUN test*, 4) abnormal dye retention in a *BSP test*, 5) a radiograph possibly showing a smaller than normal liver and 6) a *liver biopsy* showing liver pathology.

Treatment of hepatic encephalopathy depends on the underlying cause. Some congenital portal-shunts can be managed surgically by partially occluding the abnormal blood flow, thereby causing more blood to flow through the liver. The surgery requires a high degree of expertise.

Medical treatment of hepatic encephalopathy is complex and must be continued for life. Treatment includes feeding a *special diet* to reduce ammonia production, prohibiting red meat, and limiting dairy and some plant proteins. The use of **KD** and **UD** prescription foods are helpful. Bacterial production in the colon where ammonia is produced can be controlled with lactulose (Cephulac®), metronidazole (Flagyl®), or the use of antibiotics. Cleansing enemas with Betadine® are also helpful. *Seizures* must be controlled. Although the prognosis is guarded, *dietary management* and proper medication may allow the dog with hepatic encephalopathy to lead an almost normal life.

ENDOSCOPY:

Refer to *TESTS FOR GI, LIVER, AND PANCREATIC DISEASES, DIAGNOSTIC.*

ENTERITIS:

Enteritis is inflammation of the intestinal tract that occurs in the small intestine. With the exception of *Crohn's Disease* (regional enteritis of the colon), the term "enteritis" by itself specifically involves the small intestine (duodenum, jejunum, or ileum). The diagnosis of enteritis is made from *contrast medium studies*, an examination of the history of the case, and the characteristics of the feces involved. Occasionally, *biopsy* or *laparotomy* (exploratory abdominal surgery) are necessary to specifically identify the location of the inflamed intestinal tract.

ENZYMES AND HORMONES, PANCREATIC:

AMYLASE is an enzyme produced by the exocrine portion of the pancreas. It is responsible for the digestion of starches. The amylase laboratory test measures inflammation of the pancreas. Since canine amylase levels are normally five to ten times higher than those found in man, the clinical laboratory must be familiar with canine values and test protocol. Amylase is also produced by the intestine and liver. The clinician must decide if the elevated amylase values are significant.

GLUCAGON is a hormone secreted by the alpha cells of the pancreas in response to a reduction in the blood sugar level. Through a complex reaction, more glucose is made available to the blood stream. **INSULIN** is secreted by the beta cells of the pancreatic islets. Its hormonal function is to lower the blood sugar level.

LIPASE is an enzyme that is produced by the exocrine portion of the pancreas. It is used to accurately measure increased pancreatic inflammatory activity. Lipase values are more specific reflections of pancreatic activity than are amylase values. The lipase test is more difficult for a laboratory to perform than is the amylase test.

For further discussion, also refer to Chapter 4 on the ENDOCRINE SYSTEM.

ESOPHAGUS:

The esophagus is the tube that connects the throat with the stomach. It is surrounded by muscle with a sphincter muscle at either end of the tube to control the opening and closing of the esophagus. If proper nerve inner-vation from the vagus nerve is not present to allow normal movement of ingesta (food), the esophagus will stretch and fill up with food creating a *megaesophagus*. Esophageal surgery warrants several special considera-tions. Since the last half of this muscular tube is within the chest, the thoracic cavity must be invaded to perform surgery on that part of the organ. Thoracic surgery requires more expertise on the part of the surgeon and the anesthesiologist. The esophagus is very prone to healing by constricting scars. The surgeon must therefore be very careful to minimize scarring. Severe strictures after surgery prevent food from passing into the stomach normally.

FECAL EXAMINATION TECHNIQUES:

Equipment required:

-1 Microscope with 100X and 400X objectives and light source
-Microscope slides and coverslips
-Paper cups and wooden tongue depressors
-Wire tea strainer
-Either test tubes or commercial kits - Ovassay™, Fecalyzer™ or Ovatector™
-Flotation solution (1 pound granulated sugar, 12 ounces water, 2 teaspoons liquid bleach)
-Centrifuge (optional)

Flotation Technique:

1. Suspend 1 teaspoon of feces in flotation solution in paper cup. Mix with tongue depressor.

2. Filter into second cup through tea strainer.
3. Pour into test tube and centrifuge for 3 minutes OR
3a. Pour into Ovassay™, Fecalyzer™ or Ovatector™. Fill container with flotation solution. Mix and allow to sit for 15 minutes.
4. Take sample from the very top of the solution. Place 2 drops on a clean microscope slide.
5. Cover with a coverslip. View under low power (100X) over the entire coverslip area.
   Note: *Coccidia* and *tapeworm eggs* are very small and may require 400X magnification.

Direct Smear Technique:

1. Suspend small amount of fresh feces in flotation solution on a clean microscope slide.
2. Cover with coverslip. View under diminished light, first under 100X, then under 400X.
3. Use this technique to observe *Giardia*.

FECAL TRYPSIN TEST:

Refer to *TESTS FOR GI, LIVER, AND PANCREATIC DISEASES, DIAGNOSTIC.*

FECALYZER™:

Refer to *FECAL EXAMINATION TECHNIQUES.*

FISTULA, ANAL:

Another name for anal fistula is *perianal fistula* which more accurately describes the location of these openings around the anus. Although seen most commonly in German Shepherds and Irish Setters, anal fistulas can affect any breed. Males have a higher incidence than females.

Three methods of treatment are available. The conservative approach requires long term antibiotic and corticosteroid therapy. In conventional surgery, the diseased tracts around the anus are removed. In cryosurgery, the diseased tissue is frozen with either *nitrous oxide* or liquid nitrogen. Post-surgical complications include strictures and incomplete removal of diseased tissue, necessitating additional surgery. The prognosis for complete recovery is guarded to fair.

FLOTATION TECHNIQUE:

Refer to *FECAL EXAMINATION TECHNIQUES.*

FLUID IMBALANCE:

Refer to *SIGNS OF VOMITING AND DIARRHEA.*

FLUKES:

Refer to *PARASITES, INTESTINAL.*

GASTRIC DILATATION, GASTRIC TORSION, AND INTESTINAL VOLVULUS:

THE SYNDROME OF GASTRIC DILATATION (BLOAT), GASTRIC TORSION, AND INTESTINAL VOLVULUS (TWISTING OR TORSION) IS A TRUE EMERGENCY! You must seek veterinary care immediately. The veterinary emergency clinics popular in metropolitan areas are probably best equipped to handle these life threatening problems.

If you cannot reach <u>any</u> veterinary care facility in less than 60 minutes, you should consider attempting to decompress the gas build up in the stomach yourself. First, clip away the hair on the lower left anterior abdomen where the "ping" sound is loudest when tapping the abdomen with your fingers. Soak the clipped area with rubbing alcohol. Insert a large gauge needle (at least 20 gauge or preferably an 18 or 16 gauge) to the hub. If blood enters the needle, withdraw it immediately and reevaluate the best location. If gas is expressed, continue to gently press on the abdomen to remove as much as possible over a 15 to 30 minute period. *THIS PROCEDURE IS NOT A SUBSTITUTE FOR VETERINARY CARE!* However, it may give you the one or two hours of time which could be the difference between life and death.

Gastric dilatation *(simple bloat)* is the filling of the stomach with gas. It occurs in any breed, at any age. Normally, the gas build-up is relieved by vomiting or passing into the intestinal tract. Causes of gastric dilatation include abdominal surgery, over eating, *pica* (depraved appetite), spinal injuries, gulping air, vomiting, and the birth process. In older dogs, malignant tumors may cause gastric dilatation. Clinical signs of gastric dilatation are non-productive vomiting, swelling in the anterior abdomen, restlessness, and excess salivation. The diagnosis of the problem is made from clinical signs and an abdominal radiograph.

Treatment for gastric dilatation involves relieving the gas accumulation by passing a stomach tube. *Anesthesia* or *sedation* may or may not be needed to accomplish this. If gas continues to buildup, the placement of a *pharyngostomy* tube will keep the gas formation under control, allowing the dog to eat and drink normally. This simple surgical procedure is very effective. Follow-up feeding instructions after recovery from gastric dilatation include multiple light broth meals for several days, followed by multiple feedings of soft foods. After a few days, the dog may return to several small normal meals instead of a single large feeding. If a dog is troubled with multiple recurrences of gastric dilatation, changes in management of the environment and additional surgical procedures to speed up the emptying of the stomach should be considered.

Both *gastric torsion* and *volvulus* are much more life threatening than gastric dilatation. **Volvulus** or the twisting of the intestine is demonstrated by twisting both ends of a long air-filled balloon. The air now trapped in the middle part cannot escape. The clinical signs associated with volvulus are subtly different than those seen with gastric torsion. In volvulus, abdominal swelling is more generalized throughout the abdomen, no salivation is observed, and the vomiting is productive. The diagnosis is easily made by radiographs which will show long loops of gas filled intestines. The treatment for volvulus is surgical correction of the twisting and removal of any devitalized sections of intestine. If removal of intestinal sections is required, the surgeon should have better than average surgical skills. More intensive hospital post-surgical care is also needed. With rapid diagnosis and competent care, both simple gastric dilatation and intestinal volvulus have a reasonably good prognosis.

Gastric torsion complex is a multifaceted, life-threatening problem. The exact way in which it develops is not yet known. Certain breeds of dogs classified as large, "deep-chested" breeds are more prone to its development. Most of these cases are seen at night after a large meal with water is followed by exercise. A number of cases also occur with a history of *gastritis* (stomach infection).

Gastric torsion results from the following sequence of events. A late afternoon feeding with a bulky dog food is capped by a big drink of water. Within one to two hours, the dog is exercised by running. Fermentation has begun, producing gas in the stomach. Water expands the food causing it to break down. During exercise, the weight of the fluid causes the stomach to turn on itself occluding the esophagus (entry) and the intestine (exit) either partially or completely so that the gas formed cannot escape. The process continues, enlarging the stomach. As the stomach expands and occupies more abdominal space, it pushes against the diaphragm causing respiratory and cardiac embarrassment. Normal blood flow through the liver and spleen is also disrupted resulting in a deep septic shock. As the stomach enlarges, the wall of the stomach is stretched abnormally causing that tissue to die leading to further complications. Whether this scenario is completely accurate is open to conjecture, but the actual events follow those described closely. *TIME IS OF GREATEST IMPORTANCE!* An immediate diagnosis and early treatment are absolutely essential. The earlier the condition is diagnosed, the better the prognosis. If the dog can walk into the veterinary care facility, you have a chance!

Three pre-operative conditions must be treated: 1) shock due to reduced blood flow to the heart, 2) electrolyte imbalance from poor blood flow and accumulation of abnormal waste materials in the circulation, and 3) cardiorespiratory embarrassment. The exact sequence or protocol for treatment will vary from one clinician to another. The prognosis, at best, is guarded and is actually fair to poor. If you are lucky enough to own a dog that has survived gastric torsion, you should reexamine your dog management program. Change the number of daily feedings, the amount of food, the kind of diet fed and the way in which water and exercise are given. Recently several surgical techniques have been developed. They stimulate permanent adhesions between the stomach wall and the abdominal lining to prevent recurrences of torsion. **REMEMBER - TIME IS OF UTMOST IMPORTANCE IF YOU HOPE TO BE SUCCESSFUL IN COMBATTING THIS KILLER!** Also refer to *BLOAT* for further discussion.

GASTRIC TORSION:

Refer to *GASTRIC DILATATION, GASTRIC TORSION, AND INTESTINAL VOLVULUS.*

GASTROENTERITIS, EOSINOPHILIC:

Eosinophilic gastroenteritis causes signs associated with the stomach as well as both the small and large bowel. Clinically, a chronic liquid diarrhea with occasional vomiting and some weight loss is observed. While most often reported in German Shepherds and Cocker Spaniels, any breed can be affected. The cause is unknown. Some have guessed that parasitic involvement or an early phase of *regional enteritis* are the reasons for the high *eosinophil* blood count. Others feel a *food hypersensitivity* is the underlying reason. A specific diagnosis may be determined by *biopsy* and peripheral blood cell counts. This disease, while it is responsive to *corticosteroids*, frequently has relapses.

GIARDIA:

Refer to *PARASITES, INTESTINAL.*

GINGIVITIS:

Gingivitis is inflammation of the gums. If the oral disease is suspected, one should inspect the entire mouth and related structures closely. Inflammation and infection associated with the gums is often related to dental and periodontal disease. Large amounts of tartar and loose teeth are present in periodontal disease. On the other hand, gingivitis is also a single sign of a systemic disease problem as diverse as *uremic poisoning* or the *autoimmune disease, pemphigus vulgaris.* A number of diagnostic tests are required to determine the underlying cause of gum inflammation.

GLOSSITIS:

Inflammation of the tongue is called glossitis. Like gingivitis, glossitis is a sign of oral disease. A good history, clinical observation of the tongue, and diagnostic tests like *biopsies* and *impression smears* help establish a cause. Once the cause of the glossitis is known, appropriate treatment may be initiated.

GLUCAGON TOLERANCE TEST:

Refer to *TESTS FOR GI, LIVER, AND PANCREATIC DISEASES, DIAGNOSTIC.*

GLUCOSE TEST:

Refer to *TESTS FOR GI, LIVER, AND PANCREATIC DISEASES, DIAGNOSTIC.*

GLUCOSE TOLERANCE TEST:

Refer to *TESTS FOR GI, LIVER, AND PANCREATIC DISEASES, DIAGNOSTIC.*

HEPATITIS:

Hepatitis, defined as inflammation of the liver, has many causes ranging from viruses *(infectious canine hepatitis)* to toxins (*copper*, alcohol, drugs, etc.). The liver has a large reserve so that when clinical signs are seen, more than 80% of the liver has already been affected. For further discussion of the clinical signs of liver disease, refer to specific liver disorders.

HEPATITIS, INFECTIOUS CANINE:

Infectious canine hepatitis is a serious viral disease which causes acute destruction of the liver cells, inflammation of blood vessels, and clots throughout the blood stream. It is caused by an *adenovirus type I* which has been successfully adapted to a vaccine. Clinically, signs of infectious canine hepatitis include those of liver failure, high fever, uncontrolled bleeding, and *white blood cell depression*. On occasion, a *"blue eye"* occurs in one or both eyes approximately 10 to 14 days after recovery from this disease or follows the use of some vaccines. The "blue eye" is actually thought to be an immune reaction in the cornea. The cornea swells and becomes cloudy blue. Some "blue eyes" will clear with or without treatment while others will remain permanently cloudy.

HISTOPLASMOSIS:

While the respiratory tract is usually infected by the *systemic fungus Histoplasma*, the intestinal tract can become secondarily involved. If the colon is involved, a chronic bloody diarrhea results. Affected dogs will show signs such as a *cough*, emaciation, *anemia*, and generalized lymph node enlargement. A *colonic biopsy* is diagnostic. Occasionally, the causative organisms are cultured from the stool. Treatment is not rewarding but may be attempted with amphotericin B or ketoconazole. The prognosis, at best, is guarded.

HOOKWORM:

Refer to *PARASITES, INTESTINAL.*

IMBALANCE, FLUID AND ELECTROLYTE:

Refer to *VOMITING AND/OR DIARRHEA, SIGNS OF.*

INTOLERANCE, LACTOSE:

Lactose intolerance is caused by a deficiency of the *enzyme lactase* which is necessary to break down the *milk sugar*, lactose, in the small intestine. The condition is usually acquired over a period of months but is most commonly observed in three to six month old puppies. These puppies develop diarrhea after being fed milk or other products high in lactose. Treatment is accomplished by withholding lactose from the diet.

INTUSSUSCEPTION:

Intussusception means that one portion of the intestine has *"telescoped"* (invaginated) into an adjacent section of gut. It most commonly occurs at the region where the small intestine, cecum, and large intestine meet. The exact cause is not known but increased intestinal *peristalsis* is a factor. Clinical signs include pain, occasional vomiting, passing blood and mucous from the rectum, and the presence of a mass in the abdomen. A definitive diagnosis requires radiography and exploratory surgery. The treatment for intussusception is the surgical resection of the part of the intestine that has "telescoped" in order to prevent recurrence. After surgery, recovery care is the same as for any intestinal surgery.

ISOSPORA:

Refer to *PARASITES, INTESTINAL.*

LIPASE:

This is the pancreatic enzyme necessary for fat digestion. Also refer to *ENZYMES AND HORMONES, PANCREATIC.*

LIVER DISEASE, SIGNS OF:

The specific signs of liver disease depend to some degree on whether or not the condition is acute or chronic.

Acute liver disease may cause depression, lack of appetite, fever, vomiting, and diarrhea. Specific signs include yellow jaundice, fluid buildup in the abdomen, a painful liver (anterior part of abdomen), and the presence of a coma. Chronic liver problems cause the same set of signs as the acute form except that there may be neurological signs such as behavior changes and seizures. Signs involving the nervous system are seen most often after eating. With chronic liver disease, the size of the liver may actually be smaller than normal. In both acute and chronic liver disease, there is a tendency for bleeding due to a lack of clotting factors normally produced in the liver.

MEGACOLON:

An abnormal enlargement of the colon is classified as congenital megacolon or as a *pseudomegacolon (obstipation)* which may develop later in life. *Congenital megacolon* occurs due to faulty nerve innervation to part of the colon allowing stool to accumulate without being evacuated. The pseudomegacolon results from some underlying blockage such as a broken pelvis, enlarged prostate, cancer of the colon, or any other cause of chronic constipation.

The diagnosis is made with a radiograph and a history of little or no stool passage. Treatment of congenital megacolon is surgical while pseudomegacolon is treated with stool softeners, laxative diets, and frequent exercise.

MEGAESOPHAGUS:

Megaesophagus is an enlargement of the esophagus. When megaesophagus occurs in puppies, it is the result of improper nerve innervation or a stricture preventing a bolus of food from entering the stomach. When found in older dogs, faulty vagus nerve innervation to the esophagus prevents the passage of food from the throat to the stomach. Management of this condition is difficult as *aspiration pneumonia* is a common sequelae. Affected dogs should be fed a gruel mixture. Their food bowls should be elevated to encourage gravitational passage of food to the stomach. The long term prognosis is guarded.

MISSING TEETH:

Refer to *ANODONTIA.*

MOTION SICKNESS, DRUGS USED FOR:

While riding, some dogs are affected by automobile motion which causes them to salivate and/or vomit. The use of drugs like *Dramamine®* *(dimenhydrinate)* for motion sickness given at the rate of 25 to 50 mg. every eight hours or as needed, aids in controlling these signs. For best results, medicine should be given one hour before the car ride is initiated. *Phenothiazine tranquilizers* like acepromazine maleate may also be beneficial in controlling motion sickness.

NANOPHYETUS SALMINCOLA:

Refer to *PARASITES, INTESTINAL.*

NEMATODES:

Refer to *PARASITES, INTESTINAL.*

NEORICKETTSIA HELMINTHOECA:

Refer to *PARASITES, INTESTINAL.*

OBSTRUCTION, FOREIGN BODY:

The ingestion of non-food objects can cause serious consequences. Young Doberman Pinschers may have *pica (depraved appetite)*. Therefore, they will eat rocks, metal objects, plastic, or other indigestible materials. As these indigestible objects begin their journey through the gastrointestinal system, they may become lodged in areas where the esophagus, stomach, or intestinal tract cannot dilate enough to allow continued movement. The location of the lodged object determines the clinical signs that are observed.

In the esophagus, the usual locations of foreign body obstruction are at the thoracic inlet (where the esophagus enters the chest), at the base of the heart, or at the exit of the esophagus from the thoracic cavity (where the diaphragm separates the chest from the abdomen). If lodged in these locations, clinical signs include salivation, difficulty swallowing, regurgitation of solid food, and retention of liquids.

Complete obstructions of the stomach are rare. Occasionally, foreign objects will descend into the stomach and then swell, preventing either movement into the intestinal tract or regurgitation. Clinically, these dogs exhibit intermittent *vomiting* and weight loss.

In the intestinal tract, obstructions are classified by the location of the blockage. A "high" obstruction is located in the area where the stomach empties into the small intestine (pylorus), the first part of the small intestine (duodenum), and the first portion of the subsequent section of gut (jejunum). High obstruction causes projectile vomiting. If present for a long period of time, severe *dehydration* and *electrolyte* imbalance result. A "low" obstruction occurs in the last part of the jejunum, the ileum and the entire large bowel (colon and rectum). Low obstruction causes the accumulation of gas in the intestinal tract. Over an extended period this may lead to septic shock and death. The dog has a much larger esophagus-intestine ratio than does man. Because of this fact, a dog can swallow something that cannot pass through its intestine.

Treatment for foreign body obstruction involves reestablishing a normal hydration and electrolyte balance. Only then is removal of the obstruction possible. The surgical procedure may be as simple as making an incision just ahead of the object and removing it or as complicated as removing a section of gut or esophagus that has been irritated to the point of tissue devitalization. The later surgical procedure requires more skill and more nursing care. The prognosis is generally good. However, many dogs will repeatedly ingest foreign objects.

PANCREATIC DISEASE, SIGNS OF:

The signs seen in pancreatic disease vary dramatically. The acute form of pancreatitis is readily distinguished from the chronic form. *Acute pancreatitis* is manifested by a rapid onset of abdominal pain and vomiting. The temperature is either elevated or depressed depending on whether or not shock is occurring. Rapid loss of body water may cause severe *dehydration* and *depression*. Intense abdominal pain causes the dog to walk with a very arched back or assume a "praying" position with its front legs down and rear legs standing. Signs of *chronic pancreatitis* are more variable than those observed with the acute, fulminating form. In general, dogs that have chronic pancreatic problems develop *diabetes mellitus*. Diabetes has an entirely different set of clinical signs. The most common signs of chronic pancreatic disease are weight loss with a voracious appetite, poor hair coat, and clay colored, loose, voluminous stools.

PANCREATITIS, ACUTE:

Acute pancreatitis is a rapidly fulminating disease that can cause death. Clinically, a wide variety of signs are observed. However, abdominal pain and *vomiting* are cardinal signs. If the onset is very rapid, nausea, retching, and salivating are observed. An affected dog may attempt to place its painful abdomen on a cool surface or assume a praying posture with the front legs down and the rear legs standing. When these dogs stand, they have an arched back. Most dogs that develop acute pancreatitis are overweight and have a history of consuming a large amount of food several hours before the disease process began. The affected dog also shows signs of rapidly progressing toxic shock. The dog's temperature is usually elevated, however if severe shock is present, the temperature will be below normal.

To help make a definitive diagnosis, both blood work and radiographs are necessary. In many affected individuals, the serum appears cloudy from high levels of fasting lipids. The *white blood cell count* is elevated. Increases in *serum amylase* and *lipase* are normally expected in acute pancreatitis. Treatment of acute pancreatitis involves resting the secretory activity of the pancreas. The dog should receive NOTHING by mouth for at least five days. Intravenous and subcutaneous maintenance fluids and electrolytes are essential. All medications should be given parenterally (IM, IV, or Sub Q) and not orally. *Atropine* is the drug of choice to decrease pancreatic secretion and stimulation. Broad spectrum antibiotic therapy should be instituted in all cases. If shock occurs, appropriate therapy should be promptly started. Currently, it is felt that the benefits of *corticosteroids* outweigh the potential for exacerbation of the condition. They also should be utilized in shock therapy.

The prognosis for acute pancreatitis is guarded since death from shock is always a possibility. Hospitalization with intensive care for up to two weeks is necessary. Recurring attacks are minimized by feeding a strict diet, reducing excess weight, providing adequate exercise, and discouraging the tendency to scavenge for food.

PARASITES, INTESTINAL:

Intestinal parasites that affect dogs are either *nematodes* (like *roundworms),* cestodes (like *tapeworms), flukes,* or *protozoans (*like *Coccidia* or *Giardia).* Each parasite has a specific life cycle. Information about the life cycle is important in the management of these diseases in a kennel environment. Some parasites have public health importance since they also cause disease in man. *Ascarids* cause *visceral larval migrans. Ancylostoma (hookworm)* causes *cutaneous larval migrans. Echinococcus (tapeworm)* is the most serious zoonotic infestation. *Dipylidium (tapeworm)* is spread by fleas. The ingestion of fleas by people can cause infestation with this species of tapeworm. It is not clear whether or not man can be infested with the canine *protozoan Giardia species.*

ASCARIDS (ROUNDWORMS) consist of two main species that can be differentiated on fecal flotation, *Toxocara canis* and *cati* and *Toxascaris leonina.* These are the most common internal parasites of dogs.

Toxocara canis and *cati have a rough outer shell and show a deeply pigmented center. Toxascaris leonina* has a very smooth shiny shell and a lighter colored inner structure. *Toxocara canis* has a complex life cycle that includes larval migration through body tissues and transplacental and lactogenic (milk) transmission to puppies. Bitches infested with *Toxocara canis* give birth to puppies with worms. Puppies also become infected from nursing an infested bitch. Conversely, there is no evidence that *Toxascaris leonina* has this kind of life cycle and thus, if these internal parasites are controlled in the bitch, puppies will be born free from them.

Signs of ascarid infections include pot-bellied pups, unthrifty and unkempt hair coat, *diarrhea, vomiting, anemia,* and even the expulsion of parasites in the stool or vomitus.

Treatment should include treating a bitch before or during pregnancy to lower her worm burden and eliminate puppy transplacental and lactogenic parasite transfer. The use of fenbendazole twice daily for two weeks or once daily from the fortieth day of pregnancy until two weeks after the pups are born will greatly cut the parasite load for bitch and pups. Most wormers have some efficiency against roundworms. *Diethylcarbamazine for heartworm prevention* helps keep the ascarid burden low. Toxocara canis should be treated at least two times at three week intervals or until a negative microscopic stool exam is obtained.

Next to ascarids, HOOKWORMS are the most common internal parasite. Two species of hookworms occur in the United States: *Ancylostoma* and *Uncinaria.* The *hookworm* is a blood sucker which is devastating to small puppies because the anemia produced is life threatening.

The life cycle of Ancylostoma is direct. A free-living phase is necessary for the larval form. A dog becomes infected in one of several ways: lactogenic (through nursing), orally, or larval penetration of the skin and possibly through the placenta before birth. This parasite flourishes in moist, warm climates with sandy soils where the free living larva mature and become infective. Clinical appearance of hookworm disease in puppies is one of anemia, bloody diarrhea, and depression. The puppy's tongue and gums appear pale gray-white.

Treatment is accomplished by using an effective wormer. The treatment should be repeated in 3 to 4 weeks if a microscopic stool examination indicates the need. Supplemental to the treatment of the dog is the treatment of the environment in which the dog lives in order to eliminate the free living larval form. These larvae mature and penetrate the unbroken skin causing reinfestation. VIP Hookworm Concentrate™ (produced by VIP Products) is used to treat infested ground to aid in hookworm larva control.

Trichuris infection *(WHIPWORM)* is more serious in some areas of the country than in others. Whipworm lives in the large intestine and cecum. It causes intermittent hemorrhagic diarrhea, anemia, weight loss, and a general loss of condition. Its direct life cycle has no migration through the body tissues. Several newer wormers have been shown to have a high degree of efficiency on whipworm. These products include mebendazole, fenbendazole and butamisole. While the first two are given orally on three consecutive days, butamisole is injectable.

Several different *TAPEWORMS* infest the dog. Of these, two are very common while the third is only mentioned because of its serious public health ramifications. *Echinococcus tapeworm* is uncommon in most parts of the United States. It causes very serious problems in humans when it is ingested, using man for the intermediate host instead of sheep and rodents. Bunamidine and praziquantel are used to treat Echinococcus infection.

Dipylidium tapeworm is a common tapeworm in the dog. The normal intermediate hosts are fleas and lice although humans become infested by ingesting fleas or lice. This tapeworm is commonly diagnosed by finding "rice granules" (dried tapeworm segments) attached to the hair around the anal orifice. *Microscopic fecal flotation tests* may not identify the presence of tapeworm ova because all tapeworms have eggs that are heavier than most other parasite ova. Control of Dipylidium tapeworm involves first eradicating fleas and lice.

Taenia tapeworm is another common kind of canine tapeworm. Its intermediate hosts are rabbits, rats, and mice. If a dog eats any of the intermediate hosts, it becomes the final host of this parasite. Treatment for both Taenia and Dipylidium tapeworms is the same as for Echinococcus. The newer tapeworm drugs are much more effective and "more gentle" on the dog's system than the old purgative types. Successful eradication depends on control of the intermediate host.

Clinical signs of tapeworm infection vary from slight to severe weight loss, mild intestinal upsets, and general unthriftiness. Occasionally, anal itching or rubbing is a sign of tapeworm infestation, but more likely those signs are due to *anal sac impaction.*

The FLUKE, *Nanophyetus salmincola*, is mentioned here only because of the very serious disease for which it serves as a vector and reservoir. In the Pacific Northwest, a disease called *salmon poisoning* is caused by an infectious agent, *Neorickettsia helminthoeca*. The fluke *Nanophyetus* is the carrier of this organism. Dogs are infected by eating raw salmon and other fish. The life cycle is somewhat complex and passage through a snail is part of the cycle. The incubation period after ingestion of affected salmon is approximately five days. The clinical signs are severe vomiting, hemorrhagic diarrhea, swollen lymph nodes, and high fever. Death is not uncommon. The disease is diagnosed by finding fluke eggs in the feces and the rickettsia on a *lymph node biopsy*. Treatment is supportive with intravenous fluids and oxytetracycline antibiotic. Hospitalization is necessary with a guarded prognosis.

Of the protozoan parasites, *COCCIDIOSIS* is the most common. This disease is caused by many species of Isospora. *Coccidiosis* is very serious in young puppies and is capable of mimicking diseases like *canine distemper*. This parasite has a life cycle that develops both within the body and in the environment.

The clinical signs of *coccidiosis* are similar to those of other protozoan diseases. The most common signs are watery or bloody diarrhea, loss of appetite and dehydration. Coccidiosis is more common in crowded environmental conditions. Therefore, a combination of treatment of the affected dogs and of cleaning up the environment is necessary to eradicate the disease. The use of *sulfadimethoxine* for two weeks is very effective in the control of coccidiosis.

GIARDIA as a cause of watery diarrhea is somewhat controversial since these motile protozoans are occasionally found in normal stools. *Giardia* have a direct life cycle. Puppies become infected after eating cysts from contaminated food, water, or stools.

Clinical signs vary from none to an explosive, mucoid diarrhea, depression, weight loss, and loss of appetite. Diagnosing Giardia is best done from a *direct smear* of stool suspended in saline solution and observed under low microscopic light. Treatment is best accomplished with metronidazole given two times daily for three days.

STRONGYLOIDES STERCORALIS, is an unusual parasitic infection that causes two different syndromes. In young puppies, the *intestinal syndrome* may include a blood-tinged diarrhea, anemia, and even death. This phase is preceded by coughing, loss of appetite, and a purulent infection of the eyes. The other *syndrome* seen in older dogs results in very itchy red skin lesions where the Strongyloides larva penetrates the body. These *rhabditiform larvae* are found in the stool. Treatment is with thiabendazole, dithiazanine, or ivermectin.

PARVOVIRUS, CANINE:

Canine parvovirus (CPV) is a new intestinal viral disease of dogs. It was first found in the dog population after 1977. Early in the history of the disease, widespread outbreaks were common affecting dogs of all ages. A vaccine was rapidly developed and now most outbreaks are limited to puppies from 6 to 16 weeks of age.

Clinical signs of parvovirus infection are a high fever, extreme depression, lack of appetite, vomiting, and the passage of watery or hemorrhagic diarrhea. The degree of depression is profound with a rapid onset. A complicating factor in CPV is the presence of heart involvement in young puppies because their heart muscle cells are growing and dividing rapidly. These cells are readily attacked by the parvovirus.

A tentative diagnosis of canine parvovirus is made from a *blood count*. About 50% of affected dogs have a very low *white blood cell count (leukopenia)*, more specifically, a low *lymphocyte* count. A definite diagnosis is made by identifying the virus from a stool sample under examination with an electron microscope. If the dog does not survive, samples of intestine examined under the light microscope may provide certain answers. A number of tests use serum to determine the presence of parvo antibody. While these tests may give one an indication that CPV is or was present, they are not considered to be definitive.

The treatment of the disease must be aggressive. Because of the rapid onset, *dehydration* occurs early and must be dealt with properly. Treatment is supportive, requiring either hospitalization or an I.V. set up at home for continued supplementation of fluids. Using oral medication is difficult because of the vomiting and extreme diarrhea. Parenteral antibiotics are important because the immune system is depressed. Treatment may continue for upwards of two weeks with a guarded prognosis.

While canine parvovirus is a highly contagious virus, immunization is available. Canine origin parvo vaccine gives a more dependable response. Puppies must receive a series of vaccinations until they are at least 16 to 18 weeks of age. Also, live virus vaccines provide greater immunity than killed vaccines.

PERISTALSIS:

Peristalsis is the worm-like movement by which the intestinal canal uses longitudinal and circular muscle fibers to propel its contents.

POISONING, SALMON:

Refer to *PARASITES, INTESTINAL.*

ROUNDWORMS (ASCARIDS):

Refer to *PARASITES, INTESTINAL.*

SALMON POISONING:

Refer to *PARASITES, INTESTINAL.*

SERUM ALKALINE PHOSPHATASE TEST:

Refer to *TESTS FOR GI, LIVER, AND PANCREATIC DISEASES, DIAGNOSTIC.*

SERUM AMYLASE TEST:

Refer to *TESTS FOR GI, LIVER, AND PANCREATIC DISEASES, DIAGNOSTIC.*

SERUM BILIRUBIN TEST:

Refer to *TESTS FOR GI, LIVER, AND PANCREATIC DISEASES, DIAGNOSTIC.*

SERUM ELECTROLYTE TEST:

Refer to *TESTS FOR GI, LIVER, AND PANCREATIC DISEASES, DIAGNOSTIC.*

SERUM GLUTAMIC PYRUVIC TRANSAMINASE (SGPT):

Refer to *TESTS FOR GI, LIVER, AND PANCREATIC DISEASES, DIAGNOSTIC.*

SERUM LIPASE TEST:

Refer to *TESTS FOR GI, LIVER, AND PANCREATIC DISEASES, DIAGNOSTIC.*

SERUM PROTEIN TEST:

Refer to *TESTS FOR GI, LIVER, AND PANCREATIC DISEASES, DIAGNOSTIC.*

STENOSIS, PYLORIC:

One cause of delayed stomach emptying is pyloric stenosis, either congenital or acquired. Clinically, the congenital form is seen in young puppies about two to four hours after eating. They vomit undigested food. Over a period of weeks, the puppies become emaciated. The acquired form shows the same signs but is due to a space occupying lesion or a foreign body. A diagnosis is made with contrast media radiographs which show delayed stomach emptying.

The congenital form when corrected surgically has a good prognosis. The acquired form also involves surgery. If the obstruction is removed, a good prognosis may also be given.

STRONGYLOIDES STERCORALIS:

Refer to *PARASITES, INTESTINAL.*

TAENIA TAPEWORM:

Refer to *PARASITES, INTESTINAL.*

TAPEWORM:

Refer to *PARASITES, INTESTINAL.*

TEETH ERUPTION, AGE OF:

Deciduous (puppy or temporary) teeth start to erupt at two to three weeks of age. By the end of the first month of life, a puppy will have four deciduous incisors and two canine teeth in place in each jaw. The outer most incisors are erupted by six weeks of age. The temporary premolars make their appearance between four and eight weeks. By two months of age, ALL of the deciduous teeth should be in place. Puppies have 28 "baby" teeth rather than the 42 adult teeth that will take their place by seven to eight months of age. Almost immediately after the eruption of the deciduous dentition, the roots are reabsorbed in preparation for the replacement by adult teeth. Proper radiographs at five to six months of age will show whether or not all adult teeth are present for eruption.

The schedule of *adult teeth eruption* is as follows. Six upper and six lower incisor teeth (the teeth located between the large 'fangs' on the upper and lower dental arcade) will be in place between three months and five months of age. The four adult canines ('fangs') erupt at five to six months of age. The first premolar (behind the 'fangs') erupt at five to six months of age; the second and third premolars at six months of age; and the fourth premolar (the largest in the upper jaw) at four to five months of age. There are two upper molars on both sides in the upper jaw. The first upper molar erupts from five to six months of age and the second molar is in place at six to seven months. The lower jaw contains three molars on each side. Eruption is similar to the upper jaw on the first and second while the third molar (the largest in the lower jaw) should be in place by seven months of age.

TEST, FECAL TRYPSIN:

Refer to *TESTS FOR GI, LIVER, AND PANCREATIC DISEASES, DIAGNOSTIC.*

TESTS FOR GI, LIVER, AND PANCREATIC DISEASES, DIAGNOSTIC:

A number of tests are performed to assist in the diagnosis of GI tract, liver and pancreatic diseases. Included here are various tests that the clinician may feel are necessary to help define the problem.

BLOOD TESTS:

LIVER:

1. *Alanine aminotransferase (ALT)* - Formerly known as *serum glutamic pyruvic transaminase (SGPT)*, ALT is the most useful liver disease test in dogs.
2. *Serum alkaline phosphatase (SAP)*
3. *Total serum bilirubin*
4. *Bromsulphalein® retention test (BSP)*
5. *Blood ammonia* and *ammonia tolerance test* - Because it requires special handling, blood ammonia is difficult to do.
6. *Serum protein*
7. *Glucose (blood)*

PANCREAS:

1. *Glucose (blood)*
2. *Serum lipase* - the most accurate enzyme determination of pancreatic damage
3. *Serum amylase* - Results are hard to interpret.
4. *Glucose tolerance test* - helpful in diagnosis of diabetes mellitus
5. *Glucagon tolerance test* - test for pancreatic tumors

GI TRACT:

1. *Serum electrolytes* - alterations seen with *diarrhea* and *vomiting*
2. *Complete blood count (CBC)*

COLONIC BIOPSY: Colonic biopsies are useful in identifying the cause of recurring lower GI tract diarrhea. A colonic biopsy helps to distinguish between bowel tumors, inflammation, allergic reactions and infection. Special instrumentation and expertise on the part of the clinician are required. Biopsy samples are submitted to a pathologist for microscopic determination of the kind of lesion.

HEPATIC BIOPSY: The hepatic biopsy procedure is a technique that although not utilized frequently enough, provides information for a more exact diagnosis. With this information, the clinician more easily formulates an appropriate treatment plan. Prognostic information for the owner and veterinarian is also acquired from the biopsy.

Each method used in a liver biopsy procedure has both advantages and disadvantages. Some techniques require specialized equipment such as a biopsy needle and a laparoscope. Blood clotting tests should be performed before the biopsy is done. Knowledge of the status of the liver enzyme and serum protein levels is necessary to determine whether a hepatic biopsy should be done and which technique will be safest. The most common potential complications of a liver biopsy procedure are hemorrhage, bile peritonitis, and infection. The use of a liver biopsy in appropriate situations is an important diagnostic tool for the veterinarian. The important information gained generally outweighs the risks of the procedure and anesthesia required.

CONTRAST MEDIUM X-RAY STUDY: *Barium sulfate,* the most common contrast medium, is given as a swallow for upper GI tract studies or as an enema for lower GI tract studies. Barium sulfate itself has a soothing effect on irritated tissues. Therefore, the test itself can be therapeutic. Preparation of the dog before contrast studies is very important. For most studies, the dog should be fasted for 24 hours and have a Fleet® enema eight to twelve hours before the x-rays are taken.

Another *contrast medium* used for GI studies is organic iodide like *Gastrografin®* . Organic iodides are safely used in stomach or intestinal perforations without fear of foreign body reactions.

ENDOSCOPY: This relatively new diagnostic aid in veterinary medicine requires special instrumentation and expertise in evaluating the results. As the use and availability of this equipment increases, exploratory surgical procedures of the lower bowel and stomach may become obsolete.

FECAL EXAMINATIONS: Two kinds of fecal examinations are done as an aid in diagnosing intestinal parasites. The *standard fecal flotation test* carried out in most veterinary offices involves the suspension of a fecal specimen in a flotation medium, such as zinc sulfate, sodium nitrate, or saturated sugar solutions. After centrifuging the specimen to force the heavy particles to the bottom of the tube, the surface of the flotation medium is examined for parasite eggs. Flotation is effective for all intestinal worms except tapeworm and possibly *Strongyloides*. Some fluke eggs can be found with this method while others will require specialized techniques. *Direct fecal examination* is necessary if *protozoan diseases* are suspected. Direct smear technique will help diagnose *Giardia, Trichomonas,* and *Balantidium* infections. The direct smear must be examined very quickly after the stool is passed as the protozoan parasites disappear rapidly. Although it is a protozoan parasite, *coccidia* can be found on the routine fecal flotation test.

FECAL TRYPSIN TEST: The trypsin test is important in determining the amount of the enzyme trypsin being produced by the pancreas. Most veterinarians are able to perform either the film strip digestion test or the more accurate gelatin tube procedure.

SUDAN III STAIN: This dye, used to demonstrate the presence of fat droplets in the stool, may give presumptive evidence of pancreatic inactivity.

TOXASCARIS LEONINA:

Refer to *PARASITES, INTESTINAL.*

TOXOCARA CANIS:

Refer to *PARASITES, INTESTINAL.*

TOXOCARA CATI:

Refer to *PARASITES, INTESTINAL.*

TRICHURIS:

Refer to *PARASITES, INTESTINAL.*

VOMITING:

Vomiting is a reflex act that results in the forceful expulsion of stomach contents. Causes of vomiting are classified into two categories - abdominal causes and causes from outside the abdomen. Abdominal causes include blockage of the intestinal tract, inflammatory causes like peritonitis, *pyometra,* and *pancreatitis,* as well as infectious causes like *coronavirus* or *parvovirus* infections and parasitic infestations.

Treatment of vomiting is directed toward identifying the underlying cause and either eliminating or treating it. Long term vomiting creates some very serious physiological changes such as *dehydration*, potassium and sodium depletion, and metabolic alkalosis.

VOMITING AND/OR DIARRHEA, SIGNS OF:

In order to help determine the cause of vomiting and/or diarrhea, observe the type, frequency, consistency, and length of time after eating that the condition occurs. Vomiting that is prolonged will cause serious metabolic upsets. *Sodium, potassium,* and *chloride* levels are greatly depleted resulting in a metabolic alkalosis. *Dehydration* occurs from loss of more fluids than are being replaced.

Fluid and electrolyte losses also occur in chronic diarrhea situations. Diarrhea is more common in dogs than in many other species because of their relatively short colon surface. The colon is the portion of the large bowel responsible for fluid absorption. If large amounts of fluids are presented to the short portion of bowel, only a small percentage of the total volume will be reabsorbed into the system.

WHIPWORM:

Refer to *PARASITES, INTESTINAL.*

X-RAY STUDY, CONTRAST MEDIA:

Refer to *TESTS FOR GI, LIVER, AND PANCREATIC DISEASES, DIAGNOSTIC.*

Chapter 6

MUSCULOSKELETAL SYSTEM

BONES, MUSCLES, LIGAMENTS, TENDONS

ACETYLSALICYLIC ACID:
Refer to *DRUGS USED FOR LAMENESS.*

ACHONDROPLASIA:

Achondroplasia is a form of canine dwarfism that is present at birth and is inherited as an autosomal dominant lethal gene. Bone growth of the front and back legs is retarded. Distinguishing achondroplasia from other forms of dwarfism which occur within some breeds is very difficult.

ANCONEAL PROCESS, UNUNITED:
Refer to *DYSPLASIA.*

ARTHRITIS - OSTEO AND RHEUMATOID:
Because a number of classifications of arthritis exist, only the most common forms, *osteoarthritis* and *rheumatoid arthritis,* will be considered.

Degenerative joint disease is called *OSTEOARTHRITIS.* In this condition there is no inflammation in the joint lining nor any systemic signs of joint disease (no fever or *increased white blood cell count*). Many older dogs suffer from this condition. Fragmenting of the weight bearing surfaces of the bones, a loss of cartilage, and new bone formation characterizes this problem.

The most frequent locations of osteoarthritis are the hips, stifles, shoulders, and elbows. While signs of lameness are seen in young adults, it gets progressively worse with age. Stiffness when rising that the dog can "warm" out of as it moves is a clinical sign of degenerative arthritis. After a considerable period of time, stiffness and lameness are almost constant.

Several facets of care are helpful in osteoarthritis therapy. If obese, the dog should lose weight. *Analgesics* like *aspirin* and *phenylbutazone* may help relieve pain. Periods of properly controlled exercise are important as are periods of rest during the day.

RHEUMATOID ARTHRITIS is an inflammatory, noninfectious form of arthritis with an immunological basis. This disease, primarily found in young adults of smaller breeds, is very erosive to the joints. However, it may occur as late as eight years of age and in any breed.

Clinical signs of rheumatoid arthritis are a shifting lameness and joint swelling, most frequently involving the pastern and hock joints. Common signs are fever, depression, lack of appetite, and swollen lymph nodes.

A number of lab tests are used to determine the etiology of the lameness. Radiographs of the swollen joint are helpful. White blood counts are often elevated. A decrease in *serum albumin protein* and an increase in alpha-2 gamma globulin protein can also be present. About 25% of the affected dogs have positive *rheumatoid factor tests*. The cause of this disease is unknown but an immunologic basis is suspected since the disease responds to powerful drugs that suppress the immune system.

Treatment of canine rheumatoid arthritis is started with a *corticosteroid* resulting in a dramatic improvement. However, as further exacerbations occur, the cortisone levels must be increasingly elevated. Ultimately even high doses will not cause remission. The best therapy is a combination of either *cyclophosphamide* and *prednisolone* or *azathioprine* and *prednisolone*. Since these drugs suppress blood forming cells, weekly and then monthly *blood counts* should be done to ensure a good response with minimal side effects. The dosage of the medications is tapered to as low a maintenance level as possible.

ASPIRIN:

Refer to *DRUGS USED FOR LAMENESS.*

ATAXIA:

Refer to *GAIT, DYSFUNCTIONS AND DEFINITIONS.*

ATROPHY, MUSCLE:

Muscle atrophy or the shrinking of the muscle mass or number of muscle cells has a number of causes. A cast leg will shrink from disuse. Atrophy may also be generalized as in old age or from the use of long term *corticosteroids.*

AUTOIMMUNE PANEL:

Refer to *MUSCULOSKELETAL SYSTEM DISEASE, TESTS FOR.*

AZATHIOPRINE:

Refer to *DRUGS USED FOR LAMENESS.*

BANAMINE® :

Refer to *DRUGS USED FOR LAMENESS.*

BIOPSY, MUSCLE:

Refer to *MUSCULOSKELETAL SYSTEM DISEASE, TESTS FOR.*

BONE BIOPSY:

Refer to *MUSCULOSKELETAL SYSTEM DISEASE, TESTS FOR.*

BUTAZOLIDIN® :

Refer to *Phenylbutazone in DRUGS USED FOR LAMENESS.*

CANINE "WOBBLER" SYNDROME:

Refer to *SPONDYLOPATHY, CERVICAL.*

CHONDRODYSPLASIA:

Chondrodysplasia or *dyschondroplasia* is a pathological condition resulting in abnormal growth of cartilage at the ends of long bone shafts and abnormal cartilage present near the *growth plates.* Clinical signs of *dwarfism* are produced. The body is normal length but the legs are bowed and shorter than normal.

Chondrodysplasia has been identified in several breeds. It is a simple recessive trait in the Alaskan Malamute. A concurrent form of anemia and altered trace mineral binding in the liver accompany it. The Norwegian Elkhound, the Great Pyrenees, and the Miniature Poodle also have a form of chondrodysplasia which again is of simple recessive inheritance. It is coupled with a kidney dysfunction which allows sugar to pass in the urine without an increase in the *blood sugar level.* To date, it has not been identified in the Doberman Pinscher.

This condition is diagnosed by radiographs of affected limbs as early as two weeks of age in the case of the Alaskan Malamute and by eight to ten weeks in other breeds. In this form of dwarfism, the head appears normal, the body length is normal or only slightly compressed, and the limbs are very short with thickened joint areas. Most affected offspring die prematurely because there is no treatment for the condition. If they do survive, they have difficulty in reproducing.

CHONDROSARCOMA:

Refer to *TUMORS, BONE.*

CORONOID PROCESS, FRAGMENTED OR UNUNITED:

Coronoid process disease is a potential cause of *elbow lameness* in medium to giant breeds. It has been found in sporting and working dogs with some regularity. Because of loose pieces of cartilage, degenerative joint disease results. It is unclear whether the coronoid process fails to join the adjacent ulna (forearm bone) in its developmental stage or whether some traumatic act has fragmented the process causing the degenerative changes to progress.

Diagnosis of coronoid process disease is difficult, but high quality radiographs taken in different positions will allow the clinician to discover the problem. Normally the bony process is covered with cartilage and is attached to the ulna bone by fibrocartilage or connective tissue.

Treatment of the coronoid process lameness is surgical. Removal of the unattached or fragmented bony processes will stop the degenerative joint condition and alleviate the pain. Prognosis for recovery of normal gait is good.

CORTISONES:

Refer to *DRUGS USED FOR LAMENESS.*

CPK ENZYME TEST:

Refer to *MUSCULOSKELETAL SYSTEM, TESTS FOR.*

CRABBING:

Refer to *GAIT, DYSFUNCTIONS AND DEFINITIONS OF.*

CREATININE PHOSPHOKINASE ENZYME TEST (CPK):

Refer to *MUSCULOSKELETAL SYSTEM DISEASE, TESTS FOR.*

CROSSING OVER:

Refer to *GAIT, DYSFUNCTIONS AND DEFINITIONS.*

CYCLOPHOSPHAMIDE:

Refer to *DRUGS USED FOR LAMENESS.*

CYTOXAN® :

Refer to *DRUGS USED FOR LAMENESS.*

DRUGS USED FOR LAMENESS:

AZATHIOPRINE or *Imuran®* is a cytotoxic drug used in combination with corticosteroids to manage immune mediated lameness such as *rheumatoid arthritis* and *systemic lupus erythematosus*. With a dosage every other day, its principle toxic side effects are gastrointestinal and hematologic.

ASPIRIN or *acetylsalicylic acid* is an anti-inflammatory drug commonly used to alleviate the discomfort associated with *osteoarthritis*. Some dogs are sensitive to the increased gastric acidity associated with aspirin administration requiring the use of a buffered product. Administration can be from 1 to 3 times daily.

BANAMINE® or *flunixin meglumine* is a very potent nonsteroidal analgesic with anti-inflammatory and antipyretic (temperature lowering) activity. Although it is used in dogs, the FDA clearance is only for horses. It can be given intravenously, intramuscularly, or orally in granular form. Banamine® should not be used more than 1 or 2 days in dogs since longer term administration may contribute to the development of fatal gastric perforations.

BUTAZOLIDIN® - Refer to *Phenylbutazone*.

CORTISONES - Of the cortisones used to treat lameness, the most common are *prednisone, prednisolone* and *triamcinolone*. Corticosteroids are anti-inflammatory agents that depress the adrenal glands when used either at high doses or for long periods of time. In the case of *rheumatoid arthritis*, the initial dramatic relief will disappear with time. Most cases will require combination therapy regimens with *Cytoxan®* or *Imuran®* .

CYCLOPHOSPHAMIDE or *Cytoxan®* is an anticancer drug sometimes used in combination with corticosteroids to treat immune mediated lamenesses. This relative of nitrogen mustard can cause reversible bone marrow depression. Administration is either oral or intravenous.

PHENYLBUTAZONE or *Butazolidin®* is an anti-inflammatory nonsteroidal drug used to treat inflammation and lameness. Given either orally or intravenously, long term usage may cause a *blood dyscrasia*.

DWARFISM:

Refer to *PITUITARY DWARFISM* in Chapter 4 on the ENDOCRINE SYSTEM, *ACHONDROPLASIA*, and *CHONDRODYSPLASIA*

DYSPLASIA:

The term dysplasia is defined as an abnormality in development.

ELBOW DYSPLASIA *(ununited anconeal process)* is a developmental disease which causes clinical lameness due to an instability of the elbow joint. This condition probably has a genetic basis. The lameness occurs because the anconeal process has not united to the ulnar bone in the elbow. In most breeds of dogs, the anconeal process does not have a separate bone growth center. In some dogs, however, the growth of the anconeal process occurs separately from the remainder of the ulna bone and then does not unite to form a stable elbow joint. Normally, closure and unification of the anconeal process is complete by 4 ½ months of age.

The main clinical sign is that of elbow lameness that may elicit pain on flexion and extension of the suspicious limb. Many affected dogs will appear to "toe out" as they walk. The diagnosis is made from a lateral radiograph with the elbow in flexion. The "beak-like" anconeal process is not united with the ulnar bone. Many times the lameness is unilateral even though both elbows are abnormal.

Two surgical procedures are done to treat elbow dysplasia. A surgical screw can be placed in the ununited anconeal process to connect it to the ulna or the anconeal process can be removed. Either type of surgery results in a good prognosis if done before severe degenerative elbow joint changes have occurred. Removing the anconeal process is technically easier surgery. The resulting joint instability is not a problem. On the other hand, surgical screw placement requires specialized equipment and a higher degree of surgical skill.

HIP DYSPLASIA is a malformation in the development of one or both ball and socket joints in the hip. The hip joint is composed of the socket which is formed by the bones of the pelvis and the "ball" (head) of the thigh bone (femur). Normally, this joint is a very tight fitting articulation lined with a smooth, lubricated, articular cartilage. The femoral head is connected to the acetabulum (socket) with a strong ligament.

Hip dysplasia is a multifactorial, genetically based disease which is greatly influenced by environmental factors. No "black or white" exists in dealing with the disease. Normal hipped dogs can produce offspring with all degrees of hip dysplasia and dysplastic dogs can produce normal offspring.

Clinical signs of hip dysplasia vary from minimal to severe pain in the area of the hips with pronounced lameness. The disease may be apparent by 3 ½ to 4 months of age at one extreme. However in an older dog, it may only involve stiffness and reluctance to walk. All puppies will appear normal radiographically at or shortly after birth. The degenerative changes occur with growth if the genetic and environmental factors for hip dysplasia are present. Affected dogs may shift their weight forward to remove some pressure from the hip joints. These dogs prefer to sit and as a result will not exercise freely. Subtle disposition changes may also be noticed.

A definitive diagnosis is made by pelvic radiograph. Some controversy surrounds the need for *anesthesia* and/or *sedation* in taking pelvic x-rays. Positioning of the dog is very important in determining minor or early changes in the hip joints. Properly positioned dogs lie on their backs with rear legs extended parallel to each other and the tail. Dogs with bony backs, deep-chested dogs, and dogs that have abnormal curvatures to their rear legs are difficult to position correctly. The ideal pelvic radiograph will show both sides of the pelvis as a "mirror image." The thickness of the pelvic bones and the size of the "holes" (foramen) in the bony pelvic girdle will be similar. If the pelvis is tilted, one side of the hip joint will appear shallow while the other side appears very deep.

Treatment of hip dysplasia is directed at alleviation of pain. The use of drugs like *aspirin, phenylbutazone,* or *corticosteroids* are partially effective in pain control. Surgery to relieve the spasm produced by the contraction of the pectineus muscle provides pain relief in some dogs affected with hip dysplasia. The surgical procedure involves cutting the pectineus muscle or its tendon of insertion. Another important facet of hip dysplasia therapy is exercise. With slow, gradual increases in walking exercise, the pelvic and thigh muscles become strengthened. These muscles help support the already weakened hip joints. Affected dogs are reluctant to exercise because of the pain. Lack of exercise weakens the involved muscles, which in turn adds to the overall weakness. The snowballing "cause and effect" problem must be handled with slow increases in exercise to increase muscle tone. *Anti-inflammatory drugs* used during the early phases of the exercise program are not needed continually after the muscle tone has improved. Recently, attempts have been made at total hip joint replacement surgery. These techniques replace the entire ball and socket joint on both sides with a stainless steel joint. The success rate of replacement surgery appears to be higher in dogs that weigh less than 50 to 60 pounds. The surgery requires a high degree of skill, is very expensive, and requires a long convalescent period.

Manipulation of environmental factors have been proposed as part of the control of hip dysplasia. These procedures include *pectineus muscle surgery* in young dogs, mega doses of *vitamin C* administered to bitches and their offspring during the formative months, cage confinement of growing puppies, and caloric restriction during puppy growth. These procedures are presented here with no opinion as to their worth just that they have been advocated by some over the years.

Hip dysplasia is controlled by radiographing all breeding stock and selecting away from severely affected dogs. The use of dogs with hip dysplasia should be limited to those that are truly outstanding in other traits important in the breed. Refer to the section on the ORTHOPEDIC FOUN-DATION FOR ANIMALS (OFA) for current statistics on the number of Doberman Pinschers that have been radiographed during the past ten years and the incidence of hip dysplasia in the breed.

POLYOSTOTIC FIBROUS DYSPLASIA is an uncommon genetically based disease which causes the replacement of normal bone with fibrous tissue and immature bony tissue. The normal bone is lysed, eroded, and seriously weakened by the cystic formation that occurs.

Clinically, the dog is presented with lameness and swelling generally above the pastern joint. In cases of older dogs, pathological fractures occur from weaknesses in the bone. Diagnosis is made on radiographic examination. Since this condition is thought to be hereditary in the Doberman Pinscher, blood lines should be studied in affected dogs. Treatment is the surgical scraping of the cystic areas. Bone grafting is used in areas where pathological fractures are present. The cause is unknown.

ELBOW DYSPLASIA:

Refer to *DYSPLASIA.*

ELBOW LUXATION:

Refer to *LUXATION.*

ELECTROMYOGRAPHY (EMG) TEST:

Refer to *MUSCULOSKELETAL SYSTEM DISEASE, TESTS FOR.*

ENOSTOSIS:

Refer to *PANOSTEITIS.*

EOSINOPHILIC MYOSITIS:

Refer to *MYOSITIS.*

EOSINOPHILIC PANOSTEITIS:

Refer to *PANOSTEITIS.*

FIBROSARCOMA:

Refer to *TUMORS, BONE.*

FRACTURES:

A fracture is defined as a break in the continuity of a bone or cartilage. The break may be partial or completely through the bone. Usually a fracture is accompanied by damage to the tissue surrounding the bone (muscle, connective tissue, blood vessels, and nerves).

These questions are raised when classifying fractures. Is there an open wound at the fracture site? How extensive is the damage to the bone? What is the direction and location of the fracture? How stable is the fracture?

The types of fractures under these classifications follow:

1. *Avulsion fracture* is the separation of a small amount of bone with its attached tendon, ligament, or muscle. The most common site is the tibial crest of the shin bone where the kneecap tendon attaches.

2. *Closed fracture* is a fracture with no break in the skin.

3. *Comminuted fracture* is one that fragments into a number of small pieces.

4. *Complete fracture* is completely through the bone walls (cortex) and usually accompanied by displacement of the fracture ends.

5. *Compound fracture* is another name for an "open fracture" where the fractured bones communicate to the outside of the body. Infection and delayed healing is often a problem.

6. *Fissure fracture* is a fracture where cracks penetrate the bone wall (cortex) while the covering of the bone (periosteum) is still intact.

7. *Green-stick fracture* is a fracture of growing puppies where one side of the bone wall (cortex) is broken but the opposite side is only bent.

8. *Impacted fractures,* generally resulting from falls from high places, are those in which the fragments are driven into each other by force.

9. *Multiple fracture* is a fracture where three or more pieces have no common meeting point.

10. *Nonunion fracture* is a type of fracture that has not healed due to infection, lack of blood supply, lack of nutrients, or instability of the fracture site.

11. *Oblique fracture* is a fracture where the fracture line is diagonal to the bone and will slip away from alignment without stabilization because of muscle contraction.

12. Open fracture - refer to *Compound Fracture.*

13. *Physeal fracture,* which occurs in growing puppies, is a separation along a growth plate (epiphyseal line).

14. *Spiral fracture* is a break in a curved bone due to inherent instability. Fixation of the fracture is required.

15. *Stable fracture* is a break where the bone elements are interlocked and are not moveable under normal circumstances.

16. *Transverse fracture* is a fracture line at right angles to the long axis of the bone.

17. *Unstable fracture* is a break that is moveable or unstable due to the way in which the break occurred. Several of the above fractures such as oblique, spiral, and compound fractures are examples of unstable fractures that will require fixation to stabilize them.

Clinical signs of a bone fracture are pain, crepitus (a crunching sound on palpation), swelling, and deformity. A definitive diagnosis is made by taking two radiographic views. In the the treatment of fractured bones, reduction is attempted to bring the fragmented ends into apposition. Reduction is followed by fixation to keep the ends in position until healing occurs.

The *rate of healing* is greatly influenced by age. Dogs under three months of age only require 2 to 4 weeks of fixation for clinical union to occur. Puppies from 3 to 6 months require anywhere from 4 to 12 weeks. Older puppies from 6 to 12 months of age need 5 to 20 weeks. Adult dogs require from 2 to 12 months for clinical union of a fracture to occur.

GAIT, DYSFUNCTIONS AND DEFINITIONS OF:

The term gait defines the manner or style of moving. Definitions of different kinds and types of gait will be provided here, however discussion of movement and reasons for faulty movement will be limited.

ATAXIA - a lack of muscular coordination resulting in a weak and weaving type of gait

CRABBING - the movement of a dog with its back at an angle to the line of travel

CROSSING OVER - also known as Weaving - the swinging of the legs in an arc crossing each other

FLAPPING - refer to *Padding*.

GALLOP - a fast running gait (two kinds of gallop - single and double suspension gallop)

GOOSE STEPPING - refer to *Hypermetric gait*.

HACKNEY ACTION - the exaggerated, high lifting of the front leg with the pastern and paw pointing downward.

HYPERMETRIC GAIT - *("Goose Stepping")* - an exaggerated gait indicating central nervous system dysfunction.

HYPOMETRIC GAIT - a shuffling, sliding gait due to central nervous system dysfunction

LEVEL GAIT - a form of movement in which the withers do not rise or fall

LUMBERING - a heavy, awkward, clumsy gait seen predominantly in large overweight dogs

PACE - a gait in which the front and rear left feet are on the ground at the same time that the front and rear right feet are in the air and vice versa - considered to be a lazy gait

PADDING - *("Flapping")* - the opposite of the hackney action where the pad actually touches the ground before the normal full forward swing of the front leg occurs

PADDLING - a circular motion of front legs as a canoe paddle would move

SIDE WHEELER - refer to *Crabbing*

SINGLE TRACKING - the movement of the individual paws toward a single imaginary line from the center of the body as the gait speed increases - legs incline inward toward the center line

TROT - a diagonal gait in which the right front and the left rear touch the ground at the same time while the left front and right rear are in the air

WEAVING - refer to *Crossing over*

GALLOP:

Refer to *GAIT, DYSFUNCTIONS AND DEFINITIONS*.

GOOSE STEPPING:

Refer to *GAIT, DYSFUNCTIONS AND DEFINITIONS*.

GROWTH PLATE (AVULSION AND PREMATURE CLOSURE):

Growth plates are the areas of the bones in young dogs where elongation (increase in size) occurs. These sections of bone are not as strong as adjacent areas not possessing this specialized function. *Avulsion of growth plates* or *physeal fractures* occur in the growth plates above the carpus (pastern). Serious deviation of the paw may occur if not treated properly.

Premature growth plate closure can occur throughout the body creating a *dwarf* or *chondrodysplasia* situation. When premature closure occurs in individual bones, it causes a deformity of the long bone conformation. This condition is illustrated in the foreleg where two bones, the radius and ulna, are growing at the same rate. If the growth plate on the ulna closes and the radial plate remains open, the leg below the pastern will deviate toward the outside. Correction of these problems requires an experienced orthopedic surgeon.

HACKNEY ACTION:

Refer to *GAIT, DYSFUNCTION AND DEFINITIONS.*

HEMANGIOSARCOMA:

Refer to *TUMORS, BONE.*

HIP DYSPLASIA:

Refer to *DYSPLASIA.*

HIP LUXATION:

Refer to *LUXATION.*

HOCKS, POPPING:

Popping hocks are hocks that bend forward and/or sideways indicating joint and ligament instability. In many cases, the rear leg conformation does not have enough angulation to keep the hock joint in its proper anatomic relationship. Treatment of severe popping hocks involves the surgical tightening of the ligaments. Straight stifled rear leg conformation cannot be changed.

HYPERMETRIC GAIT:

Refer to *GAIT, DYSFUNCTIONS AND DEFINITIONS.*

HYPERPARATHYROIDISM:

Hyperparathyroidism is a disorder in which the amount of hormone secreted by the parathyroid gland is too great. The disease may be primary or secondary to either a nutritional problem or a kidney deficiency.

The most common clinical signs are lameness, multiple fractures in older dogs, and a stiff gait. Other signs are apparent if kidney problems are present. Resorption of bone calcium causes the bones of the face and jaws to become very soft and bendable. Since the jaw does not close properly, the term *"rubber jaw"* is utilized. The condition is diagnosed by measuring blood calcium, phosphorus, and alkaline phosphatase enzyme levels. Radiographs also help in the diagnosis.

HYPERTROPHIC PULMONARY OSTEOARTHROPATHY (HPOA):
Refer to *OSTEOARTHROPATHY, HYPERTROPHIC PULMONARY.*

HYPOMETRIC GAIT:
Refer to *GAIT, DYSFUNCTIONS AND DEFINITIONS.*

IMURAN® :
Refer to *DRUGS USED FOR LAMENESS.*

INSTABILITY, CERVICAL VERTEBRAL:
Cervical vertebral instability is necessary for clinical signs to be observed in the *"wobbler"* or *cervical spondylopathy syndrome.* The vertebral instability occurs in the articulations that connect one vertebra to another. It may also be part of the ligaments that are either over or under developed. Instability of adjacent vertebrae causes trauma to the cervical spinal cord which is manifested as signs of neurological disease.

INTRAMUSCULAR INJECTION (IM) TECHNIQUE:
Intramuscular injections convey medications to the bloodstream more quickly than subcutaneous injections and less quickly than the intravenous or intraperitoneal routes. The most commonly used muscles for injections are those of the posterior lateral thighs. Lumbar muscles, cervical, or shoulder muscles are also used for IM injections.

The technique for administering an IM injection involves grasping the muscular posterior portion of the thigh halfway between the hip and stifle. A sharp needle is introduced into the muscle mass to a depth of 1/2 inch (depending on the size of the dog). Before injecting into the muscle, the syringe plunger is pulled back (aspirate) to make sure that no blood appears in the needle hub. If blood appears, the needle is pulled out completely and reintroduced into a new area. The aspiration is then repeated. Steady pressure is used on the injection of the syringe plunger.

Complications from IM injections include the placement of the medication too close to a nerve causing temporary or permanent lameness and the development of a sterile abscess around the material that was injected. Drugs that should be injected intramuscularly include most *antibiotics*, some forms of *steroids, rabies vaccines,* and drugs present in an oil vehicle like *hormones* and *fat soluble vitamins*.

LAMENESS:
Lameness is classified as either weight bearing or non-weight bearing. Among the causes of *lameness* are joint diseases, fractures, tumors, *bone infections,* muscle inflammation, metabolic bone diseases, neurological diseases, as well as ligament and tendon injuries. Laboratory aids and tests which are necessary to diagnose the cause of lameness include palpation of the involved area, biochemical tests, radiographs, neurological exams, and blood exams.

LEGG-CALVE-PERTHES DISEASE:

Legg-Calve-Perthes bone disease is seen in small dogs. In young dogs of toy breeds, for some unknown reason, the blood supply to the head (cap) of the femur bone which forms the hip joint loses its blood supply. The cartilage and bony tissue deteriorate as the body attempts to absorb this diseased tissue. If untreated, secondary *arthritis* and a continual painful *lameness* remain. Treatment is surgical removal of the diseased portion and the femoral neck. The dog's body creates a false joint and freedom from pain. Hereditary implications are present.

LEVEL GAIT:

Refer to *GAIT, DYSFUNCTIONS AND DEFINITIONS.*

LIGAMENT, RUPTURE OF ANTERIOR CRUCIATE:

The stifle joint is a complex structure that is stabilized by a number of ligaments, tendons, and the patella (kneecap). One of the major stabilizing forces of the stifle joint is the crossed cruciate ligament pair - anterior and posterior. A higher incidence of rupture of the anterior cruciate ligament occurs in middle aged heavy females.

The history usually presented with this problem is one of sudden lameness after exercise, pain on movement of the stifle joint, and loss of use of the leg. Examination of the stifle joint for the characteristic *"sliding drawer syndrome"* may require *anesthesia* or *deep sedation* because of the pain elicited from manipulation of the affected joint. Radiographs may also be necessary to determine the degree of instability.

Treatment is generally surgical in nature. However, in some cases where total separation of the ligaments is not evident, complete rest for thirty days results in healing. Surgical procedures vary from construction of a new ligament to placing a mattress configuration of artificial suture material in the side of the joint tissue to reduce the looseness in the entire stifle region. With proper treatment, the prognosis is good for regaining use of the leg. Problems in treatment can occur if a closed surgical approach is employed since other structures may be damaged requiring that they be repaired before total clinical soundness is restored.

LION'S JAW:

Refer to *OSTEOPATHY, CRANIOMANDIBULAR.*

LUMBERING:

Refer to *GAIT, DYSFUNCTIONS AND DEFINITIONS.*

LUXATION:

Luxation is defined as the dislocation of a joint. While luxation occurs in any joint, the most common three locations are the hip, the kneecap (patella), and the elbow.

HIP LUXATION is the most common form of dislocation in the dog, usually occurring as a result of trauma. If the case is diagnosed within four days, closed reduction of the dislocated hip is satisfactory unless severe soft tissue and cartilage damage have occurred. Dogs with *hip dysplasia* are more likely to require open or surgical reduction of a dislocated hip because of their shallow hip socket (acetabulum). The diagnosis of hip luxation is made from clinical signs and radiographs. Clinically, pain and crepitus (crunching) is present on manipulation of the hip joint. The affected leg appears shorter than the weight bearing leg. X-rays to verify that there are no fractures around the hip joint are required for a definitive diagnosis. An additional radiograph to verify the reduction is necessary after the hip is reduced. The reduced joint is immobilized by a sling for 3 to 10 days allowing the surrounding soft tissue to heal. The open surgical reduction which is necessary in some cases carries with it a more guarded prognosis for recurrence.

ELBOW LUXATIONS are traumatic in origin and generally occur laterally (outside) because of the structure of the bones and ligaments forming the elbow joint. Clinical signs are of a *non-weight bearing lameness* with the elbow flexed and the radius and ulna (bones of the foreleg) deviated to an extreme degree. Radiographs insure that no fractures or serious ligament damage are evident.

For the reduction of the luxation, *general anesthesia* is necessary. Most can be reduced in a closed manner, but rare instances require open surgical reduction. After reduction, utilization of a modified support splint for several days is required. The elbow joint should be flexed and extended to keep its range of motion. Restricted activity for several weeks is important. If ligament damage necessitates surgery, the healing process will be slower with a less favorable prognosis.

PATELLAR LUXATION *("slipped stifle") ("slipped patella")* is a common problem in all sizes of dogs. Dislocations of the kneecap (patella) can be either to the inside (medial), to the outside (lateral), or in some cases, both ways. The abnormal structure of the stifle joint and associated muscles and tendons above it may cause patellar luxation. The position of the tibial crest on the bone below the stifle joint (the shin bone or tibia) also affects patellar luxation. Patellar luxation can be due to a traumatic accident or to abnormal anatomical structures. *Medial (inside) patellar luxation* is more common in dogs that are bow-legged. Conversely, *lateral (outside) patellar luxation* is more common in cow-hocked dogs.

Four stifle (knee joint) structures are important in maintaining normal patellar function. The quadriceps muscle group on the thigh bone must be in a normal location so the patellar (kneecap) tendon is not pulled abnormally to one side or the other. The kneecap must normally "ride" in a groove in the lower part of the thigh bone. The collateral ligaments that attach to the kneecap from the inside and the outside must not be too long or too short. The bony attachment of the patellar tendon on the shin bone (tibia) must be directly under the kneecap to avoid any abnormal pulling on the tendon. If these above structures are not in their normal positions, the possibility for dislocation of the kneecap exists. Clinical signs of medial (inside) patellar luxation are more apparent as the dog turns a corner, suddenly elevating the pivoting leg into a flexed position. Pain is very intense in first time dislocations, but is less severe in repeat luxations. Generally, lateral (outward) luxations do not cause the pain response that medial luxations do. Occasionally, radiographs are used in the diagnosis. However, most are diagnosed by palpation of the suspicious joint structure. Treatment in the acute case is directed to returning the kneecap to a normal position and massaging the thigh muscles to keep them from contracting, "forcing" the kneecap out of its normal position. In chronic cases where the patella continually luxates or in cases in which the kneecap does not maintain a normal anatomic position, surgical intervention is necessary. Luxations are graded from 1 to 4 and the degree of deviation from the normal dictates the kind and amount of corrective orthopedic surgery. The prognosis after competent surgical repair is good for freedom from pain and use of the leg. Evidence has been found linking the development of medial patellar luxation in family lines. Dogs with *hip dysplasia* have a higher incidence of lateral patellar luxation.

MANDIBULAR PERIOSTITIS:

Refer to *OSTEOPATHY, CRANIOMANDIBULAR.*

MULTIPLE MYELOMA:

Refer to *TUMORS, BONE.*

MUSCLE BIOPSY:

Refer to *MUSCULOSKELETAL SYSTEM DISEASE, TESTS FOR.*

MUSCULAR DYSTROPHY:

Two forms of muscular dystrophy occur in the dog. The form found in young dogs is characterized by the swelling of the muscles in the neck, back, and shoulders. During muscle swelling, the muscle fibers are actually undergoing degeneration. The muscle cells are being replaced with scar tissue and fat cells. Clinically, the dog becomes progressively weaker resulting in a more stilted and stiff gait. Specific diagnosis is made by *muscle biopsy* and *electromyography (EMG)*. The prognosis is poor since no treatment arrests the insidious nature of the disease.

The other form, which occurs in older dogs, is the form most closely related to muscular dystrophy in man. Except for the lack of muscle swelling, clinical signs are similar to the young dog variety. Diagnosis is made by muscle biopsy and EMG. Again, the prognosis is poor. Information about the hereditary basis of this disease is sketchy.

MUSCULOSKELETAL SYSTEM DISEASE, TESTS FOR:

An AUTOIMMUNE PANEL is composed of a number of blood or tissue tests necessary in the diagnosis of immunological diseases. Autoimmune diseases which affect the muscles or bones include *systemic lupus erythematosus, rheumatoid arthritis,* and possibly *panosteitis* and *myasthenia gravis.* An *anti-nuclear antibody test (ANA), an LE Prep,* a *rheumatoid factor,* and a *Coombs (direct and indirect)* compose an autoimmune panel.

A BONE BIOPSY is technically a difficult procedure requiring an accomplished surgeon with specialized equipment. If a space occupying lesion is situated on the bone, a sample of the bone is necessary. Before the bone sample is examined by a histopathologist, it must undergo special processing. A bone marrow biopsy is performed much more easily.

The CREATININE PHOSPHOKINASE ENZYME (CPK) TEST is an enzyme test used to determine muscle deterioration. CPK enzyme is normally in high concentrations in skeletal muscle. Increased levels in the blood plasma indicate muscular degeneration. This fact is useful in diagnosing certain kinds of *myositis.*

The ELECTROMYOGRAPHY TEST measures electro-potential at the muscle fiber membrane. For this test to be valid, the nervous system must be intact and functioning properly. Normal neuromuscular functions have predictable characteristic waves. Both visual and auditory disorders produce abnormal EMG results.

MUSCLE BIOPSIES are examined microscopically. The muscle sample should not be taken from areas near intramuscular injection sites or EMG sites. The sample of muscle is preserved in formalin after having been placed in a biopsy clamp to keep it from contracting.

RADIOGRAPHY (X-ray) is useful in the diagnosis of bone and joint disorders. Views taken from several angles are necessary to adequately diagnose some fractures and joint pathology.

SERUM ASPARTATE AMINOTRANSFERASE (AST) (FORMERLY SERUM GLUTAMIC-OXALOACETIC TRANSAMINASE OR SGOT) ENZYME TEST is indicative of muscle damage if the enzyme level is elevated and no other liver enzyme levels are increased. After the liver, skeletal muscle contains the largest amount of the SGOT enzyme. By itself, the SGOT enzyme test is of limited value.

MYASTHENIA GRAVIS:

Myasthenia gravis is classified as both a muscular system disease and a nervous system disease. The disease is characterized by a deficiency of a chemical that transmits the nerve impulse to the muscle. While this can occur in a generalized state, the muscles of the face and neck are most commonly involved. As the disease progresses, chewing and swallowing become difficult and leg muscles grow weak. Severely affected dogs die from failure of the respiratory muscles.

Myasthenia gravis is diagnosed by clinical signs, EMG findings, and a positive response to Tensilon® . While not absolute, the use of Tensilon® IV will make an affected dog appear normal within one minute. The effect lasts for about fifteen minutes before the muscle weakness reappears. Oral doses of neostigmine or pyridostigmine control the disease but treat only the symptoms. However, since myasthenia gravis may be autoimmune in nature, *steroids* are the treatment of choice. Life long drug therapy is essential to control signs although occasional remissions do occur.

MYOSITIS:

Myositis, the inflammation of muscle fiber bundles, has varied causes. Traumatic injury produces severe inflammation of affected muscle groups. Some parasites have an affinity for muscle tissue. In the dog, *Toxoplasma gondii* causes a muscular weakness by initiating a myositis. *Leptospirosis* bacteria also cause a severe myositis. The three forms of myositis which occur in the dog, each of undetermined origin, have similar treatment.

EOSINOPHILIC MYOSITIS occurs in young adults with a predilection for the muscles of the head. The affected muscles may swell at first but later become painful making eating difficult. This disease is diagnosed by the characteristic bony facial appearance, by a high *eosinophil cell count,* and by a *muscle biopsy* which also contains eosinophils. The cause is not known. Recurrence is common with muscular control becoming more difficult each time.

ATROPHIC MYOSITIS also involves the muscles of the face and head initially. As it continues, the shoulder and other body muscle groups are affected. After the initial inflammatory response, affected muscles atrophy. In the case of the head and face, the bony outline of the skull becomes prominent. Little pain is associated with this condition. Diagnosis is made from clinical signs and muscle biopsy.

POLYMYOSITIS is a generalized muscular inflammation involving a number of muscle groups in the body. While pain is present on acute involvement, the usual clinical sign is weakness. This form of myositis occurs with some systemic conditions like *systemic lupus erythematosus, rheumatoid arthritis,* and some malignancies. Diagnosis is made by association with other conditions, muscle biopsies, and serum enzyme tests from *CPK* and *SGOT enzymes.*

Treatment for the three forms of myositis includes cortisone in addition to the removal of any underlying cause if one is found. Exacerbations are common. Therapy is required for life. The prognosis is guarded.

MYOTOMY OR TENOTOMY, PECTINEUS:

This surgical procedure is performed to relieve pain associated with the shortening of the pectineus muscle in *hip dysplasia*. The small pectineus muscle originates on the bony pelvis and inserts via a long tendon on the inner surface of the femur (thigh bone). It can be palpated in the groin area near where the pulse is felt. Normally tube-shaped, the pectineus muscle shortens in cases of hip dysplasia joint instability. The surgery involves completely severing the tendon of insertion on the femur, relieving the muscle spasm and associated joint pain. Although the surgical procedure does not change the dysplastic nature of the hip joints, for some dogs this is a salvage operation.

ORTHOPEDIC FOUNDATION FOR ANIMALS (OFA):

The OFA foundation has served as a registry for several serious canine orthopedic diseases since 1966. Located at the University of Missouri, their address is:

> Orthopedic Foundation for Animals, Inc.
> University of Missouri - Columbia
> Columbia, MO 65211
> (314) 442-0418

OFA will read a hip radiograph at any age but will not issue an OFA number unless the dog is 24 months old at the time of the radiograph. The submitted x- ray is read by three independent veterinary radiologists. The majority opinion is then expressed in one of the seven classifications developed by the OFA.

Numbers 1-3 are given OFA breed numbers.

#1 — *EXCELLENT HIP JOINT CONFORMATION* - superior hip joint conformation compared to other individuals of the same breed and age

#2 — *GOOD HIP JOINT CONFORMATION* - well-formed hip joint conformation compared to other individuals of the same breed and age

#3 — *FAIR HIP JOINT CONFORMATION* - minor irregularities of hip joint conformation compared to other individuals of the same breed and age

Numbers 4-7 are ineligible for OFA Breed Numbers.

#4 — *BORDERLINE HIP JOINT CONFORMATION* - marginal hip joint conformation of indeterminate status with respect to hip dysplasia at the time of the x-ray - recommend repeat study in 6-8 months

#5 — *MILD HIP DYSPLASIA* - radiographic evidence of minor dysplastic changes of the hip joints

#6 — *MODERATE HIP DYSPLASIA* - well-defined radiographic evidence of dysplastic changes of the hip joints

#7 — *SEVERE HIP DYSPLASIA* - radiographic evidence of marked dysplastic changes of the hip joints

Between 1974 and 1984, 2,619 Doberman Pinschers or 0.4% of the eligible population of Dobes had hip radiographs submitted to OFA. Of this number, 8.1% were dysplastic. Breed numbers were awarded to 90.3% having either a fair, good, or excellent classification. Of the submitted radiographs, 1.6% were considered borderline with recommended repeat evaluation in 6-8 months.

OFA will also evaluate breeds for elbow dysplasia. Radiographs taken and submitted to OFA become their property. Proper positioning for OFA quality radiographs is very important, necessitating chemical restraint in most cases. The dog must be lying on its back with its rear legs extended and parallel to each other.

Worthy of notation is the fact that the percentage of dysplastic Doberman Pinschers has decreased from 10.6% in the evaluations from 1966 to 1973 to 8.1% during the following ten year period.

OSTEOARTHROPATHY, HYPERTROPHIC PULMONARY (HPOA):

This uncommon bone disease is the result of a *lung tumor* or in rare cases, other thoracic conditions like *heartworm disease*. In this disease, new bone is laid down on the lower legs causing a thickened, painful extremity. The cause is unknown.

HPOA is diagnosed by radiograph. The clinical signs are *lameness* with thickened bones in the feet and lower legs. After radiographs of the legs are taken, a lateral chest x-ray is done to look for the thoracic "mass" that has initiated the leg pathology. The prognosis is poor since in a high number of cases, the accompanying *lung tumor* is inoperable. If, however, the lung pathology is resolved satisfactorily, the new bone proliferation on the legs will be resorbed causing the lameness to disappear.

OSTEOCHONDRITIS DISSECANS:

Osteochondritis dissecans (OCD) is a specific bone disease that refers to breaking or separation of joint cartilage from the underlying bone resulting in this degenerative joint disease. The first description was in the shoulder joint involving the cartilage on the humerus (upper arm bone). Now, however, OCD has been found in the elbow, hock, and stifle joints with some regularity.

The clinical signs depend on the location and the degree of cartilage involvement. In general, lameness and possibly swelling of the joint will be evident especially if the hock joint is involved. In the case of the shoulder joint, extension of the leg will elicit pain. A "clicking sound" is heard in the joint. Clinical signs are first seen around six months of age. In over 70% of the cases, both shoulders or sides will be involved. Incidence in sporting breeds and working dogs, especially the giant breeds, is very high, occurring about five times more frequently in males than females.

The diagnosis of OCD is made by clinical signs, history, and finding radiographic lesions. Positioning of the affected area is very important if a radiographic diagnosis is to be obtained. The shoulder is examined from the side extending the limb by pulling the shoulder joint forward and away from the neck. If the lameness is in the elbow, a medial oblique, anterior-posterior radiograph will show the inside condyle of the upper arm where OCD lesions occur. The elbow is extended and rotated outward for proper positioning. Standard positioning is adequate for the diagnosis of OCD in the stifle region. Common practice includes radiographing the opposite leg joint after a lesion is found because many dogs are affected bilaterally. Treatment is subject to some controversy. The conservative approach rests the dog in confinement for two to three months. Others feel that corrective surgery should be done early before serious degenerative changes have occurred. Before making a decision about treatment, consider that any dog with corrective OCD surgery is no longer eligible for competition in American Kennel Club events. On the other hand, dogs that are confined will probably not cause further damage to their shoulders. If healing does not occur, surgical correction can always be undertaken at a later date. Use of pain killers (analgesics) is also questionable. Because the dog feels better during confinement, the dog is more difficult to keep quiet therefore increasing the chances of further damage. Complications from surgery are few, other than the development of seromas (serum pockets) at the site of surgery which may require surgical drainage. The surgical procedure is designed to remove any loose cartilaginous pieces or flaps from the affected area. The resulting defect becomes covered with new cartilage over the next year. If both shoulders are affected, some surgeons advocate surgery on both at the same time so recovery is only necessary once. The post-surgical recovery period lasts from 2 to 8 weeks during which confinement is required.   The prognosis is generally good following either successful conservative therapy or surgery done by a competent surgeon. Whether this condition or tendency toward this condition is inherited is also open to debate. Much evidence points toward a familial tendency but no definitive tests have been done.

OSTEODYSTROPHY, HYPERTROPHIC:

Hypertrophic osteodystrophy is also called *canine scurvy* since some think *vitamin C deficiency* is the underlying cause of this obscure long bone disorder. Clinical signs are normally observed between three and seven months of age in large rapidly growing puppies. The most common site for lesions is in the bones of the forelegs just above the pastern joint. The affected bones are swollen, warm, and painful to the touch. The puppy is depressed, has no appetite, and is reluctant to stand or move around.

Definitive diagnosis of hypertrophic osteodystrophy is made by radiographs of the affected bones. Occasionally, bones other than the forelegs are affected. Because the exact cause is unknown, symptomatic treatment includes the administration of *aspirin* and *phenylbutazone* for pain relief. Nothing definite is known about hereditary factors.

The prognosis is guarded. Many dogs recover completely but some develop bony degenerative problems and become deformed. Death from hypertrophic osteodystrophy is unusual.

OSTEOGENIC SARCOMA:

Refer to *TUMORS, BONE.*

OSTEOMYELITIS:

Osteomyelitis is an inflammation of the bone marrow and adjacent bone tissue. Although a number of causes exist for osteomyelitis a bacterial infection or a mycotic (fungus) infection is normally the underlying cause. Bacterial infections are frequently the result of a contaminated wound from foreign body penetration, *compound fractures,* or internal bone fixation equipment. *Staphylococcus* or *streptococcus* organisms are usually isolated. Lameness, pain, loss of appetite, and fever are all clinical signs. Diagnosis is made by radiograph and from bone cultures. Antibiotic therapy is used, with the possibility of further surgery to remove any free pieces of infected bone or foreign bodies. The prognosis is good but long term treatment is necessary.

Mycotic osteomyelitis, commonly caused by the systemic fungus disease *coccidioidomycosis,* is also seen in *blastomycosis, actinomycosis,* and *nocardiosis.* Treatment is the long term use of *amphotericin B* or *ketoconazole.*

OSTEOPATHY, CRANIOMANDIBULAR:

Craniomandibular osteopathy, also called *Lion's Jaw* and *mandibular periostitis,* is a noncancerous, noninflammatory, proliferating bone disease. Both mandibles (lower jaws), temporal bones, and occipital bones of the skull are involved. Most cases are recognized between three and six months of age. While most cases occur in Scottish and West Highland White Terriers, other breeds including the Doberman Pinscher have been affected.

Clinical signs include pain when the mouth is opened, excess salivation, fever, depression, and hard swellings on the lower jaws. Diagnosis is made by radiographic evidence of the proliferation of bony tissue on the jaws or skull. Both lateral (side) and ventrodorsal (bottom to top) radiographic views should be taken.

Treatment depends on the number of bones involved so it may be both surgical and medical. If the dog is not able to open its mouth to eat or to drink, the placement of a *pharyngostomy tube* is necessary. The condition is self-limiting. After the skeleton has stopped growing, the disease process may regress and completely disappear. In a very severe condition where supportive therapy can not buy enough time to allow the skeleton to mature, euthanasia is the only alternative.

The prognosis ranges from guarded to good depending on the degree of involvement. Presently it is believed that this condition has a genetic basis. Suspension of further reproduction of the sire and dam should be seriously considered.

PACE:

Refer to *GAIT, DYSFUNCTIONS AND DEFINITIONS.*

PADDING:

Refer to *GAIT, DYSFUNCTIONS AND DEFINITIONS.*

PADDLING:

Refer to *GAIT, DYSFUNCTIONS AND DEFINITIONS.*

PANOSTEITIS:

Panosteitis begins at about six months of age. The cause is unknown. Other names include *enostosis, eosinophilic panosteitis,* and *wandering lameness.* It is far more common in males (5 to 1),. The clinical signs of this bone disorder are *lameness,* reluctance to walk, occasional inappetence, and fever. If the affected leg is firmly squeezed, pain responses are elicited. In differentiating pain associated with panosteitis from other lamenesses, isolating the painful area on the long bone is important. The panosteitis pain area is located in the middle of the bone while pain from areas of *hypertrophic osteodystrophy* and *rheumatoid arthritis* are near the joint. Recurring lameness may involve the same leg or affect another leg. Numerous episodes occur over several months with each period of lameness lasting from 1 to 30 days.

Diagnosis is made from history, clinical signs, and radiographic findings. Three phases can be differentiated on x-ray providing the affected bone is included in the radiographic evaluation. Each phase reflects a separate period in the progression of the disease.

Treatment is symptomatic using *aspirin, phenylbutazone,* and *cortisone* for pain relief. Panosteitis is self-limiting and causes no permanent changes. On occasion, however, pain is severe enough to cause a compensatory deviation in normal movement. Sometimes this deviation remains after the disease has run its course. Panosteitis occurs in certain families. Although inherited traits have not yet been proven, it appears to be passed on through asymptomatic brood bitch carriers.

PHENYLBUTAZONE:

Refer to *DRUGS USED IN LAMENESS.*

RADIOGRAPHY:

Refer to *MUSCULOSKELETAL SYSTEM DISEASE, TESTS FOR.*

RHABDOMYOMA:

Refer to *TUMORS, MUSCLE.*

RHABDOMYOSARCOMA:

Refer to *TUMORS, MUSCLE.*

"RUBBER JAW":

Refer to *HYPERPARATHYROIDISM.*

SARCOMA, OSTEOGENIC:

Refer to *TUMORS, BONE.*

SGOT ENZYME TEST:

Refer to *MUSCULOSKELETAL SYSTEM DISEASE, TESTS FOR.*

SIDE WHEELING:

Refer to *GAIT, DYSFUNCTIONS AND DEFINITIONS.*

SINGLE TRACKING

Refer to *GAIT, DYSFUNCTIONS AND DEFINITIONS.*

"SLIPPED STIFLE":

Refer to *LUXATION.*

"SLIPPED PATELLA":

Refer to *LUXATION.*

SPONDYLOLISTHESIS:

Spondylolisthesis is defined as the subluxation (displacement) of one vertebra in relationship to another. Subluxation in the neck is part of the *"wobbler" syndrome*. Surgical stabilization of the vertebra to prevent trauma to the spinal cord is necessary.

SPONDYLOPATHY, CERVICAL:

Because cervical spondylopathy, an abnormality of the cervical (neck) vertebra or associated structures, causes neurological dysfunction, it is discussed under the MUSCULOSKELETAL SYSTEM in Chapter 6. Cervical spondylopathy *(canine "wobbler" syndrome)* is seen primarily in large breeds, especially the Doberman Pinscher and the Great Dane. The cardinal sign is a progressive incoordination of the hind limbs. The forelimbs are not affected or are only minimally affected. Clinical signs appear any time after three months of age and as late as four to five years of age. In cases where the onset of signs is very sudden, the dog may become weak or paralyzed on all four legs. Pain is elicited from manipulation of the neck in acute cases.

A variety of changes occur in this syndrome, including osteochondrosis dissecans of adjacent vertebrae, dislocation (subluxation) of the vertebrae, and deformation of the vertebra and associated cartilage. The most commonly affected vertebrae are the last three cervical (neck) vertebrae, C_5, C_6, and C_7. More than one deformity can occur in the same dog.

The cause of the *"wobbler" syndrome* is not known. However, several contributing factors have been incriminated. The most commonly mentioned factors are the presence of a large head, selection toward a long neck and rapid growth. Possibly over-nutrition in the form of excess *protein, calcium,* and *phosphorus* may induce various skeletal changes that precipitate the *"wobbler" syndrome*.

The diagnosis of cervical spondylopathy is made by clinical signs, breed of dog, and radiographs. Proper positioning for diagnostic radiographs is important. A standard lateral (side) view should be compared to a lateral flexed cervical radiograph looking for anatomical abnormalities. On occasion, the use of *myelography* is necessary to show the contrast between normal and compressed areas of the cervical spinal cord.

Treatment of cervical spondylopathy is designed to decompress the spinal cord and to stabilize any unstable vertebral structures. In acute cases where the dog is paralyzed or very weak in all four legs, use of *mannitol, steroids,* and surgical procedures to decompress the affected spinal cord must be done very early to achieve satisfactory results. Various surgical procedures for stabilization of the cervical vertebrae exist in the veterinary literature. These procedures require a surgeon with above average skills.

Prognosis for satisfactory resolution of this condition depends on many factors including the surgeon's skill. Affected dogs should not be used in a breeding program until more is known about the possible hereditary implications.

SPONDYLOSIS:

Spondylosis is the bony fusion of vertebral bodies which limits movement, causing pain in a certain range of movement. Primarily, spondylosis is seen in older dogs.

SQUAMOUS CELL CARCINOMA:
Refer to *TUMORS, BONE.*

SUPPLEMENTATION, MINERAL:
With current high quality balanced dog foods available, the need for mineral supplementation is minimal. In fact, over-supplementation can be detrimental to the dog by creating such problems as *osteoporosis* or *osteopetrosis.* Indiscriminate supplementation of minerals also leads to severe imbalances within the body. Only during times of rapid growth is supplementation needed. Calcium requirements must be met during teething, bone, and body growth. Deficiencies in zinc, sometimes found in growing puppies, necessitate the addition of zinc to the diet.

Essential minerals can be divided into those associated with electrolytes and fluid balance *(sodium, chloride, potassium)*, those associated with bones *(calcium, phosphorus)*, and the trace minerals *(zinc, copper, selenium, manganese, iodine, cobalt, iron)*. Collectively, all of these minerals are called *ash content.*

The amounts of most of the minerals necessary for proper growth and maintenance in dogs have been determined. However, some optimal trace element amounts are still unknown. The established calcium level should exceed phosphorus by 1.2 parts to 1 in the diet. Most name brand commercial dog foods are balanced to meet that ratio.

SYNOVIAL-CELL SARCOMA:
Refer to *TUMORS, BONE.*

SYSTEMIC LUPUS ERYTHEMATOSUS (SLE):
Systemic lupus erythematosus (SLE) is a serious immunologic disease that affects many body systems. *Lameness* is caused by *arthritis* and muscular weakness. Clinical signs include reluctance to walk, difficulty in rising, a low grade fever, and lack of appetite. If the condition has been present for some time, muscles atrophy. Pain is present when the joints are manipulated.

SLE is diagnosed by blood tests *(ANA, LE Prep, Coombs Test)* and a negative *rheumatoid factor test.* If other body systems are involved, additional tests are required. Treatment is with high doses of *cortisone* which are decreased over a short period of time to establish a maintenance level. The prognosis is guarded. Watching for infections during long term cortisone therapy is important.

TETANUS:
Tetanus is a bacterial toxin disease classified under either the neurological or the musculoskeletal section. The toxin produced by *Clostridium tetani* acts on the nerve receptors. Tetanus causes muscular rigidity and finally respiratory muscle paralysis and death. Also refer to NEUROLOGICAL DISEASE in Chapter 7.

TROT:

Refer to *GAIT, DYSFUNCTIONS AND DEFINITIONS:*

TUMORS, BONE:

Seven tumors will be mentioned in this section. The four most common bone tumors are *osteogenic sarcoma, chondrosarcoma, fibrosarcoma,* and *hemangiosarcoma.* Unfortunately, a very high percentage of bone tumors are malignant. Rapid diagnosis and treatment are necessary for a reasonable prognosis. However, in most instances, the tumor has already spread by the time it is diagnosed. In those cases, the prognosis is poor.

OSTEOGENIC SARCOMA, most common in large and giant breeds, accounts for at least 85% of the bone tumors in dogs. Males appear to be affected more frequently than females with an average age of seven years at the time of diagnosis. Osteogenic sarcoma has been diagnosed in dogs as young as eight months of age and as old as fifteen years. The most common locations for the tumor are on the front legs just above the pastern joint near the shoulder joint and on the rear legs near the stifle joint, hip joint, or hock joint. The tumor involves the long bones near the above mentioned joints and not the joints themselves.

The first clinical sign observed is pain, followed by *lameness* and swelling at the tumor site. The initial diagnosis is made by radiograph. After a bone tumor has been discerned, the definitive diagnosis is made from a *bone biopsy* examined by a histopathologist.

In spite of advancements in cancer chemotherapy, surgical removal of the affected limb remains the treatment of choice for osteogenic sarcoma. The prognosis, even with amputation, is poor as only 10% of amputees live for one year after surgery. One must contemplate the following three questions when considering amputation: 1) Has the tumor spread from the leg? (a radiograph of the lungs is a must!) 2) Can the large to giant breed dog get along on three legs? and 3) Is the postoperative period of recovery and learning to use three legs realistic? If you can answer all of these questions affirmatively, have the surgery done as soon as possible.

Ten percent of the bone tumors are CHONDROSARCOMAS, making it the second most common bone tumor in dogs. Most frequently it is seen in five to nine year old large breeds (e.g. Doberman Pinscher). The bones most commonly involved are the ribs, nasal bones, and pelvic bones.

Clinical signs of this tumor depend on which bones are involved. For instance, if the nasal bones are involved, *sneezing, nasal discharge,* and *bleeding* occurs. If the ribs are involved, many times the tumor is much larger in the thoracic cavity, impeding normal breathing. Other involved bones would obviously cause pain, swelling, and lameness.

Diagnosis is first made by a radiograph although definitely distinguishing an osteogenic sarcoma from a chondrosarcoma on an x-ray is nearly impossible. A bone biopsy would provide the differential. Surgical removal from accessible bones has a guarded to fair prognosis since chondrosarcomas spread much later than the osteogenic sarcomas. Chondrosarcomas infrequently reappear at or near surgical sites years after surgical removal of the tumor.

The FIBROSARCOMA, although it is the third most common form of bone tumor, is rather rare. About two-thirds of the time this tumor involves the facial and head bones. The other third involves the long bones. Those on the head and face are more highly malignant. Diagnosis is made the same way as other bone tumors; radiograph initially and then biopsy of the affected tissue. If the affected bone can be surgically removed, a long term cure is possible because the tumor spreads slowly.

The HEMANGIOSARCOMA arises from either bone or from soft tissue like muscle. While uncommon, it occurs in large dogs after five years of age. However, it has been diagnosed in dogs as young as two years. The most commonly affected places are the ribs and the upper arm near the shoulder joint.

Clinically, this neoplasm causes *lameness,* pain, and lysis of bone. Radiographs show minimal soft tissue swelling and lysis of the involved bone. Unfortunately, this tumor is always well advanced by the time it is presented for diagnosis. Early metastasis (spreading) makes surgical treatment less than rewarding.

SQUAMOUS-CELL CARCINOMAS, also rather uncommon, occur in dogs past nine years of age. The most commonly affected site is the toes. Clinical lameness and swelling are observed. Early surgical resection or amputation of the affected toes increases the chance of survival.

The SYNOVIAL-CELL SARCOMA is very uncommon and is normally located around the stifle joint. Radiographs show soft tissue swelling with tumor cells involving more than one bone. Early amputation may produce over a year of survival since the joint capsule is not normally penetrated.

Another complex tumor that affects bone is MULTIPLE MYELOMA. This tumor involves the pelvis, thigh bone, lower spine, or upper arm of aged dogs (over six years). Typical lytic bone lesions are identified on a radiograph. Additional helpful diagnostic data are the presence of *Bence Jones protein* in *urine* and a very high *plasma protein* level. Treatment of multiple myeloma includes plasmapheresis, *cytotoxic drugs, antibiotics,* and *cortisones.* The prognosis is guarded to fair.

TUMORS, MUSCLE:

Primary tumors of skeletal muscle are uncommon. A benign tumor of skeletal muscle, the RHABDOMYOMA, is encapsulated within muscle tissue. The malignant counterpart, the RHABDOMYOSARCOMA, spreads (metastasizes) to the abdominal organs or thoracic structures.

WANDERING LAMENESS:

Refer to *PANOSTEITIS*

WEAVING:

Refer to *GAIT, DYSFUNCTIONS AND DEFINITIONS.*

"WOBBLER" SYNDROME:

Refer to *SPONDYLOPATHY, CERVICAL.*

X-RAY:

Refer to *MUSCULOSKELETAL SYSTEM DISEASE, TESTS FOR*

Chapter 7

NEUROLOGICAL SYSTEM

ACQUIRED EPILEPSY:

Refer to *EPILEPSY, TRUE.*

ACUTE POLYRADICULONEURITIS:

Refer to *POLYRADICULONEURITIS, ACUTE.*

ADDISON'S DISEASE (HYPOADRENOCORTICISM):

Refer to *DISEASES, METABOLIC, AFFECTING THE NERVOUS SYSTEM.*

ALTERED ADRENAL METABOLISM AS A CAUSE OF NERVOUS SYSTEM DISEASE:

Refer to *DISEASES, METABOLIC, AFFECTING THE NERVOUS SYSTEM.*

ALTERED CALCIUM METABOLISM AS A CAUSE OF NERVOUS SYSTEM DISEASE:

Refer to *DISEASES, METABOLIC, AFFECTING THE NERVOUS SYSTEM.*

ALTERED GLUCOSE METABOLISM AS A CAUSE OF NERVOUS SYSTEM DISEASE:

Refer to *DISEASES, METABOLIC, AFFECTING THE NERVOUS SYSTEM.*

ANTIBIOTICS, TOXICITY OF:

Antibiotics of the aminoglycoside type can cause several neurological reactions if given for an extensive periods. *Deafness* is the most common neurological problem from high prolonged doses of *gentamicin, dihydrostreptomycin, kanamycin, neomycin,* and *streptomycin.* These antibiotics can also cause the *vestibular disease, head tilt.* These neurological dysfunctions can occur together or individually. While deafness is usually permanent, the head tilt can correct itself if the drug is discontinued early enough.

ANTICONVULSANT DRUGS:

Refer to *DRUGS, ANTICONVULSANT.*

ASTROCYTOMA:

Refer to *TUMORS OF THE NERVOUS SYSTEM.*

ATAXIA:

Ataxia, failure of muscular coordination, is characterized by a staggering, *weaving,* swaying gait with either exaggerated or depressed leg movement. Causes of neurological ataxia include loss of balance, loss of sensory function to one or more legs, and motor ataxia in which nerve impulses to the legs are abnormal.

AUDIOMETRY:

Audiometry, a neurological test, measures the ability to hear sounds. An *electroencephalogram* that is performed on a sleeping dog measures changes in brain wave activity in response to sounds. Measurement of hearing ability by observing the dog's response to sound stimulus is more practical making the usefulness of audiometry limited in veterinary medicine.

BACTERIAL MENINGITIS:

Refer to *MENINGITIS, BACTERIAL.*

BEHAVIOR OR PERSONALITY CHANGE:

Behavior or personality changes can be due to either neurological or psychological abnormalities. Neurological abnormalities affecting personality most commonly arise from the frontal lobe of the brain. These altered personality traits include dementia, the inability to learn, *pacing* or *circling,* lack of owner recognition, and excess sleeping or coma. To determine the origin of the neurological signs, various ancillary neurological tests should be performed.

BLASTOMYCOSIS:

Blastomycosis is a *systemic fungus* which can affect the nervous system and eyes. When neurological signs are present, treatment is very difficult. The prognosis is poor. Refer to Chapter 10 on the *SENSORY SYSTEMS.*

BLOOD TESTS FOR NEUROLOGICAL DISEASE:

As an aid in the diagnosis of neurological disease, the following blood tests are important. A good gauge of liver activity is provided by *BSP retention,* a measurement of dye excreted by the liver. This test is also useful in the diagnosis of *hepatic encephalopathy*. *Blood ammonia* testing is also valuable in diagnosing hepatic encephalopathy and its associated *seizure* activity. Because the sample of blood must be iced down and the test performed within 30 minutes of collection, it is very difficult to run. A complete blood count *(CBC)* should be part of every diagnostic work-up. It provides information about *anemia* and *lead poisoning*. *Blood gas tests* determine the degree of acidity or alkalinity of the blood as it reacts to the presence of disease. Although the tests are difficult to have run, the results are meaningful. Serological tests *(serum titers)* determine the presence of protozoan and fungal diseases in the body. *Blood sugar* tests measure the change in the blood glucose level. Both low and high blood sugar levels can cause neurological signs.

BOTULISM:

Botulism is a rare disease caused by a neurotoxin from the bacteria, *Clostridium botulinum,* which is found in spoiled food. Clinical signs similar to those of *tick paralysis* and *coonhound paralysis* are seen 24 to 36 hours after eating the tainted food. Fortunately, dogs are fairly resistant to the affects of botulism neurotoxin. However, if the bacteria is present in large amounts, the clinical signs may progress quickly with death occurring in 24 hours. The most common sign is a flaccid paralysis of all four legs.

Diagnosis is made from a history of ingesting tainted food, the injection of serum from a sick dog into a lab mouse causing its death, or isolation of the neurotoxin from the stomach contents. Treatment consists of the use of a specific antitoxin during the five days following ingestion, high doses of *penicillin*, and nursing care. Prognosis ranges from poor to fair depending on the amount of botulism toxin ingested. Slightly affected dogs recover in approximately four weeks.

CANINE DISTEMPER:

Refer to *DISTEMPER, CANINE.*

CATAPLEXY:

In the Doberman Pinscher, cataplexy is the most common sign of the neurological disease *narcolepsy*. In this condition, the dog collapses abruptly into a flaccid paralyzed position from which it can be aroused quickly. No reflexes are evident while in the collapsed state. If the collapsed dog is not stimulated, actual REM (rapid eye movement) sleep can occur. The eyeballs will move from side to side and the toe muscles may twitch.

To diagnose whether a dog has a mild form of cataplexy, the *physostigmine provocative test* is useful. Within 5 to 15 minutes after the drug physostigmine salicylate is administered intravenously, a cataplectic attack is likely to occur in a narcoleptic Doberman Pinscher. Also refer to *NARCOLEPSY.*

CEREBROSPINAL FLUID (CSF) ANALYSIS FOR NEUROLOGICAL DISEASE:

The brain and spinal cord are suspended in a medium called *cerebrospinal fluid (CSF)* which acts as a cushion for the sensitive nerve tissue. Diseases of the nervous system affect the production of the cerebrospinal fluid, the kind of cells present, and the appearance of the fluid itself.

Because a special spinal needle is necessary for sampling cerebrospinal fluid, some expertise is required for the procedure. Fluid may be obtained at the base of the skull, from the cisterna magna, or from the lower lumbar region in the back. While the risk is minimal, some chance of brain stem injury is present.

Evaluation of the spinal fluid cell content must be made within 20 minutes from the time of collection. Spinal fluid pressure is measured with a spinal fluid manometer while the fluid is being collected. Compression of the spinal cord, presence of tumors, and inflammation are all evaluations available from a 2 ml. sample of cerebrospinal fluid.

CERVICAL VERTEBRAL MALFORMATION (WOBBLER SYNDROME):

Refer to Chapter 6 on the *MUSCULOSKELETAL SYSTEM.*

CHLORAMPHENICOL:

Chloramphenicol (*Chloromycetin*®) is a broad spectrum bacteriostatic *antibiotic* that passes the blood-brain barrier and thereby becomes useful in the treatment of bacterial infections in the nervous system. In human medicine, life-threatening side effects make this antibiotic a "last resort." Side effects in dogs, even after long term high level doses of chloramphenicol, are very uncommon. Also refer to *DRUGS USED IN NEUROLOGY.*

CHLORINATED HYDROCARBONS:

Refer to *HYDROCARBONS, CHLORINATED.*

CIRCLING:

Circling is a sign of neurological dysfunction. The neurological lesion is located in the *vestibular* apparatus which controls balance and movement. Circling is toward the side which has the disturbed vestibular function. Other *vestibular signs* such as *head tilt,* jerking of the eyeballs (nystagmus), leaning and rolling may accompany this condition.

CONGENITAL HYDROCEPHALUS:

Refer to *HYDROCEPHALUS.*

CONGENITAL NEUROLOGICAL DISORDERS:

Refer to *NEUROLOGICAL DISORDERS, CONGENITAL.*

COONHOUND PARALYSIS:

Refer to *POLYRADICULONEURITIS, ACUTE.*

CORTICOSTEROIDS FOR NERVOUS SYSTEM USAGE:

Glucocorticoids are the drugs of choice for the treatment of acute inflammation of the nervous system. *Dexamethasone,* the glucocorticoid of choice for immediate intravenous usage, can be given orally after the initial critical period has passed. Other useful steroids in the treatment of nervous system inflammation are *prednisolone, triamcinolone,* and *methylprednisolone.*

CRYPTOCOCCOSIS:

Cryptococcus neoformans is a *systemic fungus* that can cause central nervous system disease. Manifested initially by a chronic *nasal discharge,* the disease eventually progresses through the nasal bony plates into the area of the nervous system which is important for smell and behavior. Eye diseases commonly occur concurrently. Treatment is often difficult resulting in a guarded prognosis, at best.

CUSHING'S DISEASE (HYPERADRENOCORTICISM):

Refer to *DISEASES, METABOLIC, AFFECTING THE NERVOUS SYSTEM.*

DIAZEPAM:

Diazepam is the drug of choice for controlling *seizures*, especially those due to *true (idiopathic) epilepsy*. When given intravenously, diazepam is very effective in controlling seizures. However, the oral form of the drug is not effective in stopping seizures in the dog. A combination of diazepam with another anticonvulsant may benefit dogs with seizures that are difficult to control. Oral diazepam can provide muscular relaxation in dogs that suffer from disc pain.

Also refer to *ANTICONVULSANTS, TRUE EPILEPSY,* and *STATUS EPILEPTICUS.* The use of this drug is also discussed in Chapter 1 on *ANESTHESIA.*

DIMETHYL SULFOXIDE:

Refer to *DMSO USE IN NEUROLOGY.*

DIPHENYLHYDANTOIN:

Diphenylhydantoin (*Dilantin®*), a drug used to control *seizures* in dogs, has one serious side effect. If the antibiotic *chloramphenicol* is administered concurrently with Dilantin® , *cardiac arrhythmias* can occur leading to cardiac arrest. Also refer to *ANTICONVULSANT DRUGS.*

DISCOSPONDYLITIS:

Discospondylitis is a bacterial infection of the vertebrae and associated intervertebral discs. More than one area along the vertebral column can be involved simultaneously. Dogs of any age or sex are infected. The most common clinical signs include pain in the area around the affected vertebrae, difficulty in rising, and weight loss. Some dogs are depressed, febrile, and have a poor appetite. Specific neurological signs vary with the extent and location of the infection.

Radiographs are used to confirm the diagnosis of discospondylitis. *Complete blood counts*, blood *cultures, serological testing* for <u>*Brucella canis*</u>, and *CSF analysis* are helpful in monitoring the progression of treatment. If severe neurological signs are not present, long term antibiotic therapy is the treatment of choice. Anti-inflammatory agents like *phenylbutazone* and *aspirin are* also helpful. *Cortisone* usage with a bacterial infection is not generally recommended. Surgical scraping of the vertebrae and immobilization of the spinal column are necessary when severe neurological signs or failure of conservative antibiotic therapy are present.

The prognosis varies greatly and is dependent on the kind of infection and the degree of neurological involvement. Chronic cases can have recurrences up to a year after apparent cures.

DISEASE, INTERVERTEBRAL DISC:

Intervertebral disc disease occurs fairly frequently in the Doberman Pinscher, usually between the ages of five and ten years. Most disc disease is due to an upward prolapse of disc material against the spinal cord. The fifth to seventh cervical vertebrae are most commonly affected.

The clinical signs range from neck pain with a reluctance to move the head to a gradually worsening *ataxic gait* and leg weakness (paresis). Fortunately, severe paralysis of the limbs from cervical (neck) disc disease seldom occurs. The presence of calcified discs is uncommon in Dobes.

Diagnosis of intervertebral disc disease is made with lateral *radiographs* and *myelography*. While a narrowed space between two adjacent vertebrae is occasionally seen on radiographs, myelography is necessary to pinpoint the area for surgical intervention. The use of myelography to identify the lesion locations has some risk.

Treatment of intervertebral disc disease can be either medical or surgical. Conservative medical treatment may result in future exacerbations. The surgical removal of disc material requires a high level of skill. If the surgical procedure is successful, the chance of a recurrence at the same site is much less than with medical treatment. Several surgical techniques are used in the repair of cervical disc lesions. Both *cortisone* and *diazepam* are useful post-surgically in controlling inflammation and muscle spasms. Following successful surgical intervention, the prognosis for a normal recovery is good. The earlier the surgery is done, the better the prognosis.

DISEASES, FUNGAL, OF THE CENTRAL NERVOUS SYSTEM:

The three *systemic fungal diseases* that may affect the central nervous system are *histoplasmosis, blastomycosis,* and *cryptococcosis.* Since several body systems are affected, the signs, treatment, and prognosis are discussed in chapters pertinent to each system. In general, if the central nervous system is affected, the prognosis for recovery is poor.

DISEASES, INFECTIOUS, OF THE NERVOUS SYSTEM:

The following infectious diseases can cause dysfunction of the nervous system. Refer to each individual topic for further discussion.

BACTERIAL CAUSE:	*PROTOZOAL CAUSE:* Toxoplasmosis
Meningitis	*VIRAL CAUSE:*
Discospondylitis	*Adenovirus 1*
FUNGAL CAUSE:	*Distemper*
Blastomycosis	*Herpes*
Cryptococcosis	*Rabies*
Histoplasmosis	

DISEASES, METABOLIC, AFFECTING THE NERVOUS SYSTEM:

The nervous system is affected by *hypoglycemia, hypocalcemia,* and *hypoadrenocorticism,* and *hyperadrenocorticism.* Even though signs of nervous system dysfunction are observed, correction of the basic metabolic disability is necessary before complete neurological recovery will occur.

Addison's disease (hypoadrenocorticism) can cause a generalized weakness. However, at this time, whether the nerve and muscle weakness is due to an increased *potassium blood level* or to the lack of *cortisone* itself is unclear.

In *Cushing's disease* (hyperadrenocorticism), a generalized stiffness, reluctance to move, and some muscle atrophy are present. The excess cortisone can be from a *tumor in the adrenal gland* or from tablets taken for skin disease.

Treatment of cortisone abnormalities is related to returning the body's corticosteroid level to normal. The neuropathy and myopathy signs will disappear over a period of months.

DISTEMPER, CANINE:

Canine distemper, a *paramyxovirus* which affects most of a dog's body tissues, has an affinity for nerve tissue. The disease can occur at any age. Prevention is possible with an appropriate vaccination program including annual booster *vaccinations.*

The clinical signs observed depend on the affected part of the nervous system. Most young dogs show respiratory and digestive tract signs rather than neurological involvement. Older dogs more commonly show signs of neurological disease early in the course of the problem. In rare instances, postvaccinal neurological signs are seen about 2 to 3 weeks after a dog receives a modified live virus *vaccination for canine distemper*. While the cause is unknown, *encephalomyelitis* is the result.

Clinical signs of distemper affecting the nervous system include *ataxia*, "chewing gum" fits with excessive salivation, *circling, pacing*, head pressing, and severe seizures. One curious manifestation is a self-mutilation syndrome in which the dog constantly chews its legs and tail.

Diagnosis is made from the clinical signs, the presence of viral inclusion bodies in tissue samples, and various *serological tests*. With treatment being symptomatic, months of nursing care are necessary. The prognosis is very guarded to poor.

DMSO USE IN NEUROLOGY:

Dimethyl sulfoxide (DMSO) is a very hygroscopic (water absorbing) liquid solvent approved for topical use in dogs and horses. In acute spinal cord trauma cases, DMSO has been injected intravenously, thereby improving the condition of the spinal cord and decreasing inflammation. Current data, however, shows that intravenous usage does not reduce acute spinal cord inflammation. A gel form of DMSO can be massaged over the back for *lumbar disc neuropathy (disease)*.

DRUGS, ANTICONVULSANT:

True epilepsy is managed by several drugs called anticonvulsants. Drug therapy should be initiated if seizures occur more frequently than once a month. The three drugs used in seizure prevention are *phenobarbital, primidone*, and *diphenylhydantoin (Dilantin®)*. *Diazepam* and *sodium pentobarbital* will stop seizure activity occurring at the time of their administration.

The treatment of choice for controlling a dog in *status epilepticus* (continual seizures) is intravenous diazepam (Valium®). Once the seizure activity has been controlled, sodium pentobarbital, a *short-acting anesthetic*, keeps the dog "under" until the excessive electrical activity in the brain has diminished. When seizure activity has ceased and consciousness has returned, the dog is then given an oral maintenance anticonvulsant.

Phenobarbital is most commonly used in large dogs because it is the least costly of the oral anticonvulsants. The dosage required to control seizures may also cause *sedation*. Particularly useful in dogs that seizure frequently, phenobarbital is also highly effective in excitable dogs because of its sedative effect. The peak activity level is attained about 12 hours after administration.

Primidone, a combination of phenobarbital and several other active ingredients, is expensive for large dogs. Like phenobarbital, primidone also has a sedative effect. Possible side effects include increased appetite and water consumption with the most serious side effect being *liver necrosis*.

For this reason, dogs taking primidone should have yearly *liver function tests.* Seizure control can usually be accomplished with less than the recommended therapeutic dosage. A minimum maintenance level that can be increased in the face of a stressful or exciting change in the dog's environment should be established.

Diphenylhydantoin *(Dilantin®), is the most expensive and the least effective drug used for seizure control.* Administration is three times daily while primidone and phenobarbital are given twice. Because it has little or no sedative effect, diphenylhydantoin is the drug of choice for show and working dogs. A therapeutic level in the blood stream is reached in 7 to 10 days severely limiting its usefulness in clustered seizures.

Anticonvulsant therapy should not be stopped abruptly since this triggers multiple seizure activity. When changing from one drug to another, always taper the dosage of the previous anticonvulsant while concurrently increasing the dosage of the new drug. The use of drugs in combination to control seizure activity is a possibility.

DRUGS USED IN NEUROLOGY:

Each of the different drugs used in neurology is discussed in other sections of the book under its individual listing. Refer to the index for the exact page. An alphabetical list of these drugs follows:

- Anticonvulsants
- Diazepam
- Phenobarbital
- Primidone
- Diphenylhydantoin
- Sodium Pentobarbital
- *Corticosteroids*

- *Chloramphenicol*
- *DMSO (Dimethyl Sulfoxide)*
- *Glucose, 50%*
- *Levodopa*
- *Mannitol*
- *Reserpine*
- *Tribrissen®*

ECLAMPSIA:

Eclampsia, also called *periparturient hypocalcemia* because it occurs at whelping time, generally is due to a deficiency in body calcium. Clinically, bitches in a poor nutritional state are more commonly affected. Muscle twitching, generalized convulsive *seizures,* and an elevated temperature may be present. The diagnosis is made by clinical signs and the time proximity to whelping (before, during, or after).

Treatment is the administration of *calcium* intravenously while monitoring the heart sounds and rate. Maintenance is then accomplished by subcutaneous or oral calcium during lactation. Puppies should be removed from the mother and raised as orphans should it recur. Prognosis for recovery is good, but recurrences are common.

EEG:

Refer to *ELECTROENCEPHALOGRAM.*

ELECTROENCEPHALOGRAM (EEG):
Electroencephalography is a means of recording the electrical activity of the cerebral cortex. The *electroencephalogram (EEG)* is a technique that can be performed on most dogs. *Sedatives* or *tranquilizers* should not be used to help restrain dogs being examined with an EEG.
For an EEG, the dog is placed on its side in a comfortable, dimly lit area. Five electrodes and eight leads are then attached to the head area. Cotton is placed in both ears and the eyes are covered by a mask. The brain wave activity is then recorded. The EEG by itself is not diagnostic. However, the EEG in combination with a thorough history, clinical signs, and other neurological tests can provide information about specific types of nervous system disorders. This advanced diagnostic equipment is only available at referral hospitals and veterinary colleges.
Some of the neurological disorders that produce abnormal EEG tracings are *hydrocephalus, hypoglycemia, hepatic encephalopathy, organophosphate* and *lead poisoning,* concussions, cerebral hemorrhage, *brain tumors,* and the inflammation of the brain due to viral, bacterial, fungal, and protozoan infections. *True epilepsy* does not cause any alteration in the EEG brain wave pattern.

ENCEPHALITIS:
The definition of encephalitis is the inflammation of brain tissue. *Encephalomyelitis* is the inflammation of both the brain and the spinal cord. This nervous system inflammation can be caused by trauma, tumor, infection, and the presence of a metabolic abnormality.

ENCEPHALITIS, OLD DOG:
Old dog encephalitis, thought to be a form of *canine distemper encephalitis,* is a central nervous system disease of older dogs. Its clinical signs, usually chronic and progressive, are *circling, pacing, blindness,* and *behavior disorders.* Test results on the nervous system are similar to those seen in distemper encephalitis. Treatment is symptomatic and unrewarding with a poor prognosis for recovery.

ENCEPHALOPATHY, HEPATIC:
Hepatic encephalopathy, one of many causes of *seizures,* may be congenital in origin or acquired as a result of chronic *liver failure.* Control of seizures caused by hepatic encephalopathy involves lowering the blood ammonia level by increasing the liver function, regulating the diet, and using intestinal antibiotics to control bowel ammonia formation. Refer to Chapter 5 on the *GASTROINTESTINAL TRACT.*

EPENDYMOMA:
Refer to *TUMORS OF THE NERVOUS SYSTEM.*

EPILEPSY, TRUE (IDIOPATHIC):

Epilepsy is classified as either acquired or true (idiopathic). Acquired epilepsy can result from a traumatic injury to the skull. *EEG test* results are often abnormal in acquired epilepsy. True epilepsy has a strong hereditary tendency, occurring primarily in purebred dogs between six months and three years of age. Generalized seizures can vary from fairly mild to extremely severe. Certain breeds tend to have groups of seizures *("cluster" seizures)* which are more difficult to control with *anticonvulsant medication.* Dogs that have had seizures should have both a physical and neurological exam including the necessary ancillary tests. If no cause is found, true (idiopathic) epilepsy should be considered. Anticonvulsant medication should be administered to animals that have more than one seizure per month. In veterinary medicine, the type of seizure is usually not classified.

Frequently, the owner's reaction during an epileptic seizure is one of helplessness. Remember, no dog has died from a single seizure. The dog is not aware of his activity. No attempt should be made to manipulate the dog's tongue during a seizure since he may close his mouth on the person's hand that is attempting to help them. Instead, position a dog having a seizure on some soft flooring away from any stairs. Make a note of the length and characteristics of the seizure (e.g. paddling on side, urinating, passing stool, foaming at mouth, etc.). Your veterinarian will want to know the duration and type of seizure for diagnostic and treatment purposes.

If medication is necessary for seizure control, the choice of drug depends on the size of the dog, the owner's ability to medicate at a given interval, and the cost of the medication. The different anticonvulsants used on dogs are discussed under *ANTICONVULSANT DRUGS.*

The prognosis for managing epileptic seizures is fair to good, depending on the breed. The Irish Setter, St. Bernard, and Belgian Tervuren are more difficult to control since they tend to have "cluster" seizures. Control of seizures is a lifelong task. Because of its hereditary nature, dogs affected with epilepsy should not be used for breeding.

FLANK SUCKING:

Refer to *SIDE SUCKER SYNDROME.*

FUNGAL DISEASES OF THE CENTRAL NERVOUS SYSTEM:

Refer to *DISEASES, FUNGAL, OF THE CENTRAL NERVOUS SYSTEM.*

GLIOMA:

Refer to *TUMORS OF THE NERVOUS SYSTEM.*

GLUCOSE, 50%:

To help reduce swelling in the brain and spinal cord, glucose in 50%

conentrations can be given orally or intravenously as a diuretic. Glucose can also be used as a source of sugar in treating seizures caused by a low blood sugar level *(hypoglycemia).*

HEAD TILT:

A head tilt, often associated with rolling eyes and circling, is a sign of neurological dysfunction. They are indicative of a lesion in the vestibular mechanism of the inner ear and cerebellar portion of the brain. Congenital idiopathic disorders, a toxicity to aminoglycoside antibiotics, an idiopathic geriatric form of the *vestibular syndrome, inner ear infections,* tumors, and trauma are all possible causes of head tilt.

In *Doberman Pinschers, an idiopathic congenital head tilt* sometimes affects one or several puppies in a litter three and twelve weeks of age. Along with the head tilt, some puppies also *circle* and are *deaf.* Puppies may learn to compensate for the *vestibular deficit,* showing only a slight head tilt after several months. If present, deafness is often permanent. All ancillary neurological test results on affected Dobe puppies are normal *(CSF exam, EEG* tests, and *skull radiographs).* Autopsy results fail to show abnormal tissues. Some evidence indicates that this disease may have a hereditary basis.

Treatment for vestibular signs is directed at the underlying cause if one can be found. Various ancillary neurological tests such as skull radiographs, EEG tests, CSF analysis, and a good clinical neurological exam should be done in an attempt to diagnose the cause. Prognosis is variable depending on the exact cause. Because compensation for head tilt in Doberman Pinscher puppies is likely, most affected pups still make good house pets.

HEAD TRAUMA:

Refer to *TRAUMA, HEAD.*

HEPATIC ENCEPHALOPATHY:

Refer to *ENCEPHALOPATHY, HEPATIC.*

HISTOPLASMOSIS:

Since it usually affects the *bowel* or *lungs,* the *systemic fungus, Histoplasma capsulatum, is discussed more fully in Chapter 3 on the CARDIOPULMONARY SYSTEM* and in Chapter 5 on the *GASTROINTESTINAL TRACT* The central nervous system can also be infected and its presence there is difficult to eliminate. The prognosis of histoplasmosis with neurological signs is poor.

HORNER'S SYNDROME:

Horner's syndrome is characterized by three specific neurological signs: *miosis* (pinpoint pupil constriction) of the eye on the affected side, *ptosis* (drooping of the eyelid on the affected side), and *enophthalmos* (sinking in of the eyeball on the affected side).

The presence of Horner's syndrome with other signs of neurological dysfunction helps to identify the location of nerve disease. An interesting condition which occurs in dog-auto accidents involves Horner's syndrome and a paralysis of the foreleg on the same side. Nerve roots that originate in the neck and extend down the leg are severely traumatized. An idiopathic Horner's syndrome also occurs for which no cause can be determined. Many of these will resolve over a period of months, with or without treatment. If Horner's syndrome is recognized, a first-rate neurological examination, with possible ancillary tests, should be scheduled in an attempt to identify any underlying lesions.

HYDROCARBONS, CHLORINATED:

The ingestion of chlorinated hydrocarbon products, through the skin or orally, causes muscle tremors, generalized *seizures,* and an exaggerated response to either noise or manipulation. Diagnosis is made by a history of exposure to a chlorinated hydrocarbon product with the presence of the neurological signs. Because no antidote is available, treatment is symptomatic. Seizures must be kept under control. For that reason, *phenothiazine type tranquilizers* should not be used since they can potentiate seizures. The prognosis is guarded, depending on the amount of chlorinated hydrocarbons absorbed into the body and the degree of success achieved in managing the neurological signs.

HYDROCEPHALUS:

The most frequent neurological disease of young dogs is hydrocephalus *("water on the brain")*. While some puppies are born with the condition *(congenital hydrocephalus)*, an infection or a parasitic infestation by *Toxoplasma* can affect other puppies early in their development. Some forms of *brain cancer* in adult dogs cause fluid build-up in the brain tissue causing hydrocephalus.

Congenital hydrocephalus is usually seen in the smallest puppy in the litter. Many times the skull has a domed appearance. He may exhibit signs of irrational behavior, aggressiveness, seizures, and may be unable to be house trained. These behavior abnormalities may not be apparent until four or five months of age.

In the acquired form, early clinical signs are similar to other central nervous system disturbances. Affected puppies or dogs may *circle,* exhibit *irrational behavior,* appear *blind,* and cry. A neurological examination with the use of ancillary tests will show abnormal nervous system signs. *EEG tracings show changes similar to adult encephalitis. Skull radiographs* with contrast media demonstrate most cases of hydrocephalus. *CSF analysis* shows changes confirming the presence of infection as a cause of acquired hydrocephalus.

Treatment of hydrocephalus is variable in kind and success. In some cases, surgical removal of fluid from the brain can be beneficial. In the congenital form, frequent *seizures* can be controlled with *anticonvulsant* therapy. An acquired form caused by an infection should be treated with *antibiotics* and possibly *steroids*.

The prognosis to become a normal dog is poor. Some young puppies will stabilize enough to allow them to be reasonably good pets, although their learning ability is markedly impaired. Because of the progressive nature of hydrocephalus, the prognosis is very poor in many young dogs.

HYPERADRENOCORTICISM (CUSHING'S DISEASE):

Refer to *DISEASES, METABOLIC, AFFECTING THE NERVOUS SYSTEM.*

HYPOADRENOCORTICISM (ADDISON'S DISEASE):

Refer to *DISEASES, METABOLIC, AFFECTING THE NERVOUS SYSTEM.*

HYPOCALCEMIA:

A low blood calcium level is a cause of *seizure* activity. Calcium levels below 7 mg./dl. can be due to *heavy lactation, pancreatitis,* and *hypoparathyroidism.* The administration of injectable or oral calcium can generally control seizures and muscle tremors caused by low blood calcium levels. Refer to *ECLAMPSIA.*

HYPOGLYCEMIA:

Low blood sugar (hypoglycemia) is the most common metabolic cause of *seizures.* Excess stress, over-exertion on an empty stomach, *insulin overdose, and the presence of an insulinoma (tumor)* are all causes of low blood sugar levels. All seizure patients should be tested for low blood sugar on admittance to the hospital. A *50% glucose* solution given intravenously will control hypoglycemic seizures but the underlying cause should then be explored. The *glucagon tolerance test* and the *glucose tolerance test* are necessary to identify the exact cause of hypoglycemia.

IDIOPATHIC EPILEPSY:

Refer to *EPILEPSY, TRUE.*

IMMUNE DISORDERS OF THE NERVOUS SYSTEM:

"Coonhound" paralysis, optic neuritis, myasthenia gravis, polymyositis, and *chronic polyradiculoneuritis* are all immune disorders that affect the nervous system. Even though these conditions are immune mediated, ancillary neurological tests should also be conducted since other causes may be found.

INFECTIOUS DISEASES OF THE NERVOUS SYSTEM:

Refer to *DISEASES, INFECTIOUS, OF THE NERVOUS SYSTEM.*

INSULIN OVERDOSE:

Refer to *OVERDOSE, INSULIN.*

INSULINOMA:

Refer to *TUMOR, PANCREATIC.*

INTERVERTEBRAL DISC DISEASE:

Refer to *DISEASE, INTERVERTEBRAL DISC.*

INTOXICATIONS AFFECTING THE NERVOUS SYSTEM:

A large number of chemical substances have a direct affect on the nervous system causing *seizures* or altering the level of consciousness causing comas. Some chemicals cause muscular twitching while others produce specific neurological signs like *deafness, circling,* and *head tilt.*

If central nervous system signs are observed following exposure to any chemical substance or plant material, call your veterinarian or contact the poison control unit in your area immediately. The **animal toxicology hot line** number is **217-333-3611.** Be prepared to give the toxicologist the name of the plant, the chemical name of the substance, or the brand name of the substance that you suspect is causing the toxic signs.

KNUCKLING OVER:

Knuckling over may be a sign of nervous system dysfunction. Standing upright in a normal manner on all four feet is normal *proprioception.* A simple *proprioceptive test* can be done by placing each foot individually in a knuckled over position, observing how long the dog takes to right itself. From this test, the neurologist can obtain important information about the function of the peripheral sensory nerves and its relationship to the cerebral cortical part of the brain.

LEAD POISONING:

Refer to *POISONING, LEAD.*

LEVODOPA (L-dopa):

Levodopa, a drug used for the treatment of Parkinson's Disease in humans, has had some success in the prevention of *spinal cord trauma* after injury in canines. Presently, its use is experimental in veterinary medicine.

LOSS OF BALANCE:

Loss of balance is a sign of neurological dysfunction in the *vestibular* area of the inner ear which functions to provide normal balance. This loss of balance results in *head tilting, circling,* and *rolling.* The varied causes of vestibular dysfunction include tumors, toxic chemicals, trauma, and infections.

MANNITOL:

A drug used to treat swelling in the nervous system with a potent diuretic action is 20% mannitol.

MENINGIOMA:

Refer to TUMORS OF THE CENTRAL NERVOUS SYSTEM.

MENINGITIS:

Meningitis, the inflammation of the membrane surrounding the spinal cord, is most commonly caused by *Staphylococcus bacteria* and *Cryptococcus fungus.* Clinical signs are neck stiffness and an exaggeratedly-stiff walking gait. A fever may also be present without involvement of other body systems.

Analysis and culture from *cerebrospinal fluid* are important aids in diagnosing meningitis. Prognosis varies from good to poor depending on the cause. Fungal infections have a poor prognosis because of the toxicity of the treatment and the length of time that therapy must be maintained.

MENINGITIS, BACTERIAL:

This uncommon disease of the lining around the spinal cord is usually localized in the brain stem (the first part of the spinal cord). The *Staphylococcus* and *Pasteurella* species of bacteria are frequently present in bacterial meningitis.

High fever and increased sensitivity in the neck are the clinical signs which reflect the area of the nervous system involved. Diagnosis is made from clinical signs, *blood counts*, microscopic *examination of cerebrospinal fluid,*and isolation of the causative agent from CS fluid. Antibiotics are used in the treatment of bacterial meningitis. The prognosis for complete recovery is fair to good.

METABOLIC DISEASES AFFECTING THE NERVOUS SYSTEM:

Refer to *DISEASES, METABOLIC, AFFECTING THE NERVOUS SYSTEM.*

MYASTHENIA GRAVIS:

Myasthenia gravis can be either congenital or acquired. Refer to the complete discussion in Chapter 6 on the *MUSCULOSKELETAL SYSTEM.*

MYELOGRAPHY:

Myelography is a special technique done to pinpoint spinal cord lesions when simple radiographs are not diagnostic. Diseases generally diagnosed with myelography include *intervertebral disc disease*, spinal cord compression, *spinal dysraphism*, meningocele, and some tumors of the spinal cord. During the procedure, the contrast substance *metrizamide*, currently the safest, is injected into the cerebrospinal fluid (CSF) at the cisterna magna (the base of the skull) or in the middle lumbar region of the back. The contrast substance mixes with the CSF and flows to the area of the compression or expansion. With the contrast substance present, a radiograph clearly shows the defect. Because some danger is associated with this technique, the risk-benefit ratio must be carefully contemplated. Side effects include increased body temperature, convulsions, and death.

NARCOLEPSY:

Narcolepsy, a genetic sleep disorder in the Doberman Pinscher, is passed to the offspring by an autosomal recessive gene. Doberman Pinscher puppies can show clinical signs by eight weeks of age. The disease is not progressive because the severity of the condition stabilizes rather than getting worse as the Dobe gets older. The severity of *cataplectic attacks* in puppies has no correlation to those which occur in adulthood. The frequency of attacks varies from over 100 in a 24 hour period to one or two per week.

The major clinical sign of narcolepsy in Doberman Pinschers is *cataplexy,* a sudden flaccid collapse (paralysis) from which the dog recovers quickly. The paralytic state can affect part or all of the body. The dog can be lying in any position. When in a cataplectic state, the Dobe's eyes, which are usually open, may follow a stimulus moving from side to side. Along with rapid eye movement (REM), the toes twitch slightly. The length of an "attack" varies from several seconds to several minutes.

This cataplectic collapse is stimulated by the presence of food, play, excitement, and sexual activity. The severity of signs can be determined by a *food-elicited cataplexy test* in which the length of time of an attack and number of attacks is measured as the dog eats 10 morsels of food. The average Dobe time is under 20 seconds. In Poodles, it may be as long as 900 seconds. Doberman Pinschers are usually less severely affected than smaller breeds.

The use of an *EEG* and an *EMG* in diagnosing narcolepsy is unrewarding. The *physostigmine provocative test* and the *food-elicited cataplexy test* described are the most beneficial diagnostic tests. *Epilepsy* must be ruled out as a consideration. In narcolepsy, urinary or fecal incontinence are not present.

Successful treatment has been obtained with several drugs. *Methylphenidate, imipramine,* and *protriptyline* have been used to diminish the cataleptic attacks. The goal of therapy is to cut down on the number of cataleptic attacks without eliminating them completely since the level of medication required for that goal is dangerously high. The prognosis for the pet to lead a normal life is good. Medication is required indefinitely. Also refer to *CATAPLEXY.*

Additional information on Doberman Pinscher narcolepsy can be obtained from William C. Dement, M.D., Sleep Disorder Center, Stanford University School of Medicine, Stanford, CA 94305.

NEURITIS, OPTIC:

Optic neuritis is a condition of the central nervous system in which the optic nerves are inflamed, impairing the dog's sight. A number of conditions have been postulated as causes of this condition. Some cases of optic neuritis appear to be *immune mediated* while virus infections, tumors, and *vitamin A deficiency* have also been mentioned as causes.

The most common clinical sign is a rapid onset of *blindness* with widely dilated eyes which fail to respond to light. Ancillary tests are not particularly useful in diagnosing optic neuritis. Response to treatment is varied. Some cases respond dramatically to initial high doses of *corticosteroids* which are decreased during the following month. Other cases show no response to the treatment or experience relapses after an initial response to therapy. Recurrences and the presence of optic nerve atrophy give an overall poor prognosis for recovery.

NEUROFIBROSARCOMA:

Refer to *TUMORS OF THE NERVOUS SYSTEM.*

NEUROLOGICAL DISORDERS, CONGENITAL:

"Congenital" means present at birth, but is not necessarily hereditary. A list of the neurological disorders which are classified as congenital follows. More detailed discussion of each can be found under the topical headings.
- *Head Tilt in Dobermans*
- *True Epilepsy*
- *Hydrocephalus*
- *Cervical Spondylopathy (Wobbler Syndrome)*
- *Narcolepsy*

NEUROLOGICAL DISORDERS, SIGNS OF:

The following list of signs of nervous system disease are discussed under each individual heading:

- *Ataxia*	- *Loss of balance*
- *Behavior or personality change*	- *Pain perception*
- *Circling*	- *Pupil abnormalities*
- *Head tilt*	- *Proprioceptive loss*
- *Horner's syndrome*	- *Seizures*
- *Knuckling over*	- *Visual loss*

OLD DOG ENCEPHALITIS:
Refer to *ENCEPHALITIS, OLD DOG.*

OLIGODENDROGLIOMA:
Refer to *TUMORS OF THE NERVOUS SYSTEM.*

OPTIC NEURITIS:
Refer to *NEURITIS, OPTIC.*

ORGANOPHOSPHATES:
The class of chemical compounds referred to as *organophosphates* is commonly used to kill parasites. The chemical may be applied topically (dip or bath) or taken internally as a *wormer.* When the organophosphate is present in *flea collars*, the dog continually absorbs the insecticide. Excessive amounts of organophosphates can cause nervous system signs like pinpoint pupils, muscle tremors, and *seizures.* Mild clinical signs include excess salivation, vomiting, and diarrhea.

The antidote for organophosphate poisoning is *atropine* and *protopam chloride (2-PAM).* If seizures are occurring, medication to control them must be included in the treatment regimen. Any organophosphate chemicals still present on the skin or hair should be removed to prevent further absorption. Organophosphate poisoning has a fair to good prognosis for recovery.

OVERDOSE, INSULIN:
An overdose of insulin can cause severe *hypoglycemia* (low blood sugar) which can lead to *seizures.* Insulin overdose is caused from the administration of too much insulin in the treatment of *diabetes mellitus* and from the tumors of the insulin producing cells of the pancreas *(insulinoma).* Treatment is in the form of sugar, either orally or intravenously.

PAIN PERCEPTION:
Altered pain perception is a sign of a central nervous system lesion. An example occurs in the skin over the lower back or neck. When a lesion involves the *intervertebral discs*, it causes pressure on the nerves or the spinal cord in that region. If the skin is lightly pricked with a pin, an exaggerated reflex movement of the skin results in the area of the disc lesion.

PANCREATIC TUMOR:
Refer to *TUMOR, PANCREATIC.*

PARALYSIS, COONHOUND:
Refer to *POLYRADICULONEURITIS, ACUTE.*

PARALYSIS, TICK:

Tick paralysis is a neurological disease produced by a toxin secreted by *wood ticks*. The toxin produces clinical signs very similar to *coonhound paralysis*, but the treatment and prognosis are considerably different. While mild signs include some rear leg weakness, a flaccid paralysis of all four legs with respiratory and swallowing difficulty is present in more severe cases. *EMG* testing can differentiate tick paralysis from coonhound paralysis.

Thoroughly examine any dog suspected of tick paralysis, looking for an engorged female tick and removing any ticks present. General supportive therapy is necessary for 24 to 48 hours. Recovery is rapid. The prognosis for complete recovery from tick paralysis is excellent when the offending ticks are removed.

PERIPARTURIENT HYPOCALCEMIA:

Refer to *ECLAMPSIA.*

PERIPHERAL NERVE INJURY:

Injury to a peripheral nerve is common in auto accidents. In a traumatic nerve injury, the nerve becomes inflamed and swollen. Early use of *glucocorticoids* like *dexamethasone* cuts down on nervous system inflammation. If edema (swelling) of the nerve exists, *50% glucose* or *mannitol* helps control this undesirable condition. After the injury of a peripheral nerve, five or six weeks may be required for normal function to return. During this period, physical therapy of the affected muscle groups is extremely important. If function has not normalized in six weeks, a permanent neurological deficit can be anticipated.

PERSONALITY CHANGES:

Refer to *BEHAVIOR OR PERSONALITY CHANGES.*

PHENOBARBITAL:

Phenobarbital is the drug of choice in controlling seizures created by excitement or in cases where cost is a significant factor. Also refer to *ANTICONVULSANT DRUGS.*

POISONING, LEAD:

Lead poisoning is a common cause of neurological dysfunction in puppies. Teething puppies may chew on items containing lead (rubber boots, golf balls, asphalt roofing, linoleum tile, caulking compounds and some ceramic dog food dishes). Acute lead toxicity will cause decreased red blood cell maturation producing *anemia* which can result in swelling of the brain and neuron degeneration.

The most common clinical signs of lead poisoning are uncontrolled running, screaming, fits, biting, and general hysteria. If the lead intoxication has occurred slowly, signs of *ataxia*, incoordinated movements, or even a total lack of functional movement may be evident. To determine the clinical difference between *distemper, rabies,* and lead poisoning is difficult. A *blood lead test* with an elevated lead poisoning content is most beneficial. *Urine lead* levels can also be determined. *Radiographs* of the abdomen may show lead items in the gastrointestinal tract.

The chelating agent calcium disodium ethylenediaminetetraacetic acid *(Calcium EDTA)* diluted in 5% dextrose solution is given subcutaneously four times daily for four to seven days for treatment. If other nervous system signs are observed, they are treated symptomatically (e.g. *seizures).*

When the treatment is started early in the course of lead intoxication, the prognosis for recovery is good. However, if the condition is chronic, irreparable brain damage can be present with a poor prognosis for recovery.

POISONING, STRYCHNINE:

Strychnine poisoning is caused by the ingestion of the chemical strychnine. Strychnine, sometimes used as a poison for varmints, is most frequently used to lace meat by a person intentionally trying to kill a dog with the poisonous chemical.

Somewhat similar to both *tetanus* and *toxaphene poisoning*, the clinical signs of strychnine poisoning are severe muscular rigidity and the head and neck being thrown back to an extreme degree. Any loud noise will cause the affected dog to have muscular spasms and *convulsions*

If strychnine poisoning is suspected, stomach contents should be saved for analysis. Seizure activity must be controlled. Oxygen should be administered as needed. The dog must be kept in a quiet, dark area on soft bedding and turned from side to side every four hours during the recovery phase. The body temperature may be elevated. However, when the excessive muscle twitching is controlled, the temperature returns to normal. The prognosis for recovery is guarded to good depending on when treatment is initiated and if the stomach contents are removed to prevent further absorption of the poison. Additional information is found in Chapter 9 under *STRYCHNINE POISONING.*

POLYRADICULONEURITIS, ACUTE:

Acute polyradiculoneuritis, a relatively common neurological disorder of dogs, is believed to have an immune origin. Because it frequently occurs after a raccoon bite, its more common name is *coonhound paralysis* has been coined. Acute polyradiculoneuritis, however, is also seen following systemic disease and *vaccinations.*

Dogs are not usually affected before six months of age. The first clinical sign of rear leg weakness quickly progresses to paralysis of all four legs.

The degree of involvement varies. In severe cases, respiratory muscles can become paralyzed causing labored breathing and possible death. The dog not only has difficulty eating and drinking but its bark is also characteristically changed. Diagnosis is from the clinical signs in addition to a history of a raccoon bite or a recent vaccination. When available, an *EMG test* is very helpful.

Extensive nursing care is important for recovery. For 7 to 14 days, assisting with fluid and food intake and aiding with excretory functions is necessary. The paralyzed dog should be placed on a water bed or sheepskin to minimize bed sores. To keep blood from stagnating in the lungs, the dog should be turned over every 4 to 6 hours. When adequate nursing care is provided for the required time, prognosis for recovery is good. Recurrences are common with acute polyradiculoneuritis.

PRIMIDONE:

Primidone, a drug used in the control of *seizures*, is considered to be the most predictable drug in the anticonvulsant group. However, in some dogs, side affects involving the liver occur. Also refer to *ANTICONVULSANT DRUGS*.

PROPRIOCEPTIVE LOSS:

Proprioception is the ability for a dog to stand in a normal manner on the pads with the legs under the body in a normal way. A loss of this ability (proprioceptive loss) is a sign of a nervous system lesion. An easy way to test for proprioceptive loss is to place the dog's paw in a knuckled over position and observe the dog to see if he corrects this abnormal posture. Failure to correct this abnormal position is evidence of a proprioceptive loss.

PROTOZOAN INFECTIONS OF THE NERVOUS SYSTEM:

Toxoplasmosis is the only protozoan infection of the nervous system that affects dogs. Refer to *TOXOPLASMOSIS*.

PSEUDORABIES:

Pseudorabies, also called "Maditch" and "Aujeszky's Disease," is a rare, rapidly fatal disease caused by a herpes virus. Most commonly seen in swine and cattle, the transmission to dogs requires ingestion of infected tissues.

The clinical signs in dogs are an uncontrollable itch, mutilation of the legs and tail, excess salivation, difficulty in swallowing, and death in one or two days. Any dog dying of these signs should be examined for rabies virus. Because no treatment or vaccine is available for pseudorabies, the prognosis is hopeless.

PUPIL ABNORMALITIES:

The ability of the pupil of the eye to constrict and dilate should be present in normal, seeing eyes. The presence of different sized pupils can be an indication of a lesion in the eye, optic nerve, or anterior portion of the brain. This difference is also seen in *Horner's syndrome*. Widely dilated pupils that do not constrict in response to bright light may indicate blindness. A tightly constricted pupil in both eyes is observed in some *chemical poisons* which affect the nervous system. Pupil constriction is seen in several other disorders of the nervous system.

RABIES:

Rabies, a fatal viral disease of all warm-blooded animals, causes a progressive *encephalomyelitis*. The disease can be prevented by timely rabies *vaccinations*. Most states have regulations concerning the frequency with which vaccinations should be administered.

The most consistent clinical sign of rabies infections is its inconsistency. Almost all cases will show a change in disposition and behavior. If the dog is NORMALLY aggressive, it will become friendly; if it is NORMALLY friendly, it will become aggressive and menacing. The variety of signs observed in rabies include fever, excess salivation, difficulty in swallowing, depression, viciousness, paresis, and paralysis of any one or all limbs.

The transmission of rabies takes place through a bite from an infected animal. The virus is transmitted from the saliva of the carrier to the bite wound of the victim. The virus travels along nerve endings to the brain where the rapidly fatal encephalomyelitis occurs. Death will occur in three to eight days from the onset of the appearance of clinical signs.

In rare instances, clinical rabies can be induced by a rabies vaccination. This condition is actually an *acute polyradiculoneuritis* and is not fatal as long as encephalomyelitis does not occur. The leg where the vaccination was given will be lame and even show signs of paralysis. The inflamed peripheral nerves recover in one or two months in most cases. This type of vaccine-induced disease only occurs when a modified-live vaccine is used.

Any dog suspected of having rabies should be handled very carefully and should be placed in a quarantine facility. If any chance of human exposure exists, a qualified diagnostic laboratory must test its brain for the presence of rabies virus after the dog dies.

The prognosis for recovering from clinical signs of rabies is hopeless. A dog that has not been vaccinated that is exposed to the bite of a known rabid animal should be quarantined for six months or destroyed.

RESERPINE:

Reserpine is a potent drug that has been used in the treatment of severe spinal cord trauma. When given within twelve hours of the injury, the reduction of hemorrhagic necrosis of the spinal cord is significant.

SEIZURES, CAUSES OF:

The causes of seizures listed here are discussed fully under each individual heading:

- Eclampsia
- Encephalitis
- Epilepsy
- Hepatic encephalopathy
- Hydrocephalus
- Hypocalcemia

- Hypoglycemia
- Insulin overdose
- Intoxications (strychnine, organophosphates)
- Lead poisoning
- Pancreatic tumor
- Uremia

SIDE SUCKER SYNDROME:

The side sucker syndrome (*flank sucking*) is fairly common in the Doberman Pinscher. Affected dogs become obsessed with an area of the flank on one side, continually licking, sucking, and chewing at that region. No skin lesions are present unless self-trauma results in inflammation and hair loss. The cause of flank sucking is open to debate. While some feel *whipworm* infestation is the underlying cause, others feel side sucking is a vice (bad habit). Still others think that it may be a form of *epilepsy*.

Therapy consists of the removal of any *intestinal parasites*. The use of *anticonvulsants* like *phenobarbital* and *primidone* can be helpful. The intramuscular use of medroxyprogesterone acetate, a female hormone, may also be of some benefit.

The prognosis for a cure is guarded unless an underlying cause is determined and removed. Relapses are common. The problem may be present throughout most of the Dobe's life.

SIGNS OF NEUROLOGICAL DISORDERS:

Refer to *NEUROLOGICAL DISORDERS, SIGNS OF.*

SKULL X-RAY:

Refer to *X-RAY, SKULL.*

SODIUM PENTOBARBITAL:

Sodium pentobarbital is a drug used in the control of nervous system *seizures* and as an *anesthetic*. Also refer to *ANTICONVULSANT DRUGS* and Chapter 1 on *ANESTHESIA.*

SPASTIC SYNDROME:

A syndrome that occurs in adult Doberman Pinschers is the spastic syndrome of the rear legs. In this condition, the dog may extend a rear leg behind him as he stands. No other nervous system signs are observed. All ancillary tests and *CSF analysis* appear normal. While it is progressive in some dogs, the disease is never very debilitating. No treatment is necessary although some veterinarians have recommended oral *diazepam*. The cause is still unknown. The prognosis for a normal life is excellent.

SPINAL TRAUMA:

Refer to *TRAUMA, SPINAL.*

STATUS EPILEPTICUS:

Status epilepticus is continuous *seizure* activity which never allows the body to return to a conscious, normal state between episodes. This life-threatening situation requires emergency veterinary care. Because of the continuing seizure activity, the body temperature elevates, greatly altering the body's metabolism. A lack of oxygen causes the brain to swell.

Treatment is directed at stopping the seizure activity. Intravenous *diazepam* and *sodium pentobarbital* are given. If the body temperature remains high, alcohol or ice baths may be necessary. *Mannitol* is used if brain swelling is suspected, followed by *corticosteroids*. Should *hypoglycemia* become a problem, *50% glucose* may be necessary.

The prognosis for the recovery from status epilepticus is fair to good depending on the underlying cause of the seizure activity. Immediate veterinary help should be sought to stop status epilepticus.

STRYCHNINE POISONING:

Refer to *POISONING, STRYCHNINE.*

TESTS USED IN THE DIAGNOSIS OF NERVOUS SYSTEM DISORDERS:

- Audiometry
- Blood tests
- Cerebrospinal Fluid (CSF) Analysis
- Electroencephalography (EEG)
- Food-elicited cataplexy test
- Myelography
- Physostigmine provocative test
- Skull X-ray

TETANUS:

Tetanus is a life-threatening disease caused by <u>Clostridium tetani</u>, the bacteria which usually occurs in deep, contaminated wounds. Although dogs are more resistant to this toxin than are horses, dogs can still be severely affected. Dogs raised around horses should receive tetanus antitoxin and possible *tetanus toxoid vaccinations* to prevent this serious neuromuscular disease.

The clinical signs of tetanus and *strychnine poisoning* are very similar. Extreme muscle twitching and rigidity are evident in both. Muscular stiffness is generalized. An affected dog walks like a wooden horse. The head and face muscles are characteristically affected. The ears are drawn back over the head, the forehead is wrinkled, and the lips are drawn back tightly. The third eyelids cover the eyeballs. Since all of the body muscles are affected, respiratory and cardiac muscle problems are also apparent. *Seizures* and difficulty in swallowing are common.

Treatment must be continued for as long as thirty days or until all muscle stiffness is gone. Initially, large doses of tetanus antitoxin (assuming no allergic reactions occur) and *penicillin G* are used to kill the bacteria and neutralize the toxin. Other signs are treated symptomatically. All wounds should be cleaned out and disinfected. Finally, the dog must be kept in a quiet, dark place and given extensive nursing care.

The prognosis for recovery is guarded. If the clinical signs become progressively more severe, the prognosis is grave. If the signs are mild, reasonable expectation of recovery after prolonged treatment can be anticipated.

TICK PARALYSIS:

Refer to *PARALYSIS, TICK.*

TOXOPLASMOSIS:

Toxoplasmosis is a *protozoan disease* that infects many body tissues causing *encephalomyelitis* and *myositis* in a dog of any age. Toxoplasmosis is spread in uncooked meats, in fecal material, and by flies and cockroaches. Public health is a definite aspect. No pregnant women should handle any animals diagnosed as having toxoplasmosis because human fetuses may be severely affected by this protozoan parasite.

The clinical signs are typical of any infection involving the brain and related tissues. Toxoplasmosis is very difficult to diagnose. Sampling blood over a two week period and checking for a rising titer to Toxoplasma is the best method.

Because treatment is difficult, long term use of *Tribrissen®* is necessary but may cause unfavorable reactions in the Doberman Pinscher. The prognosis varies. If there is a concurrent immunosuppressive disease (e.g. *canine distemper, leukemia*), toxoplasmosis will spread rapidly in the body making the prognosis poor. However, early treatment of mildly affected dogs provides a much better prognosis.

TRAUMA, HEAD:

Head trauma, internal or external, is a cause of various neurological signs. The severity of the neurological signs is determined by the degree of trauma and the injured area of the head. An external blow to the skull can cause swelling within the skull. Internally, either ruptured blood vessels or blood clots can cause head trauma. The prognosis for head injuries is guarded.

TRAUMA, SPINAL:

Spinal trauma can occur as a result of manipulation during spinal surgery, a traumatic accident (e.g. car, bad fall), damage from disc and cervical vertebrae instability, or an improper *CSF sampling* technique. The spinal cord is very sensitive to movement and pressure from any source. Hemorrhage around the spinal cord causes necrosis of the nerve tissue. If untreated, necrosis causes the cord to become nonfunctional. However, if spinal cord trauma is properly treated within twelve hours of the injury, some chance of recovery from nerve tissue dysfunction is expected.

TRIBRISSEN® :

This antibacterial drug is useful in treating nervous system infections. Tribrissen® is composed of two drugs, *sulfadiazine* and *trimethoprim*, that cross the blood-brain barrier. Administration, either orally or by injection, is once or twice daily depending on the seriousness of the infection. The antibacterial spectrum for sulfadiazine-trimethoprim is wide. Also refer to *DRUG ALLERGY* before using in Doberman Pinschers.

TRUE EPILEPSY:

Refer to *EPILEPSY, TRUE.*

TUMOR, PANCREATIC:

A pancreatic tumor (*insulinoma*) can cause *seizures* by producing large amounts of *insulin* which lower the blood sugar level creating severe *hypoglycemia*. The treatment of choice is the removal of the pancreatic tumor or the entire pancreas, which requires above average surgical skill. In partial pancreas removal, *pancreatitis* is a common post-surgical complication. Most malignant pancreatic tumors have already spread at the time of surgery. The surgeon must be alert in order to remove solitary metastasis (spread tumors). Some malignant pancreatic tumors can be partially controlled by the use of drugs that destroy beta cells and inhibit insulin production.

The prognosis for nonmalignant tumor removal by a qualified surgeon is good. The prognosis for malignant tumor management or removal is poor.

TUMORS OF THE NERVOUS SYSTEM:

Any tumor may metastasize (spread) to the nervous system. In this section, only primary nervous system tumors will be discussed. Ancillary tests for determining the presence of neoplasms (tumors) include *skull radiographs* and *CSF analysis*. Unfortunately, many tumors are only found on necropsy (autopsy). When nervous system signs are seen in middle and old age dogs, tumors are suspected.

Astrocytomas, primary tumors of the nervous system, are most commonly found in the cerebrum and middle portion of the brain. They don't usually metastasize (spread) to other tissues.

Ependymomas are found primarily in the area of the brain where the cerebrospinal fluid canals are located. They are invasive and cause much damage to surrounding tissue.

Gliomas or *glioblastomas* are tumors of specific functional nerve cells. This type of neoplasm is most commonly found as a circumscribed mass in the front part of the brain. This type of tumor is also hemorrhagic in nature.

Meningiomas are tumors of the meninges which cover the brain and spinal cord. They grow slowly, sometimes becoming calcified and very hard. As they expand toward the brain, neurological signs are observed.

Neurofibrosarcoma, a rare tumor of nervous tissue, can act like a *meningioma*. The vestibular portion of the inner ear region is affected causing *head tilt, circling,* and loss of balance. This progressive lesion will spread to adjacent tissues.

Oligodendrogliomas are primary tumors of the brain, most commonly occurring in the brain stem area. They are seen in middle and old aged dogs. Neurological signs occur which represent the area of the brain involved.

UREMIA:

A high level of urea in the blood can cause *seizure* activity. Most of the dogs that reach this level of uremia are in severe *kidney failure*. The use of *anticonvulsants* in these dogs can produce high lethal levels of the drug in the blood system since most anticonvulsants are excreted through the kidneys. *Fluid therapy* and *peritoneal dialysis* are the only methods of reducing the uremia level. Kidneys that can resume normal function after the uremia level is reduced produce a better prognosis for control of uremia induced seizures. If kidney regeneration is not possible, the prognosis is grave.

VESTIBULAR DYSFUNCTION:

Refer to *LOSS OF BALANCE, HEAD TILT, and CIRCLING.*

VISUAL LOSS:

Visual loss occurs in one or both eyes, originating either from the eye or from the central nervous system. In the case of the central nervous system, it is a sign of a nervous system lesion. Determining if the visual imparity originates in the eye or in the brain is done by performing a *neurological* and an *ophthalmological examination.* The eye is examined for pupil size and symmetry, pupil response to light, and charcteristics of the lens, retina, and optic disc. Structures associated with the eye may also be examined in a thorough eye examination. Determination of the cause of the blindness is important in establishing a method of therapy and a prognosis.

WATER ON THE BRAIN:

Refer to *HYDROCEPHALUS.*

WOBBLER SYNDROME (CERVICAL VERTEBRAL MALFORMATION):
Refer to Chapter 6 on the *MUSCULOSKELETAL SYSTEM.*

X-RAY, SKULL:
Radiographs of the skull can provide valuable information in some nervous system dysfunctions. Usually radiographs must be taken from several different angles. To be normal, the skull should be bilaterally symmetrical (both halves appear similar) when looking down at a skull from above.

Chapter 8

NUTRITION

AAFCO:

Refer to *AMERICAN ASSOCIATION OF FEED CONTROL OFFICIALS.*

ADDITIVE-FREE DIETS:

A number of additive-free diets are currently being marketed for dogs. This concept is based on the idea that "preservatives" are harmful and can cause disease or cancer when consumed. Close governmental regulation does not allow the use of harmful chemical substances in pet foods. Even "natural preservatives" such as salt and sugar may be harmful at the levels needed to prevent food breakdown and bacterial decomposition. The chance of bacterial contamination is greater in additive-free foods. While the idea of feeding an additive-free dog food may primarily be a sales gimmick, it is not harmful providing only small amounts of additive-free food are kept on hand. This kind of food will deteriorate more rapidly than "preserved" dog foods, losing its palatability and wholesomeness.

ADULT DOGS, DIETARY MANAGEMENT OF:

A quality dog food which will provide all of the *nutrients* necessary to sustain life at a maintenance level should be fed to adult dogs not under the stress of working, showing, or hunting, and to those not being bred or nursing puppies. Adults of both sexes weighing over 50 pounds, like the Doberman Pinscher, can be maintained nicely on a quality *dry food* and *water*. Canned food and supplementation is not necessary for normal health. *If canned food* is added to increase palatability, the amount of dry food should be decreased to prevent obesity. Changing food frequently is not necessary and in fact, is undesirable because these changes may cause bowel upsets like *diarrhea* and *vomiting*.

The aim of an adult maintenance dog food is to maintain optimal weight and health while eliminating excesses of certain nutrients that are harmful if fed over a long period. Quality maintenance food should be at least 75% digestible. The *protein* content should be between 18% and 25%, the *fat* content greater than 10%, the *calcium* percentage .5% to .9%, and the *phosphorus* level between .4% and .8% on a dry weight basis. The *label of the dog food* should indicate that *feeding trials* show that the diet will maintain adult dogs under average conditions. Do not merely accept the statement that *NRC* minimums have been met.

AMERICAN ASSOCIATION OF FEED CONTROL OFFICIALS (AAFCO):

In an attempt to bring some stability to the rules and regulations affecting animal feeds, the American Association of Feed Control Officials (AAFCO) was formed. Representatives from the Food and Drug Administration (FDA), the Federal Trade Commission (FTC), and the U.S. Department of Agriculture (USDA) compose the AAFCO panel that regulates animal feeds. In addition, people from the State Departments of Agriculture and the State Departments of Public Health are included.

Uniform *pet food label* regulations and a standardized testing procedure of dog food have been established. AAFCO requires that pet foods be *feeding-trial* tested on at least 10 dogs of the age specified on the food. These test-fed dogs must then be checked to determine whether the dogs have maintained their weight and health during the feeding trial. AAFCO's feeding trial regulations are much more valid to the pet food buyer than are the *National Research Council (NRC)* standards of minimal nutrient requirements. IF AAFCO is not mentioned on the dog food label, write to the company to determine if AAFCO requirements are being met or if only NRC standards are being used. For the health of your dog, only use dog food that meets AAFCO requirements!

AMINO ACIDS, ESSENTIAL AND NON-ESSENTIAL:

Amino acids are the structural components of *protein*. The dog's body cannot make *essential amino acids* so they must be provided in the diet. Ten of the 22 amino acids are essential including arginine, histidine, isoleucine, leucine, lysine, methionine, phenylalanine, threonine, tryptophan, and valine. The higher the quantity of essential amino acids in the dietary protein, the better the *biological value* of that food. A deficiency of arginine in some commercial substitutes for dog's milk can cause *cataracts* in eight week old pups.

ANOREXIA:

Anorexia is defined as a lack of appetite or loss of appetite for food. The cause should be determined when possible so that natural feeding methods may be utilized.

ANOREXIA, FEEDING METHODS FOR:

Refer to *FEEDING METHODS FOR ANOREXIA.*

APPETITE STIMULATION:

Refer to *FEEDING METHODS FOR ANOREXIA.*

ASCORBIC ACID:

Refer to *VITAMIN C.*

ASH:

The collective mineral content of dog food, ash, is determined by the extraction of *fats*, the acid and alkali digestion of *carbohydrate* and *protein*, and the burning of the food to remove *crude fiber*. What remains after burning is ash (*mineral*).

AVIDIN:

The protein avidin is highly concentrated in raw egg white. Egg yolk is high in *biotin*. Avidin binds the vitamin biotin and renders it inactive. Therefore, if the entire raw egg is fed to the dog, a *biotin deficiency* is unlikely. When the egg white is cooked, avidin is changed and will not bind with biotin.

BALANCED DIET:

A balanced diet is a diet which contains the correct amount of all the *nutrients* necessary to maintain a dog at any given life stage or activity level. A diet for proper puppy growth is a balanced diet when the necessary nutrients for growth are present in the correct amounts to insure optimum development.

Many pet foods which attempt to be "all things to all dogs" are not balanced diets. A dog has different nutritional needs at every stage of its life cycle. A food that is balanced for puppy growth is too high in *protein, fat, calcium, and phosphorus* for an older dog that is neither active nor raising puppies. Other diets may not be balanced because of the additional nutrients or vitamins given by the owner. Most commercial pet foods contain too much *sodium* for a dog with a *cardiac insufficiency*. A high sodium level can lead to hypertension in normal dogs. *"Generic"* and other very cheap dog foods do not contain enough of the necessary nutrients to be a balanced diet in spite of the fact that the package boasts of "meeting the minimum requirements of the National Research Council (NRC)."

BIOLOGICAL VALUE:

Biological value *(BV)* is the most common measurement of the quality of *protein* in the diet. BV is the percentage calculated from the difference between the amount of a *nutrient (protein)* absorbed and the amount retained in the body. This measurement is only pertinent if the dog is in a state of good nutrition and has a nonprotein source of calories to meet its food requirements. The following are biological values of some proteins: egg, 100; milk, 92; beef, 78; soybean meal, 67; whole wheat, 48; corn, 45; and gelatin, 0. Gelatin does not contain the essential amino acid, tryptophan.

BIOTIN:

Biotin is a *B complex vitamin* sometimes called *vitamin H* or *coenzyme R*. This potent vitamin is required by all forms of life. Health problems do not occur from high levels of biotin but deficiencies may cause skin problems, posterior leg paralysis, *loss of appetite*, and weakness from *diarrhea*. Egg yolk is very high in biotin. Raw egg white is high in the biotin antagonist, *avidin*. While the feeding of a whole raw egg will probably not cause a vitamin deficiency, cooking the egg will remove any possibility of a biotin deficiency.

BV:

Refer to *BIOLOGICAL VALUE.*

B VITAMINS:

The B complex group of vitamins consists of *vitamin B_1 (thiamine), vitamin B_2 (riboflavin), niacin, vitamin B_6 (pyridoxine), pantothenic acid, folic acid, biotin, and vitamin B_{12} (cobalamin)*. All are water soluble. Because all but cobalamin are not stored in the body tissues, overdosing is not a problem. Remember that physiological functions which increase fluid removal from the body may also increase the removal of the B complex vitamins resulting in deficiencies. *Kidney problems, diarrhea, vomiting,* and prolonged diuretic therapy for *heart failure* may create deficiencies that require B complex supplementation. Whole grain cereals, liver, yeast, and egg yolk are all high in B complex vitamins. Each member of the B complex group is discussed separately within the chapter.

CALCIUM:

Because of its contribution to bone, teeth, and cartilage formation, calcium is a very important mineral for normal body function and growth. Calcium is also necessary for normal *cardiac and skeletal muscle* contraction. Both deficiencies and excesses of calcium will seriously disrupt normal body function.

Early signs of calcium deficiencies include enlarged joints, splayed feet, stiffness, and *lameness. Hock hyperextension syndrome* may be partially due to a calcium deficiency. Long term low calcium levels decrease the appetite and predispose the dog to fractured bones and loose teeth. A rapid loss of calcium will cause the skeletal muscles to have *tetanic contractions.*

Calcium absorption in the gut is associated with *vitamin D* intake. Most deficiencies develop in high meat diets which are high in *phosphorus*, but very low in calcium. The proper ratio of calcium to phosphorus in the diet is 1.2 parts calcium for every 1 part of phosphorus. Meat does not have this ratio. As a rule, if a quality growth related diet is maintained during the first year of life, supplementation with calcium is not necessary. There are, however, some individual circumstances that might require the addition of calcium to the diet. Do not add it indiscriminately.

Excess calcium indirectly causes deficiencies in *zinc, iron, copper,* and *phosphorus*. High levels predispose the dog to *bloat* and *decreased thyroid function*, actually decreasing the growth rate.

CALORIES:

Calories are the amount of energy produced from food. By definition, a calorie with a lower case "c" is the amount of energy needed to raise 1 ml. of water 1^0 centigrade. In nutrition, a calorie is usually expressed as Calorie upper case "C" or kilocalorie (K calorie) which is 1,000 calories. Dog food diets talk about metabolizable or digestible calories per given amount of food. The energy from the digestible calories is first used for maintenance of normal body functions. If more energy is available, weight is gained. If less than normal energy is available, weight is lost. Certain activities in a dog's life require more calories than those found in a maintenance food. In the following example, multiply maintenance calories by the number indicated for the actual amount of calories needed for that activity:

ACTIVE DOG	1.2
HUNTING (full day in field)	1.1 to 1.4
COLD (below freezing)	1.75
HEAT (hot and humid)	2.5
PREGNANCY	1.0 up to six weeks, then 1.3 until whelping
HEAVY LACTATION with large litter	4
GROWTH	
to 2 months	3
2 to 6 months	2
6 to 12 months	1.5

The **normal maintenance dietary energy requirements** for a mature Doberman Pinscher will be 25 to 30 K calories/pound of body weight/day. Amounts needed for growth, lactation, strenuous exercise or severe environment may be approximated from the above chart.

CARBOHYDRATES:

Carbohydrates are simple and complex sugars which compose a good portion of the energy source in dog food. This source of energy is grouped into soluble carbohydrates, those utilized by the body after enzymatic breakdown, and insoluble carbohydrates or *fiber* that adds bulk to the diet for proper intestinal function. Only certain bacteria can break down fiber for absorption and energy usage. These bacteria are not found in the dog's intestinal system. Because carbohydrate fiber cannot be utilized by the dog, adding high fiber to some foods can make them useful as canine diet foods. Cooking increases the digestibility and assimilation of simple sugars from cereal sources of carbohydrates. If more carbohydrates are assimilated than necessary for maintenance, they will then be stored as fat or glycogen.

CHOLINE:

Choline, frequently grouped with vitamins, is not a vitamin because it is not needed for metabolism. Choline helps to prevent fat accumulation in the *liver* and is also necessary for proper nerve impulse transmission. A deficiency of choline may result in blood clotting problems, fatty liver formation, and a decrease in albumin in the blood stream. Too much choline can cause *diarrhea* and nerve irritability.

COBALAMIN (VITAMIN B$_{12}$):

Vitamin B$_{12}$ (cobalamin) is one of the water soluble B complex vitamins which makes it non-toxic in large doses. Over a long period of time, deficiencies may contribute to the development of anemia. Vitamin B$_{12}$ has been used with some success as an appetite stimulant.

COENZYME R:

Refer to *BIOTIN*.

COLITIS, DIETARY MANAGEMENT OF:

While drugs such as *sulfasalazine* are important in the management of *colitis*, careful regulation of the diet is also paramount to control this troublesome disease.

Prescription Diet® I/D® , dry or canned, is an easy way to feed a highly digestible, easily tolerated diet. The following homemade diet can also be utilized:

COLITIS DIET:

1/2 cup Cream of Wheat (cook to make 2 cups)
1 hard boiled egg
2 Tablespoons Brewer's yeast
3 Tablespoons sugar
1 Tablespoon corn oil
1 teaspoon potassium chloride
1 teaspoon dicalcium phosphate
1 Tums® tablet
1 balanced vitamin-mineral tablet
Cook Cream of Wheat. Cool and add other ingredients and mix well. This recipe prepares 2.2 pounds of food.

Both Prescription Diet® I/D® and the homemade diet should be fed in small, frequent meals.

COPPER:

Copper is a *trace mineral* necessary for normal body function, especially *red blood cell production.* Deficiencies of copper can be produced by excesses in *zinc* or *iron.* Bone deformities, *hair depigmentation,* or *diarrhea* can occur from copper deficiencies. Copper excesses are likely to occur in the Doberman Pinscher because some members of the breed have hepatic defects allowing for accumulation of high doses of copper. Accumulation of copper causes *liver disease.*

COPPER TOXICOSIS, DIETARY MANAGEMENT OF:

Early dietary management of copper toxicosis in the Doberman Pinscher is important in order to minimize *liver disease* caused by the accumulation of dietary copper. *D-penicillamine (Cuprimine®)* is mixed with the usual *low copper diet* to increase the excretion of copper in the urine. Puppies under nine months of age can be fed a *Prescription Diet® U/D®* supplemented with cooked eggs, hamburger, cottage cheese and 1/2 teaspoon of dicalcium phosphate. If the *U/D® diet* is used, bimonthly *blood cell counts* should be checked. Maintaining normal red blood cell levels with this ultra-low protein diet is difficult.

The homemade low copper diet is as follows:

LOW COPPER DIET:

2-1/2 cups of cooked rice	1/2 Tums® tablet
1 ounce of corn oil	1/4 teaspoon salt
1 cooked egg	1 `balanced vitamin-mineral tablet without copper.

Cook rice and mix with other ingredients to make one pound. Refrigerate unused portion.

COPROPHAGY (STOOL EATING):

While disgusting, stool eating is usually not harmful. However, *parasites* can be transmitted through this process. A bad habit which has developed and boredom are the most common causes of coprophagy (stool eating). A *pancreatic enzyme deficiency* may cause a small number of dogs to crave the "extra" ingredients that are obtained from eating stool. Rapid pickup of stool will eliminate the source helping to break the habit. Increased exercise helps to alleviate boredom. The addition of Adolph's® Meat Tenderizer to the dog food enzymatically changes the composition of the stool. The use of a highly digestible dog food also helps minimize coprophagy.

CRUDE PROTEIN:

Crude protein, the amount of protein present in dog food, is noted on the label. This is an accurate analysis of the quantity but not of the quality. In high quality foods, the digestibility and biological value of the protein are high. In low quality dog foods, a similar crude protein level will have very low digestibility and *biological value.*

DIARRHEA, DIETARY MANAGEMENT OF:

The dietary management of diarrhea is identical to the management of *colitis* except that within two weeks, normal dog food can be gradually reintroduced in the case of simple diarrhea. The basis for treating diarrhea is feeding a highly digestible, low fiber diet which does not contain disaccharides (table sugar, milk sugar).

DIETARY MANAGEMENT:

Each of the following specialized dietary situations are discussed individually within the chapter:

Adult Dog	*Obesity*
Colitis	*Old Dog*
Copper Toxicosis	*Pancreatitis*
Diarrhea	*Reproduction and Lactation*
Growing Dogs	*Stressed Dogs*
Heart Disease	*Vomiting*
Kidney Disease	*Weaning*
Liver Disease	

DIETS, SPECIALIZED:

The following specialized diets are discussed under each individual heading within this chapter:

Additive-Free Diet	*Low Mineral Diet*
Balanced Diet	*Low Protein/Kidney Disease Diet*
Food Allergy Diet	*Low Sodium/Heart Disease Diet*
Formula, Nutritious Puppy	*Meat-Free Diet*
Lactose-Free Diet	*Soy-Free Diet*
Low Copper/Copper Toxicosis Diet	
Low Fat Diet	

DIGESTIBLE PROTEIN:

Digestible protein is defined as the percentage of protein absorbed in the body in relation to the amount eaten. A good quality pet food should have protein digestibility of at least 80% in *dry food*, 85% in *soft moist* and *canned ration* forms, and up to 90% in *canned meat* types. Meat-type protein is more digestible than cereal protein.

DOG FOOD, CANNED:

Canned dog food is more palatable and more digestible than its dry counter-part. Because of its 75% water content, canned dog food is more expensive than dry food. Two varieties of canned dog food exist. The all-meat "gourmet" type may contribute to kidney problems and an appetite for only that diet when used exclusively. The other type is a mix of meat, cereals, and soybean generally balanced nutritionally to create a varied appetite. The mixture is usually less expensive than the gourmet variety. Canned foods provide between 450 and 600 K calories of utilizable energy per 14 oz. can. As with most products, you get what you pay for with canned dog food.

DOG FOOD, COMMERCIAL FORMS:

The three basic types of commercial dog food produced are *dry food, canned food,* and *soft-moist dog food.* Each of these types is discussed under its individual heading within this chapter. Remember - good and bad foods exist in all forms. A customer generally gets what he or she pays for.

DOG FOOD, DRY:

As with any form of dog food, dry dog food has both advantages and disadvantages. Dry dog food is produced in three forms: meal, kibble, and expanded form. Meal mixes the ingredients together. Kibbles are first baked and then broken into pieces. The expanded form is cooked in an extruder and forced under pressure causing further expansion. Currently, no meal forms of dry food are sold. Most foods available are the extruded type. The cooking process increases digestibility of *carbohydrates. Fats* are added after cooking by spraying them onto the product, helping to increase palatability.

Dry dog food costs less, controls tartar buildup on teeth, and allows the leisure of *free choice feeding.* One disadvantage is the lower palatability of the food. Also, the kind of ingredients that can be used in the dry food process are limited. As an example, muscle meat cannot be used in dry food. Because they are less stable, as a rule, they should be eaten within six months from the time of manufacture.

Acceptable levels of K calories would be 600 K cal. per 8 oz. cup where the dry food contained 25% fat, 300-400 K cal. per 8 oz. cup when the fat content is 8% to 24%, and in low-fat dry foods, the K calories per cup are less than 200. Once again, you get what you pay for in dry dog food.

DOG FOOD PALATABILITY:

Palatability of dog foods varies but in general, four factors are important in determining how well a dog likes a given diet. The odor of the food, the texture or mouth-feel (dry versus canned), the dog's habits, and the amount of nutrients in the diet contribute to how edible it is. Moistening dog food increases the palatability for most dogs. Adding something to increase the odor of a food may stimulate some dogs to eat more. Habit is a large factor in the eating pattern of a dog. Any changes in the diet should be made gradually by combining the new food with the old.

DOG FOOD, SOFT-MOIST:

Soft-moist dog food has the highest level of concentrated *digestible energy* of any dog food form. The "moistness" is caused by the presence of propylene glycol, corn syrup, and salt which all attract water. Soft-moist products contain 25% to 35% moisture, 25% to 30% protein, and 10% to 12% fat. Refrigeration is not required to preserve it because propylene glycol and some acids are used to retard bacterial and fungal growth. Providing the packet or pouch has not been opened, these products have a long shelf life. Generally, they are quite palatable. The cost is comparable to canned foods.

ENERGY:

Energy as related to foods is expressed in *calories. Protein, carbohydrates,* and *fats* provide energy sources. Most of the energy in dog food comes from carbohydrates and fats. Fat provides 2.2 times as much energy as the same amount of carbohydrate or protein. Energy in pet foods, expressed as *metabolizable energy*, is the amount left after elimination of stool and urine.

ESSENTIAL AMINO ACIDS:

Refer to *AMINO ACIDS.*

ESSENTIAL FATTY ACIDS:

Refer to *UNSATURATED FATTY ACIDS.*

FATS:

Fats in a dog's diet provide a source of *essential fatty acids. Linoleic acid* is the unsaturated fatty acid necessary for proper fat metabolism in the dog. Fats are essential for proper absorption of the fat soluble *vitamins A, D, E, and K.* Fat also enhances the palatability of dog foods. While not an indispensable energy source, fats become the best source of energy in the diet by providing over two times as much energy per unit as either proteins or carbohydrates. Both plant oils (corn, safflower) and animal fat (pork, butter fat) can be used as a source of energy and unsaturated essential fatty acids. High quantities of linoleic acid occur in corn and other vegetable oils. While pork and chicken fat are 25% linoleic acid, only a very small amount is contained in butter fat and beef tallow. Dogs are able to tolerate fat contents up to 40% without suffering from *steatorrhea* (diarrhea from unabsorbed fat). Up to half of the daily caloric (energy) needs can be supplied by fats in the diet. Increased fat in the diet is important during growth, whelping, lactation, and strenuous work.

FATTY ACID DEFICIENCIES:

Linoleic acid is the only essential fatty acid which must be supplied in the dog's diet. From linoleic acid, the dog's body can make *linolenic* and *arachidonic acid*, the two other fatty acids important for metabolism and health. Therefore, if enough linoleic acid is supplied, no deficiencies will occur. Fatty acids must be present for *prostaglandin* production, hair and skin health, normal wound healing, and to control skin water loss. Deficiencies can affect the skin and hair, cause *reproductive deficiencies* and *chronic ear infections*, and occasionally develop *"hot spots."*

Fatty acids in dog food become rancid with increased humidity, high temperature, or improper storage of the diet. Antioxidants such as *vitamin E* are necessary to stabilize the fatty acids in dog food.

FEEDING DOGS, METHODS OF:

The three basic methods of feeding dogs are *free choice, meal feeding with food restrictions,* and *meal feeding with a time restriction.* All three methods have both advantages and disadvantages.

Free choice feeding is the easiest form of feeding. The bowl is kept full of fresh dry dog food. This helps discourage *stool eating* and allows a non-aggressive eater time at the food bowl without competition. Because the canned variety will spoil quickly in warm and humid weather, free choice feeding is limited to dry and soft-moist forms of dog food. A dog fed by free choice is more difficult to house train because of the tendency to eat small amounts many times throughout a twenty-four hour period. However, small frequent feedings are beneficial in the management of some *liver, pancreatic,* and *gastrointestinal diseases.*

Meal feeding with food restriction is done to limit the amount of food consumed at any given time. The amount of food offered is less than the amount the dog desires so is eaten immediately. Additional feedings of similar portions are done at prescribed times during a twenty-four hour period. This method of never satisfying the dog's appetite can be used to put weight on dogs that seem to stay thin. Frequent feedings of small, high caloric meals may increase weight in "poor doers."

Meal feeding with time restriction is a common method of feeding especially for growing puppies and lactating bitches where increased caloric requirements make frequent feedings necessary. The dog is offered all that it will consume in a 20 to 25 minute period. This type of feeding can also be used to manage deep-chested dogs that have a tendency toward *gastric dilatation or bloat.*

Combinations of feeding methods may also be useful in other situations. For instance, free choice feeding of dry dog food can be combined with meal time restriction feeding of canned food.

FEEDING METHODS FOR ANOREXIA:

At least three methods of feeding the anorectic dog can be utilized at home. **Appetite stimulation** should be attempted before other methods are contemplated. The use of a highly palatable canned food either as a sole diet or mixed with normal food may be enough to stimulate an anorectic dog to eat. Sick dogs will quickly become deficient in *B vitamins and potassium.* B complex and 1/4 teaspoon of potassium chloride salt substitute should then be given to stimulate the dog's appetite. The drug *diazepam (Valium®)* is a very effective appetite stimulant when given intravenously and may also be effective orally. On occasion, anabolic steroid drugs have been used as appetite stimulants with mixed results.

Force-feeding is an effective method of feeding the anorectic dog. By placing the food deep in the throat, the swallow reflex will cause it to move into the stomach. The use of a high quality canned food or a high caloric semi-liquid diet makes force-feeding much easier. Recently, *HI-CAL LIQUID®* which contains 2,100 calories per 5 ml. (1 teaspoon), has become available through Pan American Pharmaceuticals of Grand Rapids, Michigan. An important part of force-feeding is maintaining adequate *vitamins and minerals.*

Gavage (Tube feeding) is a very easy and rapid method of feeding the anorectic dog. Most commonly, a newborn puppy that is weak, chilled, or otherwise distressed is fed in this manner. A size 8 French soft rubber or soft plastic infant feeding tube, and both a 12 cc. and a 35 cc. disposable plastic syringe are needed for this technique. Refer to *FORMULA, PUPPY NUTRITIOUS* for the most effective nutritional formula. Commercial puppy formula will keep the neonatal puppy alive but will not help him to gain weight from birth to the time he is old enough to start lapping from a pan (two weeks of age).

The following technique is used for *tube-feeding* the newborn under *FEEDING METHODS FOR ANOREXIA.* Measure from the mouth to the curvature of the last rib to establish the length of tube that can easily be passed down the esophagus. Before passing the tube, fill the entire length of tubing with warm formula to eliminate the problem of air in the stomach. Pass the tube. If you find that less than half of the tube will pass, remove the tube and repeat the process. A tube incorrectly placed in the lungs will encounter firm resistance after one-third to one-half of the calculated amount of feeding tube has been passed. The formula should be given slowly over several minutes. You will notice the stomach becoming full. The amount of formula that can safely be given will vary. If a puppy has been anorectic for several days, its stomach capacity will be less. As a rule of thumb, start with 5 ml. for every eight ounces of puppy weight and feed it six times the first day. Each day, as the puppy gains weight, increase each feeding by 2.5 ml. and decrease the number of feedings to four or five. The warmer the puppy is, the less often he requires food. If the abdomen does not become distended with your calculated amount of formula or if the puppy does not gain weight, greater increases should be instituted. After removing the tube, stimulate the puppy to eliminate its urine and stool by gently rubbing the urinary and anal region with a warm, moist piece of cotton.

Several other techniques for tube-feeding older puppies and adult dogs are available but are best utilized in a veterinary hospital setting where long-term force-feeding is anticipated. In one technique, a tube is passed through the nasal cavity into the stomach. Another technique places a tube through a surgically prepared opening in the side of the neck, bypassing the mouth. This *pharyngostomy technique* is particularly useful in broken jaw recovery where manipulation of the jaws is undesirable.

Intravenous (IV) feeding is generally done in a hospital setting. If longterm feeding is required, an indwelling catheter is placed in the jugular vein and sutured to the skin. As the caloric and metabolic needs are determined, various fluids can be given intravenously. The solutions should be warmed, taking care not to overload the cardio-respiratory system. Feeding the non-eating dog is important and must be done properly to keep the body in a positive balance. Since various methods can be utilized, finding one that is not stressful for either the owner or the dog is desirable.

FEEDING TRIAL, DO-IT-YOURSELF:

Two practical feed trials can be conducted by the owner to determine the quality of the dog food being fed. If either trial fails, change foods regardless of what is stated on the food bag label.

TRIAL I: *(STOOL VOLUME AS A MEASURE OF DIGESTIBILITY AND UTILIZATION)*
- Feed a premeasured amount of food daily for six days.
- DO NOT SUPPLEMENT AT ALL!
- Keep exercise level constant during the feed trial.
- Immediately eliminate from further consideration any food that causes diarrhea for more than two days.
- Pick up and save in a plastic bag EVERY stool for the last four days of the feed trial. Refrigerate the stool.
- At the end of the sixth day, weigh the stool and divide the weight of the stool by the weight of the food consumed. The stool should weigh less than 90% of dry food, 70% of soft moist, and 25% of canned food. These are acceptable levels of digestibility.

TRIAL II: *(THREE WEEK FEEDING TO MAINTAIN ADULT WEIGHT)*
- Feed the test food for three weeks free choice.
- Record weight of the animal at the start and again 25 days later.
- Adult unstressed weight should be maintained. If not, eliminate that food from consideration.

FLATULENCE (GAS PRODUCTION):

Flatulence (intestinal gas production) is generally due to swallowing or gulping air while eating and to the bacterial fermentation of the food. Some dog food components like soybeans are high in sugars that are not digestible so are likely to undergo the fermentation process. While most gases produced in the intestinal tract are nonodorous, gases produced from spoiled food, high meat diets, and vitamin supplements can be very odoriferous.

Gas production in the gastrointestinal tract can be controlled in several ways. Feeding small amounts of food in a quiet atmosphere helps eliminate the gulping of air. Changing the diet to eliminate soybeans, meat, or a vitamin supplementation will help control flatulence. If all changes have no effect, a physical examination and testing should be done to determine if high levels of fats are present in the stools.

FOLIC ACID:

Folic acid is classified as one of the *B complex vitamins*. Being water soluble, overdosage is not a problem. Deficiencies can depress the bone marrow causing *anemia*. Inflammation of the tongue has also been reported in folic acid deficiencies. Use of the *antibacterial drug, sulfonamide,* for long periods can cause folic acid deficiencies.

FOOD ALLERGY, DETERMINATION OF AND DIET FOR:

The determination of a food allergy requires the feeding of distilled water and a *hypoallergenic diet,* like *Prescription Diet® D/D®* , for a three week period. To prepare the dog for this food allergy determination, three cleansing enemas should be given at twelve hour intervals during a 48 hour fast. Distilled water is given but no supplements or any form of food are used. After the 48 hour fast, D/D Diet® is given for a three week period. The signs of suspected food allergy are then compared with the original symptoms. If much improvement is noted, individual food items are added to the diet weekly. Corn Flakes, Wheat Chex® , hamburger, Cheerios® and Rice Chex® all supply only one food ingredient so can be added weekly while observing for food allergy signs. Refer to Chapter 11, *FOOD ALLERGY.*

FORCE-FEEDING:

Refer to *FEEDING METHODS FOR ANOREXIA.*

FORMULA, PUPPY NUTRITIOUS:

Most of the commercially available puppy formulas will keep a puppy alive but will not allow them to gain weight. The following formula will put weight on newborn puppies who do not have bitch's milk available.

PUPPY NUTRITIOUS FORMULA
1 can (13 ounce) of condensed milk
2 cans (13 ounce can) of water
2 packages of Knox® gelatin
2 egg yolks
1 Tablespoon honey
1 Tablespoon whipping cream

Blend all ingredients and refrigerate between usage. Note, the formula will become stiff when refrigerated but liquefies when heated. Follow the directions for *Tube feeding* newborn puppies under *FEEDING METHODS FOR ANOREXIA.*

GAS PRODUCTION:

Refer to *FLATULENCE.*

GAVAGE FEEDING:

Refer to *FEEDING METHODS FOR ANOREXIA,* **Tube Feeding.**

GROWING DOGS, DIETARY MANAGEMENT OF:

Doberman puppies from weaning to six or eight months of age should be fed three times daily with a 25 minute time limit at each meal. Between the age of eight and twelve months, two feedings are sufficient. After one year of age, only one daily feeding is necessary.

Providing a good quality growth diet is very important in determining the kind of start that puppies get in their lives. Food for the growth diet should consist of 25% *protein* and 17% *fat* and be at least 80% digestible. Each pound of food should contain approximately 1,750 K calories. The *calcium* to *phosphorus* ratio should be 1.2 to 1.

Feeding should consist of one kind of food with no supplementation unless recommended by your veterinarian. Continually changing brands of food creates a finicky eater. On the other hand, over-feeding creates fat puppies that have a tendency toward obesity their entire life.

HEART DISEASE, DIETARY MANAGEMENT OF:

The dietary aim in managing heart disease is to feed the dog a low *sodium* diet. Sodium restriction helps control the fluid congestion which occurs in *heart failure.* Only distilled water should be used for drinking water, avoiding the use of soft water. Commercial *canned dog food* has over 1,000 mg. of sodium per 100 grams of dry matter, *soft moist food* over 850 mg. of sodium, and *dry food* over 500 mg. of sodium per 100 grams. Prepared diets, like *Prescription Diet® H/D®* , contain 50 to 90 mg. of sodium per 100 grams of dry matter. Dogs on restricted sodium diets should also receive extra *B complex vitamins* to replace those that are lost in the urine.

The following homemade diet is very low in sodium.

LOW SODIUM DIET:

1/4 lb. lean ground beef
2 cups unsalted cooked rice
1 Tablespoon corn oil
2 teaspoons dicalcium phosphate
1 multiple vitamin-mineral tablet

Braise meat retaining the fat. Mix in remaining ingredients. This makes one pound of low sodium diet (approximately 660 K calories).

IMBALANCE, PROTEIN:

Too much or not enough protein can be detrimental to a dog's health. Because the kidney must remove the protein waste products from the body, receiving excess protein for long periods of time subjects the dog to *kidney disease*. On the other hand, poor quality or inadequate protein intake causes the body to use both the dietary protein and protein from the body muscle to make energy. Signs of *protein deficiency* include weight loss, stunted hair growth, *ascites* (fluid in the abdomen), and swollen limbs.

IODINE:

Iodine is a mineral necessary for normal body and *thyroid gland* functions. While deficiencies are rather common, excess iodine in the body is rare. A deficiency can cause *hair loss, infertility,* and lethargy. *Myxedema* is a complex syndrome which occurs in adult dogs due to *thyroid and growth hormone deficiencies.* Iodine is supplied as a *trace mineral* in most good quality dog foods.

IRON:

Iron, an integral part of *hemoglobin,* is a *trace mineral* essential to normal *red blood cell* metabolism. Too much iron can cause death in young puppies. However, under normal circumstances, this is very unusual. Deficiencies in iron can occur from blood loss or from diets which contain inadequate iron such as milk. Atypical *anemia* results from iron deficiency.

INTRAVENOUS (IV) FEEDING:

Refer to *FEEDING METHODS FOR ANOREXIA.*

KIDNEY DISEASE, DIETARY MANAGEMENT OF:

Diets used to control kidney disease must contain low quantity-high quality protein and low amounts of *phosphorus* and *sodium.* Failing kidneys cannot process large amounts of protein waste nor remove normal levels of phosphorus. The levels of sodium in commercial dog food increase blood pressure which then increase the amount of work that the kidneys must do. When the kidneys function poorly, *B complex vitamins* are lost in the urine. Therefore, dietary management includes the addition of large amounts of B complex vitamins to the diet.

Both *Prescription Diet® K/D® and U/D® Diets* are useful in managing *kidney disease.* The following homemade diets are also very good.

LOW PROTEIN AND PHOSPHORUS DIET:

1/4 pound regular hamburger
1 hard boiled egg
2 cups of cooked, unsalted rice
3 slices of crumbed white bread
1 Tums® tablet
1 multiple vitamin tablet

Cook hamburger to retain fat and mix all ingredients together. Add 4-6 Tablespoons of water before serving. This recipe makes 1-1/4 pounds of diet yielding about 750 K calories per pound.

For dogs with serious *uremic poisoning* and end stage *kidney failure*, the following ultra-low protein diet can be used.

VERY LOW PROTEIN DIET:

2-1/2 cups of cooked rice with 1/4 teaspoon salt added
2 Tablespoons corn oil
1 hard boiled egg
1/2 Tums® tablet
1 multiple vitamin tablet

Cook the rice and mix together all ingredients. Refrigerate between feedings. This mix will yield 1-1/10 pounds of diet with about 690 K calories per pound.

LABELS, INTERPRETATION OF PET FOOD:

Pet food labeling is regulated in most states by *AAFCO*. Being able to understand the dog food label will help you better understand what you are getting for your money.

The dog food label has two basic parts. The information panel is found to the right of the display panel. The display panel must contain a statement of identity which generally includes the product name, brand name, and a statement indicating the animal for which the product is designed (e.g. "dogs," or "puppies"). The information panel must declare the quantity of the contents. Optional information such as a flavor designation indicating the kind of flavor can appear on the display panel. The flavor source must then be identified in the ingredient list. If a certain ingredient makes up more than 25% of the total diet, it must be listed. All meats or meat by-products other than cattle, pigs, sheep, or goats must be named. This specifically applies to horse meat. A nutritional statement is found on either the information panel or on the display panel. Examples of nutritional statements would be " complete puppy food," or "complete diet for pregnant bitches." By law, incomplete diets like snacks must carry a statement indicating that the "product is intended for intermittent or supplemental feeding only."

The ingredient list, the guaranteed analysis, and the name and address of the packer, distributor, or manufacturer of the dog food must all appear on the information panel. The amount or percentage of each of the contents is listed in decreasing order. The guaranteed analysis which is required states the minimum amount of crude *protein* and *crude fat* and the maximum amount of *crude fiber* and water present in the food. Other information may also appear at the manufacturer's discretion.

By reading ALL of the information on the label, you will be able to make more intelligent decisions about dog food purchases.

LACTATION, DIETARY MANAGEMENT OF:

Refer to *REPRODUCTION AND LACTATION, DIETARY MANAGEMENT OF.*

LACTOSE-FREE DIET:

Lactose is the *sugar* present in milk. Some dogs, especially puppies, lack *lactase,* the enzyme necessary for splitting lactose into simple sugars to be utilized by the body. If lactase is not present in sufficient levels and a diet containing lactose is fed, *chronic diarrhea* will occur. Many lactose-free diets are available. *Canned Prescription Diet® I/D® K/D® H/D® U/D® R/D® and D/D®* can be used. *Prescription Diet® dry R/D® I/D® and H/D®* are lactose-free as are the *homemade low protein* and *low sodium diets.*

LIVER DISEASE, DIETARY MANAGEMENT OF:

The goals of dietary management of liver disease are four fold: 1) to provide small quantities of high quality protein and an easily used carbohydrate energy source, making the job of the liver easier, 2) to help replenish the liver glycogen stores, 3) to prevent sodium retention, and 4) to keep the ammonia which results from protein breakdown from building up in the blood.

For a carbohydrate source, the diet should contain corn starch or dextrose instead of cereal grains. A high quality protein like cottage cheese or eggs instead of meat should be included. Sodium should be either moderately or severely restricted depending on the signs. The diet should be fed up to five times throughout the day.

Diets recommended for the treatment of liver disease include *Prescription Diet® K/D® I/D® and H/D®* . The homemade diets for *colitis, heart disease,* and *kidney disease* are also beneficial.

LOW COPPER DIET:

Refer to *COPPER TOXICOSIS, DIETARY MANAGEMENT OF.*

LOW FAT DIET:

Low fat diets are useful in feeding dogs that need to lose weight. These diets provide bulk but with fewer calories than normal. A long-term weight reduction program is superior to a quick, crash diet because good habits are developed by both the owner and the dog. Before initiating a diet program, your veterinarian should perform a physical examination on the dog to determine that a weight reduction program is not dangerous. To check the progress of the diet, weigh the dog monthly. The length of the diet will vary with the amount of weight reduction desired but should be maintained at least six months.

The prepared *Prescription Diet*® *R/D*® is excellent for weight reduction programs. The following homemade diet can also be utilized.

LOW FAT DIET:

1/4 pound lean ground beef
1/2 cup uncreamed cottage cheese
2 cups canned green beans
2 cups canned carrots
1-1/2 teaspoons dicalcium phosphate
1 vitamin-mineral tablet

Cook and drain fat from beef. Mix all ingredients together when cool. This mixture makes 1-3/4 pounds of low-fat diet that supplies 250 K calories per pound.

LOW MINERAL DIET:

The use of low mineral diets is primarily to dissolve specific *urinary stones* from the bladder and to prevent any recurrences. In some dogs, the chemistry of the urinary tract system predisposes them to the development of *calculi (stones)* in the urinary bladder. Dogs maintained on low mineral diets are less likely to develop stones in the urinary system. The prepared *Prescription Diet*® *S/D*® is useful in some cases where urinary bladder stones have already formed. *Prescription Diet*® *K/D*® *and U/D*® and the *low protein homemade diet* are helpful when a low mineral diet is desired.

LOW PROTEIN DIET:

Refer to *KIDNEY DISEASE, DIETARY MANAGEMENT OF.*

LOW SODIUM DIET:

Refer to *HEART DISEASE, DIETARY MANAGEMENT OF.*

MAGNESIUM:

Magnesium, a mineral essential for proper body functions, helps to maintain fluid balance, structural functions, and acid-base balances. Deficiencies of magnesium in the diet contribute to *soft tissue calcification, seizures,* retarded growth rates, and *hyperextension of the hock* and *pastern joints.* Excesses of magnesium are unusual but could contribute to the development of chronic *diarrhea.* Most quality dry dog foods contain adequate amounts of magnesium.

MANGANESE:

Manganese is a trace mineral necessary for normal body function. Deficiencies can contribute to *impaired fertility*, joint enlargements, and short, brittle bones. Too much manganese may result in the development of *albinism* and *impaired fertility.*

MEAT-FREE DIET:

Some forms of *kidney disease, meat allergies,* and purine metabolism problems are controlled by meat-free diets. The dry *Prescription Diet® K/D® and U/D®* are excellent for dogs with these problems. The *homemade very low protein diet* can also be utilized for these conditions.

MINERALS:

Although minerals only make up .7% of the body, they play a very important role. Classified by the amount present, **macro-minerals** include *calcium, phosphorus, sodium, potassium, and magnesium.* **Micro-minerals** *(trace minerals) include zinc, selenium, iodine, manganese, cobalt, copper, and iron.* The trace minerals function as a part of enzymatic activity while the macro-minerals form bone and are necessary for muscle activity. Refer to *ASH.*

NATIONAL RESEARCH COUNCIL (NRC) NUTRITIONAL REQUIREMENTS FOR DOGS IN 1985:

The National Academy of Sciences National Research Council first established minimum nutritional levels for the dog in 1974. In a study commissioned by a major pet food producer, 65 foods or 83% of the *generic foods* sampled were found to be short at least one essential nutrient. Today, the NRC requirements still do not insure that all dogs will gain or even maintain weight and health while eating these foods.

The 1985 National Research Council pet food report has made several changes helping to make the pet food labels more meaningful. Now minimum requirements, without allowances, are specified for each nutrient. Substantial changes in protein and mineral level recommendations have been made. Lower levels of these nutrients are suggested. However, if high *calcium* or *phytate* levels are present in the food, increased *zinc* is recommended. *Vitamin E* should be increased in the presence of high levels of *unsaturated fatty acids.* The values are now stated as "available nutrients." Also, food quantities are expressed in units per 1,000 K calories of *metabolizable energy* available.

As a buyer of dog food, you, the consumer, should only buy foods that have met AAFCO guidelines not just NRC minimum levels.

NIACIN:

Because of its water soluble nature, niacin is a *B complex vitamin* which in large amounts does not cause serious problems. However, on occasion, high doses may cause skin redness or flushing. Deficiencies of niacin are also uncommon with today's improved nutrition. In the past, a disease called *"Black Tongue"* was attributed to a niacin deficiency. Other signs observed from low niacin levels are *anemia* and *hemorrhagic diarrhea.*

NUTRIENT:

A nutrient is defined as any food substance that helps to support life. Life support can be accomplished in a number of ways. The six necessary nutrients in order of importance are *water, fats, carbohydrates, protein, minerals, and vitamins.* Some nutrients have multiple functions while others, like vitamins, are only required for metabolism.

OBESITY, DIETARY MANAGEMENT OF:

The goal in managing obesity is limiting the calorie intake to 50% or 60% of the normal diet. Three to four small feedings daily are superior to one large feeding. The use of *Prescription Diet® R/D®* provides high bulk, low fat dietary needs conveniently. The *homemade low fat diet* is also an excellent low calorie diet.

OLD DOGS, DIETARY MANAGEMENT OF:

For feeding purposes, all breeds except giant breeds are considered "old" after the age of seven. Giant breeds are considered "old" at five years of age. The old dog should receive less *protein, sodium, and phosphorus,* and more *unsaturated fatty acids, zinc,* and *vitamins A, C, and B complex.* The best diets for the old dog include *Science Diet® Senior®, Prescription Diet® G/D®,* and the *homemade diet which is low in protein and phosphorus.* Strict attention should be paid to maintaining normal weight levels during the dog's older years.

PANCREATITIS, DIETARY MANAGEMENT OF:

Managing pancreatic insufficiency requires a diet with high quality, bland protein sources like eggs or cottage cheese. The addition of *pancreatic enzymes* helps the digestion process. Do not give milk to the dog since the presence of lactose (milk sugar) will cause *diarrhea. Prescription Diet® I/D®* or the *homemade colitis diet* are the most desirable diets. Both are well-tolerated and digested in the presence of pancreatic enzyme supplementation.

PANTOTHENIC ACID:

Pantothenic acid is grouped as a vitamin in the *B complex group*. Being water soluble, toxicities do not occur at high levels. However, deficiencies can produce severe *gastroenteritis, seizures, hypoglycemia,* increased *BUN levels,* and depressed appetites.

PET FOOD EXAMINATION FOR WHOLESOMENESS:

The wholesomeness and quality of dog food can be determined, in part, by first examining the dog food container (e.g. can, bag) and then by carefully examining the product. *Dry food, soft-moist,* and *canned dog food should* meet certain specifications.

The dry food bag should be carefully examined for any evidence of "grease out" (soaking through of fat). The presence of fat-soaked paper will attract rats and mice creating a problem at the distributor's warehouse. A sample of food should be removed from the top and the bottom of the bag. The samples are then placed on paper and examined for color (Mold is green, white, or black.), odor (Mold is musty, spoiling fat is rancid.), and texture of the sample. If numerous fine particles within the sample are detected as being several different ingredients, the result is an overall poor quality product.

The cellophane wrappers in which soft-moist foods are packaged should be carefully scrutinized for signs of leakage or vermin contamination. The package should be opened and examined for odor, abnormal color of product, and the presence of extra moisture which causes rapid spoilage. A normal sample of soft-moist food should be soft and spongy and "slick" between the fingers. The sample, however, should not be wet. Break open the soft-moist pellet to look for a homogenous mixture of ingredients. Again, the presence of identifiable ingredients denotes lower quality.

Cans of food should be examined for swollen ends which means bacterial gas production and spoilage. Open both ends of the can, removing the contents by pushing the can lid through the can. The contents are observed for odor, color, and ingredients. Rancidity and spoilage can be determined by smell. A darkened or black area on the food may only mean that charcoal was used to indicate certain ingredients and is not necessarily indicative of spoilage. The canned food is spread out on a plate to examine the ingredients. The ration canned food should be mixed with cereal grains and small amounts of meat tissue. No foreign substances should be present. Wire, paper, feathers, and hair denote a low quality product. The meat-type canned food can be judged by the amount of undigestible protein in the form of blood vessels, tendons, and ligaments present with the chunks of muscle meat.

As is mentioned frequently in this chapter on nutrition, you, the consumer, get what you pay for in dog foods.

PHOSPHORUS:

Phosphorus, classified as a *macro-mineral,* is associated with *calcium* in bone formation. Deficiencies of phosphorus can cause *depraved appetites* and many of the same signs of calcium deficiency. Excesses of *phosphorus* lead to *kidney disease.* The most immediate affect of high phosphorus levels is to create calcium deficiencies.

PICA:

Pica, a craving for unnatural articles of food, can occur in nutritional, neurological, and reproduction situations.

POTASSIUM:

Potassium is a *macro-mineral* that will not cause toxicities unless the dog is not urinating. With decreased urination, potassium increases causing *heart toxicities* and death. Deficiencies can result from the use of diuretics, *diarrhea,* or insufficient dietary intake. If diuretics are used for heart conditions, the *blood potassium* level should be monitored every three to four weeks. The signs of potassium deficiency include muscle weakness, *wobbling gait,* and paralysis.

PROTEIN:

Protein, one of the six *nutrients* necessary for life, provides *amino acids* for body functions. Structural tissues, hormones, enzymes, and various body secretions all use protein. If the usual energy sources, fats and carbohydrates, are absent, protein can be used as a source of energy.

PROTEIN QUALITY, ESTIMATING:

Several methods determine protein quality. Although not practical, the best method of determining protein quality is to compare the amino acid content of the protein in question to the amount of *essential amino acids* needed by the dog to perform a particular function. Probably the most practical method that a dog owner can use to estimate protein quality is a feeding trial in which the dog is closely examined to insure that the protein present in the food meets all of that dog's individual needs.

PYRIDOXINE (VITAMIN B_6):

Pyridoxine is a water soluble *B complex vitamin.* Toxic levels do not occur. *Anemia* is the most common B_6 deficiency. Severe long term deficiencies result in high levels of *blood iron* and *convulsions.*

REPRODUCTION AND LACTATION, DIETARY MANAGEMENT OF:

Since very little growth occurs in the feti during the first five to six weeks of pregnancy, supplementation of the maintenance diet is unnecessary. A very good sign of pregnancy is inappetence during the third or fourth week of pregnancy. In most bitches, this occurs with each pregnancy lasting for three to five days. After the sixth week, the ration should be increased until it exceeds the maintenance level by 25% at the time of *whelping*. The diet should be high quality, contain 25% *protein* and 17% *fat,* and should be at least 80% *digestible*. There should be 1,700 to 1,800 K calories/pound of food with more *calcium* than *phosphorus* in the diet. During the last several weeks of pregnancy and through lactation, the bitch should either be fed twice daily or by free choice.

The amount fed to the lactating bitch depends on the size of the litter. A litter of less than four whelps can be raised by a two-fold increase in the bitch's food intake. Litters of up to 10 or 12 pups require at least three times the maintenance amount of food.

Several excellent commercial diets are available for pregnancy and lactation. *Science Diet® Growth®* is excellent for maintaining the nursing bitch's weight. As puppies are weaned, the bitch's diet should gradually be cut back below the maintenance level to help dry up the milk supply.

RIBOFLAVIN (VITAMIN B₂):

Riboflavin (vitamin B_2) is one of the water soluble *B complex* group. No toxicities are reported. A wide range of serious problems can occur from deficiencies including *fertility problems, pannus* (an eye condition), *dermatitis* problems, muscle weakness, and death.

SELENIUM:

Selenium is a *trace mineral* that must be provided in the diet in small amounts. Too much selenium will result in vomiting, weakness, *pulmonary edema* (fluid in lungs), and death. An overdose through injection is about the only way this kind of toxicity can result. Deficiencies of selenium are associated with a disease in the young called *"white muscle disease"* which affects both skeletal and cardiac muscles causing stiffness, lameness, and death.

SODIUM:

Sodium is a *macro-mineral* which causes either acute or chronic toxicity problems. Acute sodium toxicity occurs only if fresh drinking water is not available. Chronic toxicity can occur from high levels of sodium in pet foods fed year after year. An increase in *heart and kidney disease* has been reported with chronic toxicity. Withholding normal levels of sodium can cause pica, *slow growth, and increased urinary frequency.*

SOFT-MOIST DOG FOOD:

Refer to *DOG FOOD, SOFT-MOIST.*

SOY-FREE DIET:

Soybean protein is commonly found in dog food. Some have incriminated the presence of soybean in the diet with the development of *hypothyroidism.* Because some dogs are allergic to soy protein, soy-free diets such as the *Science Diet*® *Senior*® *and Performance*® and *Prescription Diet*® *canned K/D*® *I/D*® *and G/D*® are available.

SPECIALIZED DIETS:

The kind and amount of food fed to a dog should be coordinated with the dog's individual needs. The use of certain diets can substantially lengthen the life of dog's affected with kidney and heart diseases. The following is a list of diets discussed individually within this chapter:

Additive Free Diets	Low Fat Diet
Adult Dog Maintenance Diet	Low Mineral Diet
Balanced Diet	Low Protein Diet
Colitis Diet	Low Sodium Diet
Copper Toxicosis Diet	Meat Free Diet
Diarrhea Diet	Obesity Diet
Food Allergy Diet	Old Dog Diet
Formula, Nutritious Puppy	Pancreatitis Diet
Growing Dog Diet	Reproduction and Lactation Diet
Heart Disease Diet	Soy-Free Diet
Kidney Disease Diet	Stressed Dog Diet
Lactose Free Diet	Vomiting Dog Diet
Liver Disease Diet	Weaning Diet
Low Copper Diet	

STOOL EATING:

Refer to *COPROPHAGY.*

STRESSED DOGS, DIETARY MANAGEMENT OF:

Stress can take many forms - both physical and emotional. The calories burned up in a stressful situation are much greater than those used in a normal environment. A good diet for stress should contain at least 1,900 K calories per pound, be very digestible, and have at least 25% protein and 23% fat. Ideally, the dog should be fed a very palatable, high energy type diet at least twice a day. Two excellent diets for dogs under stress are *Science Diet*® *Performance*® and *Prescription Diet*® *Maximum Stress*® .

THIAMINE (VITAMIN B₁):

Thiamine (vitamin B_1) is a water soluble *B complex vitamin*. No toxicity has been observed at high doses. However, deficiencies can cause a wide range of clinical signs including loss of appetite, *vomiting,* paralysis, *seizures,* dehydration, and *heart disorders.* A characteristic downward flexion of the neck from a thiamine deficiency is called *"Chastek paralysis."*

TIME-RESTRICTED FEEDING METHOD:

The time-restricted method for feeding dogs is useful when house training puppies. With this feeding program, a 20 to 30 minute time period is given for the dog to consume its food. If the entire amount is consumed in less time, no more food is given at that meal. Instead, the next meal is increased by 1/3 cup. Feeding a young, growing puppy is a dynamic situation. The amount being fed to the dog each meal should either be increased or decreased based on its past meal.

TUBE FEEDING (GAVAGE FEEDING):

Refer to *ANOREXIA, METHODS OF FEEDING.*

UNSATURATED FATTY ACIDS:

Unsaturated fatty acids are discussed under *FATS* and under *FATTY ACID DEFICIENCIES.* Remember, the only essential fatty acid needed by dogs is *linoleic acid* found in large quantities in corn and safflower oil. Dogs deficient in unsaturated fatty acids must be supplemented with oil at the rate of 1 teaspoon to every 8 ounces of dry diet.

VITAMIN A:

Vitamin A is a *fat soluble vitamin* which is stored in the body. The highest concentrations occur in wheat germ, liver, egg yolk, and animal fat. Because cooking and baking destroys the vitamin, it must be added after dog food has been processed. Great excesses can cause loss of appetite, increased skin sensitivity, and loss of bone calcium. A deficiency in vitamin A may cause *poor hair coat, skin and eye problems,* rear leg weakness, and *reproductive difficulties.*

VITAMIN B₁:

Refer to *THIAMINE.*

VITAMIN B₂:

Refer to *RIBOFLAVIN.*

VITAMIN B$_6$:

Refer to *PYRIDOXINE.*

VITAMIN B$_{12}$:

Refer to *COBALAMIN.*

VITAMIN C:

Vitamin C *(ascorbic acid)* is a water soluble vitamin found predominantly in fresh fruits and vegetables. Vitamin C plays an important role in *wound healing,* in connective tissue integrity, and in the stability of capillary blood vessels. Mega-doses of vitamin C have been used as a method of reducing the incidence of *hip dysplasia.* Those proclaiming this method indicate its action is at the subcellular level. No valid clinical trials have been conducted to prove or disprove this method of joint nutrition. While toxicities from mega-doses of vitamin C have not been reported in the dog, some feel that high levels of vitamin C may increase the possibility of *urinary tract stone formation.*

VITAMIN D:

Vitamin D is a *fat soluble vitamin* capable of being stored in the body in high levels. If the amounts stored are above necessary needs, serious physiological problems can result. Natural sources of vitamin D are liver, fish oils, and cereal grain germ. For dogs, vitamin D$_2$ is the only form necessary. However, some species of animals cannot change D$_2$ to D$_3$ so must receive the D$_3$ form of the vitamin.

Because vitamin D is associated with the assimilation and use of *calcium* and *phosphorus,* deficiencies and excesses are associated with these minerals and their need in teeth and bones. Increased calcium absorption in the presence of large quantities of vitamin D causes organ and *soft tissue calcification* which can result in death. Reversing soft tissue calcification is only partially successful. The use of *cortisone* is necessary during the depletion of stored body vitamin D.

VITAMIN E:

Vitamin E is a *fat soluble vitamin* important in reproductive, muscle, and fat normalcy. Vitamin E is the least toxic of the fat soluble vitamins. Being a very unstable vitamin, Vitamin E is easily destroyed by storage and heat. Wheat germ contains the vitamin in the natural form. Deficiencies in *alpha tocopherol* (vitamin E) can cause *pregnancy failures* or *stillbirths.* Muscle cells require the correct level of vitamin E for proper development. Because of its importance in fat metabolism, quantities should be increased as the fat intake level is elevated. Mega-doses have been used in the treatment of *demodectic mange* in South America.

VITAMIN H:

Refer to *BIOTIN*

VITAMIN K:

Vitamin K is a *fat soluble vitamin* normally produced by bacteria in the intestinal tract. Vitamin K is essential for proper blood clotting. Because the body does not store it, excessive amounts are unlikely. Deficiencies cause *prolonged clotting times* and hemorrhaging.

VITAMINS:

Vitamins are grouped into *fat soluble* and *water soluble*. Each is listed here but is discussed separately within the chapter.

FAT SOLUBLE VITAMINS:	WATER SOLUBLE VITAMINS:
Vitamin A	*Biotin*
Vitamin D	*Vitamin C*
Vitamin E	*Cobalamin (Vitamin B_{12})*
Vitamin K	*Folic acid*
	Niacin
	Pantothenic Acid
	Pyridoxine (Vitamin B_6)
	Riboflavin (Vitamin B_2)
	Thiamine (Vitamin B_1)

VITAMINS, B:

Refer to *B VITAMINS.*

VITAMINS, FAT SOLUBLE:

The four fat soluble vitamins necessary for proper body function are excreted and absorbed with fat. *VITAMIN A, VITAMIN D, VITAMIN E,* and *VITAMIN K* are all discussed individually within this chapter.

VITAMINS, WATER SOLUBLE:

The water soluble vitamins include *vitamin C* and all of the *B complex vitamins.* They are listed here for reference, but are discussed separately.

Biotin	*Niacin*
Vitamin C	*Pantothenic acid*
Cobalamin (Vitamin B_{12})	*Pyridoxine (Vitamin B_6)*
Folic Acid	*Riboflavin (Vitamin B_2)*
	Thiamine (Vitamin B_1)

VOMITING, DIETARY MANAGEMENT OF:

The dietary management of vomiting is necessary until the cause of *vomiting* can be determined. Vomiting can cause dehydration and electrolyte or mineral imbalances. While occasional vomiting is normal, repeated or frequent vomiting may cause serious problems. The cause of the repeated vomiting should be sought by the veterinarian.

In the face of persistent vomiting, withhold food and water for 24 hours to help break the drink-vomit cycle. Several ice cubes on five or six occasions during the day can be given to provide small amounts of fluid. With mild dehydration, Gatorade® given in small amounts replaces some of the electrolytes lost in the vomitus. This helps to alleviate the weakness and depression caused by fluid imbalances and mineral loss. The mature Doberman should receive 2 Tablespoons of Gatorade® every two to three hours for several days.

After the 24 hour fast, start small amounts of a very bland, easily digestible diet (Refer to *COLITIS DIET*). Five small feedings are superior to one or two large feedings. Gradually increase fluid consumption using Gatorade® as the basic oral fluid for 48 hours replacing it with increasing amounts of water. Free choice water should be made available when the craving for fluids has ceased.

Identifying the cause of the vomiting is imperative, especially if the vomiting continues with a bland diet and restricted fluids.

WATER:

Water is the most important nutrient needed to maintain life. The greater the surface area on the dog per unit of weight, the more water required. This means that young puppies have higher water requirements than do adults and smaller dogs require more than larger dogs.

Three conditions can cause increased water consumption. Puppies that feel the need to compete for water will consume more than is really required. Anything that increases body fluid loss such as *diarrhea*, fever, high out-side temperature with high humidity, or nursing bitches increases fluid consumption. The need for water is also greater with increased salt intake.

The form of the dog food eaten plays some role in water consumption. Dry dog food has much less water in it than canned food. Therefore, the amount of water required is less for dogs eating canned food exclusively. If the available water is either too hot or too cold consumption can be af-fected. Hard water (water with high mineral levels) is not as palatable as low mineral water.

The rule of thumb is that palatable water should be available 24 hours per day unless fluid restriction is indicated in vomiting.

WATER SOLUBLE VITAMINS:

Refer to *VITAMINS, WATER SOLUBLE*.

WEANING, DIETARY MANAGEMENT OF:

The weaning procedure should take place gradually over a period of two to three weeks. Large litters can start as early as three weeks of age or as late as five weeks when the mother has an adequate milk supply and nursing is not detrimental to her. In extraordinary circumstances, weaning could occur as soon as the eyes open (10 to 14 days of age). However, this situation should be reserved for orphan pups or pups from mothers with poor or diseased milk supplies.

A gruel is prepared by mixing warm water with a high quality puppy food like *Science Diet® Growth®* . After a short soaking period, the gruel is either rubbed on the pup's mouth or the pup is placed face first in a shallow pan of the mixture. In a short time, the puppies learn to lap from the pan. Start with a once daily feeding and increase feedings up to four or five times daily at the time of weaning. After the pups are eating the fluid mixture, gradually decrease the amount of liquid. By five or six weeks of age, the food can be fed dry with available water in a separate bowl.

Remember, when you start feeding the pups, they will take less milk from the lactating bitch. She will then require less water and less food as the puppy formula is gradually increased. When this whole process takes 14 to 17 days, weaning is not traumatic for either the bitch or the pups. On the day that you determine weaning is complete, the bitch must be totally separated from the pups. Any nursing stimulation will continue lactation.

All puppies, even puppies weaned early (five weeks of age), should be kept together since they need this period of peer interaction to develop well-rounded personalities. As much human contact as possible is also very beneficial to their development.

ZINC:

Zinc is classified as a *trace mineral.* High doses will tie up *calcium* and *copper* causing signs associated with deficiencies of calcium and copper. Serious zinc deficiencies have been identified with the feeding of *"Generic" dog foods.* Signs of zinc deficiency are a *scaly dermatitis* with inflammation and poor *wound healing.* Also, hair thins out, a poor appetite develops, and the growth rate of puppies slows down. To reverse the signs of zinc deficiency, zinc supplementation must be provided for several years or possibly for life.

Chapter 9

POISONING

INTRODUCTION

Many poisonings require immediate attention. Use this chapter as a reference for the treatment of suspected poisoning. First, determine the name of the poison (brand name, if possible), the amount ingested, and the weight of your Dobe. Then, call either the *ANIMAL TOXICOLOGY* **HOTLINE at (217) 333-3611** (day or night) or the closest *POISON CONTROL CENTER,* generally located at a metropolitan Children's Hospital. If a specific antidote exists, they will tell you. Carefully write down the name of the antidote and any recommended supportive treatment. Next, call your veterinarian and request immediate service for the type of poison involved. If you find a home antidote in this chapter for the poison consumed, give the antidote and proceed to your veterinarian's office quickly. The *Animal Toxicology Hotline* or *Poison Control Center* telephone numbers should be posted near your telephone for ready access.

ACID POISONING, INTERNAL AND EXTERNAL:

Acids used for cleaning and etching procedures, like sulfuric, nitric, carbolic, hydrochloric, and trichloroacetic acids, are very caustic. A short contact period with any of these acids will destroy the tissue they contact. Changes in the color of the mucous membranes or skin are external signs of acid intoxication. The skin first becomes gray and then black as it is destroyed.

HOME ANTIDOTE FOR EXTERNAL ACID POISONING: Flush with large quantities of water and cover affected area with sodium bicarbonate paste.

Internal signs of acid intoxication are extreme abdominal pain, bloody vomitus, and rapid breathing. DO NOT MAKE THE DOG VOMIT!

HOME ANTIDOTE FOR INTERNAL ACID POISONING: Mix 3 egg whites and 1 ounce of liquid soap in 8 ounces of water. Orally, give an adult Dobe 4 to 6 ounces of the egg white-soap solution. Next, give olive oil (2

Tablespoons for an adult Dobe) and transport immediately to your veterinarian!

ACONITE (WILD) PLANT POISONING:

Serious cardiovascular disturbances are caused by aconite, the toxic principle of wild aconite or monkshood (Aconitum napellus). The early signs include nausea, muscular twitching, and convulsions. The heart rate becomes very slow and irregular. The tongue turns blue as breathing becomes labored. Treatment is supportive with *gastric lavage* being helpful if the signs have not yet progressed to convulsions. Prognosis is guarded and dose related.

ACTIVATED CHARCOAL:

Refer to *CHARCOAL, ACTIVATED.*

ALKALI POISONING, INTERNAL AND EXTERNAL:

Alkalis, the opposite of acids, can cause very severe burns both externally and internally. These products are frequently used as degreasers, cleaners, and washing powders. Lye is a common caustic alkali. Signs of external toxicity are very red skin accompanied by pain.

HOME ANTIDOTE FOR EXTERNAL ALKALI POISONING: Treatment for external alkali toxicity is flushing the area with copious amounts of water followed by the use of vinegar to neutralize the alkali.

Signs of ingestion of a caustic alkali include extreme abdominal pain, blood-tinged vomitus, and difficulty in breathing. DO NOT INDUCE VOMITING!

HOME ANTIDOTE FOR INTERNAL ALKALI POISONING: Attempt to neutralize the alkali by giving dilute vinegar (1:4) or lemon juice orally. Up to 4 ounces may be given to an adult Dobe. Then give albumin (give 6 to 8 ounces orally of a solution of 5 egg whites dissolved in 1 quart of lukewarm water) or olive oil (2-3 tablespoons). Immediately transport the dog to your veterinarian.

ALKALOID POISONING:

This class of drugs includes such diverse members as *atropine,* caffeine, *morphine,* nicotine, quinine, and *strychnine.* The potential clinical signs vary greatly from alkaloid to alkaloid. Refer to the individual alkaloids like strychnine within the chapter for a broader discussion.

HOME ANTIDOTE FOR INGESTION OF ALKALOIDS: Inactivate the drug by giving either 1 ml. of tincture of iodine in 4 ounces of water orally or give 3 to 4 ounces of a 1:400 dilute of strong tea (tannic acid) to an adult Dobe. Immediately transport the dog to your veterinarian for additional gastric lavage and supportive treatment. Keep the dog warm on the ride to the hospital.

ALOCASIA PLANT POISONING:

Alocasia, a member of the *Arum family,* is normally kept as an ornamental house plant. All parts of the plant are irritating to the internal membranes of the mouth and throat resulting in vomiting and diarrhea from the irritation. Generally salivation also increases. Since no systemic toxicity is seen, treatment is oral in the form of milk or olive oil to soothe the irritated tissue. One ounce is usually sufficient in an adult Doberman.

AMPHETAMINE POISONING:

Amphetamine drugs are tightly controlled by the federal government because of their potential for abuse. The drug, a potent nervous system and cardiovascular stimulator, is only used for treatment of hyperactive children, dieting, and depression. Clinical signs vary from dilated pupils and delirium, to convulsions and a very high body temperature, and finally to coma and death.

Tranquilizers or an injectable anesthesia controls the seizures. Oral lavage with *activated charcoal* removes any amphetamine from the stomach. Acidification of the urine speeds urinary excretion. If the dog lives for six hours after this treatment, the prognosis improves.

ANIMAL TOXICOLOGY HOTLINE: CALL (217) 333-3611

Several years ago, as a service to practicing veterinarians and pet owners, the University of Illinois College of Veterinary Medicine established an animal toxicology telephone service. The hotline is answered 24 hours a day, seven days a week. Consultation is designed primarily for the veterinarian, but calls from owners of poisoned pets are accepted. They attempt to provide antidote information and ideas on the symptomatic care of affected animals. KEEP THIS NUMBER NEAR YOUR PHONE - **(217) 333-3611.**

ANT POISON:

Arsenic is the active ingredient of most ant poisons. Because of the palatable taste and the slow biodegradable characteristics of arsenic, ant poisons are frequent causes of arsenic poisoning in dogs.

ANTIDOTES (HOME), AGAINST UNABSORBED POISONS:

Each of the following poisons has a home antidote which may be partially effective in neutralizing or removing unabsorbed poisons from the stomach of an affected dog. Refer to each poison within this chapter for its particular home antidote.

ACIDS, CORROSIVE	FORMALDEHYDE
ALKALI, CAUSTIC	LEAD
ALKALOIDS	MERCURY
ARSENIC	OXALIC ACID
CARBON TETRACHLORIDE	PETROLEUM DISTILLATES (GASOLINE)
COPPER	PHENOL AND CREOSOTES
DETERGENTS (ANIONIC)	PHOSPHORUS
DETERGENTS (CATIONIC)	UNKNOWN

ANTIDOTE - UNKNOWN POISON:

Refer to *UNKNOWN POISON - ANTIDOTE.*

ANTIFREEZE POISONING:

Ethylene glycol is the active ingredient in most antifreeze products. This chemical compound becomes more toxic after it is metabolized by the body. Ethylene glycol's sweet taste attracts dogs and cats. Once the diagnosis of antifreeze poisoning is made, treatment must be very aggressive. The minimum lethal dose of ethylene glycol antifreeze for a 50 pound dog is 3-4 ounces. For puppies, it is much less! At best, there is a guarded prognosis for saving the dog.

If there is to be any chance of saving the Doberman, treatment must be started before clinical signs are observed. The earliest signs of antifreeze intoxication are loss of balance and disorientation followed by *seizures* and coma. Affected dogs showing neurological signs usually die within eight hours. If the dog survives the early signs, *congestive heart failure,* kidney pain, and decreased urination may develop within several days. While ethylene glycol causes initial central nervous system signs, later *kidney failure* signs are due to the formation of oxalic acid crystals in the kidney tubules which effectively destroy kidney function.

Treatment first removes any unabsorbed ethylene glycol with activated charcoal, then corrects serious acid-base problems in the body fluids, and finally promotes the excretion of unchanged ethylene glycol through intravenous ethanol. The resulting kidney disease must be treated by maintaining a good flow of urine. If a hospitalized dog can be kept alive for five days, the chances of survival improve considerably. Early treatment is the most important element in saving a Dobe poisoned by ethylene glycol.

ANTU® POISONING:

ANTU® the abbreviation for alpha-naphthyl thiourea, is a very potent chemical used in the past as a rat poison. Because of the danger to all life, this poison is not currently used very much. After ingesting a small amount,respiratory failure results in death within eight hours. The chemical is irritating to an empty stomach which may result in vomiting. Vomiting is the only chance to save the Dobe's life. No antidote is available. Symptomatic treatment is fruitless.

ARSENIC POISONING:

Arsenic is a common ingredient in ant poison, snail bait, herbicides, insect-icides, and paint. Arsenic trioxide and sodium arsenite are the most poisonous forms. Most commonly, the poisoning is acute. However, repeated low doses can possibly accumulate causing chronic arsenic poisoning. Acute arsenic poisoning signs include extreme abdominal pain, vomiting, and weakness. The vomitus has a garlic odor. Later, bloody diarrhea and circulatory collapse are followed by coma or convulsions and death.

HOME ANTIDOTE FOR ARSENIC POISONING: Give 4 ounces of evaporated milk mixed with 3 beaten egg whites and 1 ounce of strong tea (tannic acid) to an adult Doberman Pinscher. Transport immediately to an animal hospital for intensive treatment.

In the hospital, a *gastric lavage* with *activated charcoal* is initiated. As part of the treatment, a heavy metal poisoning antidote, *dimercaprol (BAL)* is given intramuscularly for several days. Aggressive fluid therapy must be maintained for four to eight days. Pain should be controlled during the treatment period.

The signs associated with chronic arsenic poisoning are loss of appetite, body fluid loss, and weakness followed by coma and death. If chronic arsenic poisoning is suspected, hair or toenails can be analyzed for the presence of arsenic. Information on heavy metal hair and toenail analysis can be obtained from Micro-Trace Minerals, 915 King Street Suite B-43, Alexandria, VA 22314.

The prognosis for arsenic poisoning is guarded. Aggressive hospital treatment is important!

ARUM PLANT FAMILY POISONING:

The Arum plant family includes many of the common ornamental house plants - *calla lily, dieffenbachia, alocasia, caladium,* and *philodendron.* All parts of these plants are gastrointestinal irritants which irritate mucous membranes causing vomiting and diarrhea. Affected animals salivate profusely. Oral demulcents are the best form of therapy. Milk and olive oil are excellent demulcents. Give 4 to 6 ounces of milk and up to 3 ounces of olive oil for an adult Dobe.

ASPIRIN INTOXICATION (SALICYLATE POISONING):

Aspirin is tolerated better by dogs than cats, but can be abused as a drug for fever reduction or arthritic pain alleviation even in the dog. Since children's aspirin is sugar coated, dogs with "sweet tooth" tendencies will consume large quantities if given the opportunity.

A wide range of clinical signs are observed in aspirin poisoning. Panting, weakness, and *seizures* are seen acutely. The acid nature of the drug can cause vomiting. *Bone marrow depression*, bleeding under the skin, a nose bleed, and the odor of acetone on the breath are seen in chronic aspirin poisoning. Death results from a high dosage.

After administering a slurry of *activated charcoal,* treatment is directed at emptying the stomach. The metabolic acidosis problem is treated with intravenous fluid containing sodium bicarbonate. Normal body temperature must be maintained. Constant nursing care is necessary for at least 24 to 36 hours. Elimination of the aspirin from the system can be accelerated with *peritoneal dialysis* techniques. The prognosis is guarded to fair depending on the dose and signs observed.

BIRD OF PARADISE PLANT POISONING:

Ingestion of the seed pod of the bird of paradise (Caesalpinia gilliesii) can cause severe vomiting and diarrhea. The gastrointestinal signs are usually preceded by nausea. Treatment is directed toward making the patient vomit to remove any unabsorbed pod material. The administration of a mixture of 3 whole eggs beaten into 4 ounces of milk follows. Replacement of fluids lost from the vomiting and diarrhea must be continued for several days. The prognosis depends on how well fluid therapy is maintained and how quickly the GI tract recovers.

BITES:

The following bites are discussed individually within the chapter. Refer to each for a more complete explanation.

Black Widow Spider	Gila Monster
Brown Recluse and Common Brown Spider	Lizard
Coral Snake	Snake
Fire Ant	Tarantula

BLACK WIDOW SPIDER BITES:

The black widow spider is one of two genera of spiders that cause severe damage or death to a dog via a venomous bite. The black widow spider (Lactrodectus) is black with a light colored hour-glass shape on its belly. The bite marks of a spider are often difficult to find. Seeing a spider in close approximation to the dog may provide the circumstantial evidence needed for a diagnosis. After a spider bite, the first sign is localized pain at the bite site. Neurological signs like muscle spasms, jerking convulsions, and flaccid paralysis follow. Hours or days later, difficulty in breathing is observed. Heart irregularities are also seen.

A specific antivenin is available but must be given early to be very effective. *Corticosteroids* are given along with fluid therapy. Antibiotics and various pain medications are also utilized. If the Doberman survives for three or four days, the chances of recovery are good.

BLEACH INTOXICATION:

Bleaches are household cleaners that disinfect by an oxidizing action. In concentrated strengths, they are caustic to skin and mucous membranes. Diluted forms, if consumed orally, cause a gastrointestinal upset.

Treatment is directed at emptying the stomach by vomiting or lavage. Later 3 egg whites or 2 ounces of olive oil are given orally to soothe and coat the irritated tissues. If the bleach was highly concentrated, sodium thiosulfate is given to neutralize the bleach solution. Generally, there is a good prognosis for recovery providing the bleach was not too concentrated.

BLUE TAIL LIZARD POISONING:

Refer to *NEUROTOXINS.*

BOTULINUM TOXIN:

The toxin from *Clostridium botulinum* is a very potent and fatal toxin found in some spoiled foods. This toxin causes motor paralysis and coma, followed by death. Fortunately, dogs are fairly resistant to the affects of the toxin. Only the early administration of a specific antitoxin will insure success in controlling the disease progression. Also refer to Chapter 7 on the NEUROLOGICAL SYSTEM.

BROWN RECLUSE AND COMMON BROWN SPIDER BITES:

The brown recluse and common brown spiders (Loxosceles) are long-legged spiders with a dark colored violin-shaped marking on their backs. Their bite is capable of causing extreme tissue and skin necrosis. Immediately following the bite, little pain is present. However, after several hours, the area around the bite swells, becoming red and blistered. The tissue surrounding the bite becomes necrotic and dies over a one to two week period. In a very susceptible dog, systemic signs are observed ranging from fever and vomiting to convulsions and poor blood clotting. Early surgical removal of affected tissue is the primary treatment. Antibiotics and *corticosteroids* are also used, especially if severe systemic signs are seen.

BUCKEYE POISONING:

The seeds from the buckeye (horse chestnut) tree cause gastrointestinal upsets if ingested. The active ingredient, saponin, causes salivation, vomiting, nausea, and finally diarrhea. Generally abdominal pain is present. Treatment is directed toward removal of the seed material by vomiting, followed by symptomatic management of the gastrointestinal signs. When these signs are managed aggressively, the prognosis is fair to good.

BUFO TOAD POISONING:

The Bufo toad species was introduced in the southern United States forty years ago for insect control. The parotid salivary glands of the toad produce a very potent, lethal toxin. Dogs may mouth the toad as it emerges and becomes active at dusk. The toad toxin is a very complex chemical compound capable of producing different clinical signs depending somewhat on the age and condition of the dog. Old dogs with cardiac and asthmatic conditions are very severely affected. Clinical signs vary from slight salivation to convulsive *seizures*. The dog may have difficulty breathing to the point that its tongue turns blue.

Flushing the mouth and gums with copious amounts of water to remove the waxy thick toxin that sticks to the mucous membranes is one of the oldest and best forms of treatment. Induction of vomiting helps protect the exposed dog. While no specific antidote is available, proper medical treatment will increase the chances of the dog's survival. Several drugs have been used to treat affected dogs. *Atropine* dries the mouth and decreases respiratory tract secretions. *Pentobarbital anesthesia* and tranquilizers may increase the ability of the dog to combat lethal doses of the toad toxin.

The heart rhythm is frequently altered by the toxin. In dogs not previously affected with bronchial asthma, the use of a heart medication called "beta-blockers" may result in spectacular reversal of heart irregularities. *Propranolol hydrochloride* is also very effective in these instances. Aggressive treatment is necessary to counteract the affects of the complex toxin.

Where the poisoning takes place in the United States effects the death rate in dogs. While Florida mortality rates approach 95%, Texas and Hawaii are as low as 10%. Apparently the strength of the toxin varies with different strains of the Bufo toads.

CALADIUM PLANT POISONING:

The caladium is an ornamental house plant from the *Arum family*. The sap and various other parts of the plant are irritating to the mucosal lining of the digestive tract. Intoxication causes severe salivation, vomiting, and diarrhea. Treatment is the use of emollients such as olive oil or milk to soothe the irritated tissues. The prognosis is generally good.

CARBAMATE POISONING:

Carbamate compounds are used in many insecticide treatments for dogs. This effective flea, tick, and louse killer is classified as a cholinesterase inhibitor because of the way it kills insects. This compound also causes the toxic signs seen when the dog has received an overdose of the drug. Clinical signs of carbamate poisoning are pinpoint pupil constriction, excessive salivation with vomiting, and diarrhea. As the poisoning becomes more severe, muscle twitching and a *wobbly gait* are seen. Death is usually due to paralysis of the respiratory muscles.

The treatment of choice for carbamate poisoning is *atropine,* both IV and sub Q. Other therapy, such as artificial respiration, may be needed until respiratory paralysis is reversed. The administration of 2-PAM is contraindicated in carbamate poisoning. The prognosis is guarded and depends on aggressive treatment and the amount of carbamates absorbed.

CARBON MONOXIDE POISONING:

Carbon monoxide poisoning most commonly occurs in dogs transported in vans with defective exhaust systems, dogs transported in car trunks, and in animals housed near faulty space heaters. Affected dogs are depressed, undergo convulsions, and have an elevated temperature accompanied by very red mucous membranes and dilated pupils.

Treatment involves the removal of the dog from the source, pure oxygen administration, and 50% Dextrose intravenously. Dogs should be hospitalized for at least two days for observation. The prognosis is guarded to fair. Elimination of the source of carbon monoxide is a must!

CARBON TETRACHLORIDE POISONING:

Carbon tetrachloride, commonly used in fire extinguishers and cleaning solutions, is a very potent liver poison. Poisoning can occur from topical administration or oral ingestion of the chemical. Signs of nausea and diarrhea will precede those of acute liver failure. Death follows acute liver failure.

If the skin has been saturated with carbon tetrachloride, flush it with copious amounts of water. Fresh air or oxygen therapy should be sought. If ingestion has occurred, the stomach should be evacuated and activated charcoal should be used to absorb. any remaining poison in the gut. Intravenous fluid therapy is important.

HOME ANTIDOTE FOR CARBON TETRACHLORIDE POISONING: Feed a high quality protein and carbohydrate diet to help protect the liver. The high quality diet is NOT a substitute for the veterinary care necessary to treat potential acute liver failure. Prognosis for recovery is guarded at best.

CHARCOAL, ACTIVATED:

Activated charcoal is widely used in treating unabsorbed poisons. Vegetable origin activated charcoal is much more effective than either animal or mineral origin charcoal. Many different poisons, including ethylene glycol, strychnine, morphine, and mercuric chloride, can be tied up with activated charcoal. However, it is ineffective against cyanide. While activated charcoal will prevent the absorption, the poison is not detoxified. To remove the charcoal mix from the stomach, an emetic (vomit stimulator) or gastric lavage is used.

CHERRY SEED TOXICITY:

The seeds of the cherry tree contain a potent chemical, amygdalin, which will cause cyanide poisoning when chewed by a dog . The clinical signs, which include muscular twitching and convulsive seizures, occur rapidly. The odor of almonds on the breath, respiratory distress followed by coma and death are also signs of cherry seed toxicity.

Because the clinical progress is so rapid, treatment is not usually undertaken. If time is available to initiate therapy, sodium nitrite is given intravenously, followed immediately by sodium thiosulfate and repeated as needed. Oxygen is administered either in an oxygen cage or by mask. Oral activated charcoal is also given. The prognosis is poor to guarded depending on the number of seeds chewed and the severity of the signs when treatment began. Also refer to CYANIDE.

CHLORINATED HYDROCARBON TOXICITY:

Chlorinated hydrocarbons are a class of chemicals found in insecticides such as lindane, aldrin, and chlordane. They cause convulsive *seizures* and neurological irritation that must be differentiated from *strychnine, metaldehyde, 1080,* and *lead poisoning.*

Clinically, the affected dog becomes restless, its muscles twitch, its legs become wobbly, and it may convulse. Its temperature rises and breathing difficulties result. Death follows shortly.

Certain groups of dogs are more susceptible to chlorinated hydrocarbon toxicity than others. Thin dogs are more severely affected than those in prime condition. Young dogs suffer more than older dogs. Animals with a full stomach are not as severely affected as those with an empty stomach.

Chlorinated hydrocarbon toxicity has no specific antidote. If the poison was applied externally, wash the dog completely with soap and water. Internal poisoning is treated by using an emetic (vomit stimulator) and *activated charcoal* in the stomach. *Diazepam* or *sodium pentobarbital* control the seizures. Aggressive supportive therapy is needed to eliminate toxic signs and maintain respiration. The general prognosis is guarded to poor. However, if the dog lives for two days, the chances for recovery increase.

CHOCOLATE POISONING:

Poisoning from the ingestion of large amounts of chocolate candy or Baker's chocolate is actually due to xanthine compounds present in the chocolate. Most of the signs are related to nervous system irritation which vary from restlessness and excitability to general seizures. Large increases in the amount of urine excreted also are observed. If the ingestion is discovered within thirty minutes, treatment is to cause vomiting. The administration of oral aluminum hydroxide gel is important in addition to general supportive care. The prognosis depends on the amount of chocolate ingested and the time that has passed before treatment is initiated.

CHRYSANTHEMUM TOXICITY:

The resin found in the chrysanthemum flower can cause an external skin irritation. Clinical signs are exudative dermatitis from the irritative properties of the flower. The only treatment necessary is thoroughly washing the affected area and applying a steroid cream like Panalog® .

COPPER POISONING:

In Doberman Pinschers, *copper intoxication* is found in dogs that are unable to metabolize normal levels of copper in the diet. These dogs will show hepatic (liver) degeneration which, if continued, ends in *chronic liver failure* with all of the associated signs. If actual copper is ingested in toxic amounts, treatment should be directed toward preventing its absorption by giving 3 egg whites and sodium ferrocyanide in a pint of water. If the copper has been absorbed into the system, *Cuprimine®* is used for long periods to eliminate the copper from the body.

CORAL SNAKE BITE:

The coral snake found in the southern United States is the only poisonous snake in the United States that possesses a *neurotoxin*. The pit viper family of rattlesnakes, copperheads, and cotton-mouthed water moccasins are totally unrelated.

Since there is little pain at the onset of the bite, one may not be aware of the bite. Signs of the neurotoxin poisoning may not appear for one or two hours. On dogs with dense hair coats, the fang marks may not be apparent. The initial signs are difficulty in swallowing and depression. These signs progress to skeletal muscle paralysis and finally death by respiratory paralysis.

Treatment includes intravenous administration of specific coral snake antivenin which can be obtained through the State Board of Health, at some zoos, or directly from Wyeth Laboratories, Radnor, Pennsylvania. If possible, a tourniquet should be placed between the bite and the heart and left in place for up to two hours. The dog MUST be kept absolutely quiet to keep circulation of the poison in the blood to a minimum. Part of the treatment is directed at controlling shock and anaphylactoid (allergic) reactions. The tissue containing the venom should be cut away when possible. Time is of great importance! Obtaining coral snake antivenin is the only realistic chance that one has in treating the dog successfully.

The prognosis is poor to fair. The amount of time that has passed between the bite and the administration of the antivenin, the amount of venom injected, and the location of the bite all determine the severity of the case.

CREOSOL POISONING:

Refer to *PHENOL AND CREOSOL POISONING.*

CREOSOTE POISONING:

Creosote is a phenol derivative used for preserving fence posts. Topical applications of this chemical may cause skin or mucous membranes to blanch (turn white). If creosote is ingested, the odor of phenol can be detected on the breath and serious abdominal pain with vomiting occurs. After several days, signs of kidney and liver failure are observed.

HOME ANTIDOTE FOR CREOSOTE POISONING: After the injured tissues are bathed with soap and water or with alcohol rinses, treatment should include bicarbonate of soda dressings. Either 4 to 6 ounces of milk containing 3 egg whites or 2 ounces of olive oil are given orally. Rush the dog to your veterinarian immediately for further treatment and observation. Your vet will probably give *activated charcoal* and establish an IV drip to treat shock and promote diuresis (urine formation.) The prognosis is good with treatment for topical poisoning and guarded with oral ingestion of this toxic chemical.

CROW FOOT FAMILY PLANT POISONING:

All parts of the crow foot plant are toxic if ingested. A severe gastroenteritis with vomiting and diarrhea occurs. Most dogs will become weak and develop convulsive *seizures*. Treatment is directed at removing the plant parts from the stomach and then maintaining blood pressure and oxygenation of the body tissues. The prognosis is guarded to fair depending on the amount swallowed and the signs that are observed.

CYANIDE POISONING:

Cyanide, one of the most potent protoplasmic poisons today, is used in herbicides and other fumigants. Cyanide is found naturally in cherry seeds and hydrangea plants. Because it is a very rapid killer, many times treatment is too little, too late. If treatment is initiated, it involves intensive care with intermittent intravenous sodium nitrite followed by sodium thiosulfate. This procedure is repeated as needed. Concurrent oxygen therapy is a must! *Activated charcoal* is not very useful in preventing the absorption of cyanide products. The prognosis is poor to fair because death occurs so rapidly.

DETERGENTS (ANIONIC) POISONING:

Anionic detergents are salts of sodium, ammonium, or potassium, usually in Class I or Class II, light-duty or all-purpose, high sudsing types of detergents. Uncolored, unperfumed soaps are relatively non-toxic even in large quantities. However, the addition of perfume and coloring agents can cause gastrointestinal upsets.

HOME ANTIDOTE FOR ANIONIC POISONING: Administer water or milk followed by demulcents like 2 ounces of olive oil and 3 egg whites for an adult Doberman Pinscher. Before giving the fluid and the demulcent, vomiting should be induced unless the poison is a strong alkali. NOTE: Remember that some laundering agents contain strong alkalis such as lye. If this is the case, DO NOT INDUCE VOMITING! Follow instructions under HOME ANTIDOTE FOR ALKALIS instead. After administering the home antidote, take the dog to your veterinarian for further treatment. Provide the doctor with as much information about the product as possible.

DETERGENT (CATIONIC) POISONING:

Cationic detergents are those that contain chlorides and iodides. While most of the highly caustic detergents are anionic in nature, the same principle applies to cationic poisoning that applies to anionic: DO NOT induce vomiting if a strong alkali is present!

HOME ANTIDOTE FOR CATIONIC POISONING: Give large quantities of Castile soap dissolved in hot water. If an alkali is present, give egg white in large quantities. Seek veterinary care after the home antidote has been given.

DIEFFENBACHIA PLANT POISONING:

Dieffenbachia (Dumbcane) is an ornamental plant that causes mouth and throat irritations if consumed. Clinical signs include profuse salivation and some swelling in the throat and esophageal region. The use of demulcents like 3 ounces of milk or an ounce of olive oil are usually sufficient to soothe the irritated tissues until they become less inflamed. Since systemic signs are rare, the prognosis for recovery is good.

DIGITALIS POISONING:

Digitalis and digitalis derivatives are widely used in the treatment of cardiac insufficiencies. Naturally occurring digitalis-like compounds are found in foxglove, *mistletoe, lily of the valley,* and *oleander* ornamental plants. The mistletoe berries are especially toxic when consumed.

Two distinct sets of clinical signs are observed. The first signs are those of a gastrointestinal disturbance with vomiting and abdominal pain. This then leads into a very slow heart rate with disturbances in the heart rhythm.

Treatment for plant digitalis poisoning would be similar to that of a drug overdose of digitalis. First, *potassium* is administered followed by *atropine.* The dog is also placed in an oxygen cage. Occasionally "beta-blocker" drugs are used to correct irregular heart beats. If the dog lives for 24 hours, the chances of survival are quite good.

DRUG OVERDOSES (MARIJUANA, AMPHETAMINE, TRANQUILIZER):

Drugs subject to abuse are called "controlled substances." When dogs are accidently exposed to these products, the veterinarian must know to what drug or compound the animal has been exposed if the owner has that knowledge. Rapid treatment may save your Dobe's life if you let your vet know the nature of the drug overdose. Because your veterinarian is bound to confidentiality by the doctor-patient relationship, you will not be reported to the authorities even if the drug is illicit.

Other individual drugs are discussed throughout this chapter. Refer to each under its own heading.

ETHYLENE GLYCOL INTOXICATION:

Refer to *ANTIFREEZE POISONING.*

FINGER CHERRY POISONING:

The fruit from the plant referred to as the finger cherry (Rhodomyrtus macrocarpa) is very toxic. Permanent total blindness will result within 24 hours after ingestion. Treatment is directed at removal of the ingesta by inducing vomiting. No specific antidote is known. The prognosis is guarded, at best.

FIRE ANT BITES:

The fire ant which resides in the southern part of the United States is capable of producing a painful, inflamed bite or sting.. In a dog previously bitten by a fire ant, *anaphylactic allergic reactions* can occur. These can be fatal if not promptly treated by a veterinarian. Multiple (hundreds) bites simultaneously can also cause a shock-like syndrome that could be life threatening. If anaphylaxis is not a consideration, the use of injectable and topical *corticosteroids* cuts down the severe inflammation that occurs. The prognosis, with proper treatment is good.

FLUOROACETATE POISONING:

Sodium fluoroacetate (1080) is a very poisonous *rodenticide* currently used only by licensed exterminators. Its use as a predator control measure is tightly regulated today because of its extreme toxicity and the chance for accidental poisoning.

The clinical signs must be differentiated from those of the *chlorinated hydrocarbon* toxaphene. Signs may be seen as early as one hour after ingestion of 1080. Early vomiting and mucoid diarrhea with evidence of abdominal pain are observed. The affected dog appears agitated, howls, and runs aimlessly. Salivation increases and tetanus-like seizures occur with the dog lying on its side. During the seizure activity, the tongue and membranes are blue. Loud noises do not intensify the seizures caused by 1080 as in seizures caused by *strychnine*. Since no antidote exists, treatment is symptomatic. *Pentobarbital anesthesia* is of little use in 1080 poisoning treatment. Calcium gluconate is given both orally and intravenously. Once *seizures* have started, treatment is unsuccessful in most cases. The prognosis is poor, but rare cases have recovered.

FORMALDEHYDE POISONING:

Formaldehyde is an uncommon poison source used in taxidermy and in some photography procedures. Because of its acid composition, VOMITING IS NOT INDUCED. If the formaldehyde has been applied externally, copious amounts of water should be used to flush the area. Orally, the use of 0.2% ammonia water or 1% ammonium acetate are administered. At home, 3 to 4 ounces of gelatin in water or starch water may also be given orally before transporting the dog to the veterinary hospital for further treatment and observation. The prognosis is fair to good depending on the amount ingested and the quickness of the antidotes and other therapy.

GARBAGE TOXINS:

The significant garbage-produced toxins come from *Staphylococcus* and *Salmonella* bacteria and <u>*Clostridium botulinum.*</u> Staph and Salmonella food poisonings are due to the putrefaction of certain foods like ham, milk, chicken, and some vegetables. There is a proliferation of exotoxins and endotoxins capable of causing gastric distress and death. *Botulism poisoning* is fortunately very uncommon in the dog. A more complete discussion can be found under *BOTULISM* in Chapter 7.

The signs of garbage intoxication are vomiting, nausea, abdominal pain and often mucoid bloody diarrhea. Garbage poisoning has a rapid onset but is usually not lethal. A more serious form of this type of intoxication occurs with the *Staph lethal toxin* which can cause initial signs within 30 minutes and violent convulsions and death in 24 hours.

Treatment is symptomatic. Vomiting should be induced. The stomach should be lavaged to empty all contents. Intravenous fluids are very important in overcoming this intoxication. The prognosis for Staph toxin poisoning is good. For the Staph lethal toxin ingestion, the prognosis is guarded depending on when emesis (vomiting) is induced and the intensity of supportive treatment.

GASOLINE (PETROLEUM DISTILLATES) POISONING:

Gasoline poisoning occurs in three ways: by exposing large areas of the skin to it externally, by breathing gasoline vapors, and by swallowing gasoline. If large surface areas of skin are saturated with gasoline, the signs are similar to inhalation poisoning. Areas of skin that have come in contact with gasoline may be more susceptible to infection in the future, because gasoline has been absorbed through the skin and removed fats from the subcutis area. Treatment of this level of toxicity involves cleaning the affected area with soap and water, followed by general supportive therapy.

If large areas of the skin are saturated with gasoline or if the vapors are inhaled, signs of a stumbling gait and stupor occur. If the dog is given fresh air and the gasoline is washed from the skin, recovery may take place. However, some dogs progress to dilated pupils, muscle twitches, and then convulsive *seizures*. At this point, treatment is probably of little value. Treatment is oxygen therapy and support of kidney and cardiovascular function.

Oral ingestion of gasoline is rather irritating causing salivation, vomiting, and diarrhea. Treatment is *gastric lavage* with mineral or olive oil to try to prevent absorption into the body. This is followed by copious amounts of warm water. Veterinary supportive care is absolutely necessary. The prognosis is good if the gasoline can be removed from the body before muscle twitching and convulsions are observed. If the product has been absorbed into the body, signs of muscle twitching and convulsions signal a poor prognosis.

GASTRIC LAVAGE:

Refer to *STOMACH PUMPING PROCEDURE.*

GASTROINTESTINAL UPSETS, POISONS CAUSING:

A number of substances can cause GI upsets as part or all of the clinical signs observed. Each listing is discussed individually within the chapter.

Acids
Alkalis
Aconite (Wild) Plant Poisoning
Alocasia Plant Poisoning
Arsenic Poisoning
Arum Plant Family
Bird of Paradise Plant Poisoning
Bleach
Buckeye Poisoning
Caladium Plant Poisoning
Carbamate Poisoning
Carbon Tetrachloride Poisoning
Creosote Poisoning
Crow Foot Plant Poisoning
Detergent Poisoning (Anionic)
Detergent Poisoning (Cationic)
Digitalis Poisoning
Fluoroacetate (1080) Poisoning

Garbage Toxins
Gasoline Poisoning
Holly Poisoning
Household Cleaners Poisoning
Insecticide Toxicity
Iris Plant Poisoning
Lily Plant Poisoning
Mistletoe Poisoning
Mushroom Poisoning
Philodendron Poisoning
Poinsettia Poisoning
Privet Plant Poisoning
Rayless Goldenrod Poisoning
Rhubarb Poisoning
Thallium Poisoning
Wisteria Plant Poisoning
Yew Plant Poisoning

GILA MONSTER BITE:

The Gila monster (Heloderma suspectum) is one of three poisonous lizards located in the United States. They reside in the arid Southwest. Because the Gila monster is not particularly aggressive, dog bites are rare. However, if a bite occurs, the lizard has a tendency to attach itself at the bite site. To release its grip, gently pry the lizard's mouth open or light a fire under the lower jaw to stimulate it to release its grip. Do not shake it loose because teeth may break off in the multiple puncture wounds.

If venom was injected in the bite, pain at the bite site will occur within a few minutes. The venom appears to have some affect on the cardiovascular system but does not affect blood coagulation. If enough venom is injected in the bite wounds, shock and circulatory collapse may occur within hours. There is NO specific antivenin, but symptomatic treatment will produce good results if shock and circulatory collapse can be controlled. The wounds should be flushed with a saline-antibiotic solution, tetanus antitoxin should be given, and systemic antibiotics used to control potential infections.

HERBICIDE POISONING:

Two classes of herbicides are especially poisonous for dogs: the dipyridal group which includes paraquot and diquot, and the phenoxy group which includes TCDD, HCDD, "2,4-D," and "2,4,5-T." The most poisonous form of these herbicides is the concentrate before it is mixed for spraying on weeds.

Signs of toxicity to the dipyridal group (paraquot, diquot) become most severe after the majority of the chemical has been excreted. These clinical signs include severe gastrointestinal upset, vomiting, diarrhea, loss of coordination, and convulsive seizures. As the toxic process proceeds, respiratory difficulty becomes apparent and a gurgling sound of fluid is heard with each breath. Treatment is not rewarding. The prognosis is poor.

The clinical signs of phenoxy-type herbicide poisoning include depression, loss of appetite, vomiting, bloody stools, muscle weakness and incoordination, and finally coma and death. A seven day period may elapse from the time that clinical signs are first observed until death occurs. The only treatment is symptomatic support of kidney and liver function as the herbicide is eliminated over several days. The prognosis is poor to fair depending on the amount of the chemical ingested.

HEXACHLOROPHENE POISONING:

Hexachlorophene is a phenolic chemical that, because of its antibacterial properties, was included in "hospital-type" bathing soaps. However, the compound can be absorbed through the skin causing phenolic poisoning. Currently, hexachlorophene has been removed from all "over the counter" antibacterial cleaners and is no longer widely used for elimination of bacteria from the skin. Signs of hexachlorophene poisoning are similar to those caused by *phenol, creosote,* and other phenol derivatives.

HOLLY POISONING:

The berries of English holly (Ilex aquifolium) cause extreme gastrointestinal irritation resulting in vomiting, abdominal discomfort, and diarrhea. Also, a neurological affect causes stupor or loss of awareness of surroundings. The treatment is directed at removal of the berries from the GI tract by vomiting followed by *gastric lavage*. The treatment is symptomatic. If the neurological signs are not too extreme, a good recovery is anticipated.

HOME REMEDIES:

Home remedies for the following poisons are included within this chapter.

Acid Poisoning (External)	Carbon Tetrachloride Poisoning
Acid Poisoning (Internal)	Creosote Poisoning
Alkali Poisoning (External)	Detergents (Anionic) Poisoning
Alkali Poisoning (Internal)	Detergents (Cationic) Poisoning
Arsenic Poisoning	Mercury Poisoning

HORSE CHESTNUT POISONING:
Refer to *BUCKEYE POISONING.*

HOUSEHOLD CLEANER POISONING:

Most household cleaning agents are classified as bleaches, or anionic and cationic detergents. Discussion of household cleaner poisoning is found under each specific kind of cleaning agent. With supportive treatment, most cleaner poisonings have a good prognosis for recovery.

HYDRANGEA POISONING:

When eaten by a dog, the hydrangea (Hydrangea macrophylla) is highly toxic. All parts of this ornamental plant contain *cyanide* producing substances. The clinical signs are the same as those of cyanide poisoning. The prognosis for recovery is poor, but is somewhat related to the amount consumed.

INDIAN TOBACCO POISONING:

All parts of Indian tobacco (Lobelia inflata) contain the toxic substance, alobeline, a nicotine-like chemical. The clinical signs of salivation and vomiting are followed by CNS depression, pinpoint pupils, weakness, disorientation, and finally, loss of consciousness. Treatment is to first stimulate vomiting followed by *gastric lavage* to remove any unabsorbed toxic principle. General supportive treatment includes artificial respiration if necessary. *Atropine* is given to counteract some of the signs that appear. The prognosis is dose related, ranging from good to poor.

INDUCTION OF VOMITING:

Refer to *VOMITING, INDUCTION OF:*

INSECTICIDE POISONING:

Three groups of chemical compounds are used for insecticide treatments: *carbamates, chlorinated hydrocarbons,* and *organophosphates.* Since *flea collars* and flea medallions contain insecticides that are constantly being released into the hair of the dog, exposure to additional insecticides may cause a toxic accumulation.

IRIS PLANT POISONING:

The root of the flag iris (Iris) contains a resin that produces a severe irritation to the gastrointestinal tract. The clinical signs include vomiting, abdominal discomfort, and diarrhea. Removal of the root material from the stomach by stimulation of emesis (vomiting) and gastric lavage will cure the irritation. Intestinal protectants like kaolin and pectin soothe the gut in severe cases. The prognosis for recovery is good following treatment.

JESSAMINE PLANT POISONING:

All parts of the jessamine plant (Gelsemium sempervirens) contain a number of alkaloid chemicals capable of causing a diverse number of clinical signs.

Signs commonly seen are dilated pupils, dry mouth, generalized weakness followed by convulsions, and respiratory failure. Occasionally, signs of gastrointestinal disturbance appear early after ingestion of this poison. Treatment is induction of vomiting followed by symptomatic therapy which includes artificial respiration. The prognosis is guarded to fair depending on the amount ingested.

LAUREL PLANT POISONING:

The mountain laurel (Kalmia latifolia) contains the resinoid, andromedotoxin, that can cause severe gastrointestinal upsets which progress to paralysis or convulsions. Although all parts of the laurel contain the resinoid, the leaves are especially toxic. The induction of vomiting will remove the toxic element from the stomach. Supportive therapy follows until signs subside. Prognosis is fair if treated early and if the dose ingested was not extremely large.

LEAD POISONING:

Some of the many articles in our environment which contain various forms of lead are paint, batteries, linoleum, caulking compound, and various plumbing supplies. If lead is present in the GI tract over an extended period, toxic amounts may be absorbed in the blood stream.

Both gastrointestinal upsets and central nervous system signs can be seen. The GI signs include poor appetite, occasional diarrhea, vomiting, and abdominal pain. The nervous system signs are personality changes, *seizures, blindness,* and hysteria. This type of poisoning is diagnosed by clinical signs, by blood lead levels over 40 mg/dl, and on *radiograph* by finding opaque objects within the intestinal tract.

Effective treatment involves the prevention of absorption of any more lead. Enemas or emetics can help remove any residual lead. The treatment of choice for lead poisoning is calcium versenate given four times daily for five days. If neurological signs occur, adjunctive treatment for seizures may be needed. The prognosis for complete recovery is very good.

LETHAL STAPH TOXIN:

Refer to *GARBAGE TOXIN.*

LILY PLANT POISONING:

Several different plants use the name lily as part of the common name *calla lily, glory lily,* and *lily of the valley.* The *CALLA LILY* causes irritation to the mouth and gastrointestinal tract. The signs accordingly are salivation, vomiting, and diarrhea. The use of milk or olive oil to soothe the irritation is the only treatment necessary.

The *GLORY LILY* produces the chemical, colchicine. This causes abdominal discomfort, delayed vomiting, and finally diarrhea. Treatment is removal of the toxic substance and symptomatic therapy until signs subside.

LILY OF THE VALLEY produces signs of *digitalis poison*ing. Refer to *DIGITALIS POISONING* for further discussion.

LIZARD BITES:

Three lizards in the United States are considered poisonous: the blue tail lizard, the Gila monster (Heloderma suspectum), and the Mexican beaded lizard (Heloderma horridum). Refer to GILA MONSTER BITES and NEUROTOXIN POISONING for further discussion. The clinical signs and treatment principles would be different for blue tail lizards.

LUPINE PLANT POISONING:

Lupinine and other alkaloids are found in all parts of the lupine plant but are especially concentrated in the berries. Ingestion of this plant causes convulsions and general cardiorespiratory failure. Many affected animals will appear paralyzed. The treatment is symptomatic after vomiting is induced. Respiration must be supported and convulsive *seizures* controlled. The prognosis is guarded.

MANCHINEEL PLANT POISONING:

The sap from the manchineel plant (Hippomane mancinella) is very irritating to the skin and mucous membranes. Skin that comes in contact with the sap will blister and peel. Removal of the sap from the skin with soap and water or alcohol comprises the treatment. If severe blistering has occurred, secondary infection must be prevented until new skin has formed.

MARIJUANA POISONING:

Marijuana poisoning is becoming much more common in veterinary medicine as pets get into the owner's supply of marijuana or hashish. The toxic principle in marijuana is tetrahydrocannabinol. As the owner of a dog that may have been poisoned with marijuana, you must convey this information to your veterinarian so that he can provide expert treatment for the problem. Doctor-patient confidentiality enables you to trust your vet.

The clinical signs are rapidly changeable. Either excitement or depression is seen. The dog is wobbly, weak, and confused. Treatment is supportive in nature. If the poisoning is discovered within 90 minutes, vomiting should be induced to remove any residual marijuana from the stomach. Two to three days may pass before the dog returns to normalcy. Usually, recovery is complete.

MERCURY POISONING:

The sources of mercury poisoning are vague. Some is found as a residue from burning fossil fuels while other is used as a fumigant on farms. Heavy metal poisoning is the result primarily affecting the central nervous system. The signs associated with central nervous system toxicity are exaggerated gait, loss of vision, rear leg stiffness, a wobbly weak gait, and convulsions.

Since there is no specific antidote, the HOME ANTIDOTE FOR MERCURY POISONING should be given if it can be administered within an hour of ingestion of the mercury poison. Give 1 pint of milk with 3 beaten egg whites. Magnesium oxide may be helpful. Starch (1 part to 15 parts hot water) aids in detoxifying the mercury. Between 25 and 35 grams of *activated charcoal* helps prevent absorption of the poison. Further treatment is directed at controlling the central nervous system signs and convulsions by tying up the mercury after it gets into the blood stream. *BAL (dimercaprol)* is an injectable antidote used in heavy metal poisonings. The dog is hospitalized so that necessary treatment and antidotes can be administered. The prognosis is guarded when central nervous system signs are seen.

METHALDEHYDE POISONING:

Methaldehyde, a polymer of acetaldehyde, is widely used as a slug and snail bait for gardens. When combined with *arsenic,* it becomes a *rodenticide.* In recent years, chemical baits have been altered making them less attractive to pets. Because muscle tremors and salivation are characteristic in all of three poisons, distinguishing metaldehyde *poisoning* from strychnine and toxaphene poisonings is essential.

The group of clinical signs seen in metaldehyde poisoning is due to the extreme acidosis which occurs after the chemical is ingested. A very rapid heart beat is present and muscular twitching results in muscle spasms. Early in the intoxication, the dog is extremely agitated, pants continually, and appears anxious. Because of the muscle twitching, panting and rapid heart rate, the body temperature may become seriously elevated (over 105°F). In a few individuals, after what appears to be a recovery from the central nervous system signs, the dog will die of *liver failure.* Liver failure occurs when the liver attempts to metabolize the metaldehyde poison resulting in the degeneration of the liver tissue.

Treatment consists of removal of any unabsorbed metaldehyde by *gastric lavage* or vomit induction. Muscle tremors or convulsions are controlled by *diazepam* or *general anesthesia.* The metabolic acidosis is corrected with bicarbonate fluid therapy. Occasionally, muscle tremors can be controlled with *Robaxin®* . Anesthesia treatment may be needed for two or three days. With intensive therapy, the prognosis is guarded to fair. The use of *liver function blood tests* is helpful four to five days after recovery to determine whether permanent liver damage has occurred.

MISTLETOE POISONING:

All parts of the ornamental plant mistletoe (Phoradendron flavescens) contain a *digitalis*-like toxic principle. The concentration of this toxic ingredient is especially high in the mistletoe berries. The signs of mistletoe poisoning are similar to other digitalis poisonings.

MUSHROOM POISONING:

The toxins produced by the Amanita species of mushrooms cause different clinical symptoms. Amanita muscaria produces an alkaloid that causes lethal affects in minutes. The fungus, Amanita pantherina, causes central nervous system signs very rapidly. However, the poison produced by Amanita phalloides may not cause signs for up to 12 hours with symptoms lasting for weeks.

The clinical signs seen early are severe gastrointestinal involvement, cramping, vomiting, bloody mucoid diarrhea, pupil constriction, salivation, cardiovascular collapse, severe agitation, coma, and death. In the types of amanita toxins that have delayed affects, both liver and kidney failure signs occur.

No antidote is available for this potent toxin. Therefore, the treatment is symptomatic. Rapid gastric lavage with tannic acid (1:400) or activated charcoal may help to keep the toxin from being absorbed. If no central nervous system signs are observed, *atropine* can be helpful. A prolonged course of therapy is essential to keep the liver and kidneys from complete failure. *Sedatives* are also necessary if the central nervous system is involved. The prognosis for mushroom poisoning is poor to guarded depending on the type and the amount of the toxin ingested.

NEUROTOXIN POISONING (SNAKE, LIZARD, TOAD):

The *coral snake*, a member of the cobra family, is the only snake in the United States that produces a neurotoxin. Bufo toad neurotoxin is discussed more fully under the *BUFO TOAD* heading. A neurotoxin is also produced by the *blue tail lizard* living in the southeastern United States.

The clinical signs involve the central nervous system including agitation, salivation, twisting of the neck, incoordination, and death. Treatment is only symptomatic because no antidote is available. Gastric lavage and control of nervous system signs with sedatives and anesthesia are necessary. The prognosis is guarded.

NEUROLOGICAL POISONING: LIST OF CAUSES

Aconite (Wild) Plant Poisoning
Alkaloids
Amphetamine Poisoning
Antifreeze
Arsenic Poisoning
Aspirin Toxicity
Black Widow Spider
Blue Tail Lizard Poisoning
Botulinum Toxin
Brown Recluse Spider Bite

Bufo Toad Poisoning
Carbamate Poisoning
Carbon Monoxide Poisoning
Cherry Seed Toxicity
Chlorinated Hydrocarbon Toxicity
Chocolate Poisoning
Coral Snake Bite
Cyanide Poisoning
Finger Cherry Poisoning
Fluoroacetate (1080) Poisoning

Gasoline (Petroleum Distillates)
Hydrangea Poisoning
Herbicide Poisoning
Holly Poisoning
Indian Tobacco Poisoning
Insecticide Poisoning
Jessamine Plant Poisoning
Laurel Plant Poisoning
Lead Poisoning
Lupine Plant Poisoning
Marijuana Poisoning

Mercury Poisoning
Metaldehyde Poisoning
Mushroom Poisoning
Organophosphate Poisoning
Peas Plant Poisoning
Phenol and Creosote Poisoning
Rodenticide
Strychnine Poisoning
Thallium Poisoning
Tranquilizer Overdose

Each of these poisons is discussed separately within the chapter.

NON-PLANT POISONING:

Acid
Alkali
Alkaloid
Amphetamine
Antifreeze
ANTU®
Arsenic
Aspirin
Blue Tail Lizard
Bufo Toad
Carbonate
Carbon Monoxide
Carbon Tetrachloride
Chocolate
Copper
Creosote
Cyanide
Detergents (Anionic)
Detergents (Cationic)
Fluoroacetate

Formaldehyde
Gasoline
Herbicide
Hexachlorophene
Household Cleaner
Insecticide
Lead
Mercury
Methaldehyde
Organophosphate
Oxalic Acid
Petroleum Distillate Products
Phenol and Creosol
Phosphorus
Strychnine
Thallium
Tranquilizer
Vacor
Warfarin
Zinc Phosphide

Each of these non-plant poisons is discussed individually within the chapter.

OLEANDER PLANT POISONING:

The toxic principle, oleandrin, found in all parts of the ornamental plant oleander (Nerium oleander), contains *digitalis*-like properties which is toxic to the cardiovascular system.

ORGANOPHOSPHATE INSECTICIDE POISONING:

Organophosphates, classified as acetylcholinesterase inhibitor chemicals, are found in insecticides and in some parasiticides. Dichlorvos, diazinon, ronnel, malathion, trichlorfon, and ciodrin are some of the common chemical names from this group.

These chemicals most commonly affect the central nervous system but can also cause vomiting and diarrhea. The clinical signs observed are salivation, pinpoint pupils, muscle tremors, incoordinated gait, and convulsions. Respiratory involvement may be evident because of excessive bronchial secretions making breathing difficult, causing a bluish tint in the mucous membranes, and causing death.

The antidote for organophosphate poisoning is 2-PAM and *atropine* intravenously. Any residual poison should be removed from the skin with soap and water. When swallowed, gastric lavage and a saline (salt) cathartic (laxative) will aid in the elimination of the chemicals. After these measures, residual signs such as respiratory difficulty and convulsions must be treated symptomatically. Remember - *phenothiazine tranquilizers* are CONTRAINDICATED in organophosphate poisoning! They actually increase the clinical signs of poisoning. Common phenothiazine tranquilizers are *acepromazine,* Sparine® and *Tran-Vet®* . The prognosis is guarded to fair depending on the amount of poison assimilated and the quality of treatment.

OXALIC ACID POISONING:

Oxalic acid is found naturally in *rhubarb* leaves as well as chemically in many cleaning agents. This acid should not be neutralized by alkalis since all alkalis except calcium hydroxide are too soluble and will cause the build-up of oxalates in the kidneys. Oxalates will quickly destroy the functional tissue of the kidney tubules.

Early clinical signs are those typical of caustic acids. Initial signs include excessive salivation and ulcerations of the mouth and throat followed by bloody vomiting and diarrhea. If the oxalic acid is absorbed, *uremia* and signs of *kidney failure* will be seen.

The antidote for oxalic acid toxicity is calcium given as calcium hydroxide (0.15%), chalk, or as other calcium salts. Magnesium sulfate is given orally for its laxative effect. If absorption of oxalic acid has occurred, intravenous fluids should be given to stimulate urine flow and prevent calcium salts from developing in the kidneys. Sodium bicarbonate is administered for the extreme acidosis build-up in the body. *Antifreeze (ethylene glycol) poisoning* is also due to the accumulation of oxalate crystals in the kidneys. The prognosis is guarded depending on the amount of oxalic acid that was absorbed and the affect on the kidney tissue.

PEAS PLANT POISONING:

Peas (Lathyrus) can cause poisoning if ingested. The entire plant is poisonous, but the seeds are the most toxic. The clinical signs are primarily neurological, including paralysis and convulsions. Respiratory embarrassment and a weakened pulse are also seen. Treatment is only symptomatic. Following *gastric lavage,* the dog is supported as needed. *Seizures* must be controlled and occasionally respiration must be supported. Prognosis is guarded depending on the severity of the convulsions occurring.

PETROLEUM DISTILLATE PRODUCTS POISONING:

Refer to *GASOLINE POISONING.*

PHENOL AND CREOSOL POISONING:

Phenolic compounds vary from wood tar and wood preservatives to antibacterials like phenol and *hexachlorophene.* While cats are especially sensitive to phenolic compounds, dogs can also be poisoned. The clinical signs observed from these compounds include necrosis of mucous membranes and skin, swelling of the brain, and a variety of liver and kidney degenerations. The dog may merely show depression or it may be comatose. Its skin and mucous membranes can turn yellow. Signs of *uremia* may develop. Treatment is supportive. The compounds must be washed from the skin and mucous membranes. Once signs of toxicity are observed, the prognosis is guarded, at best. Also refer to *CREOSOTE POISONING.*

PHILODENDRON PLANT POISONING:

The philodendron is a member of the Arum plant family. Refer to *ARUM PLANT FAMILY POISONING* for further discussion.

PHOSPHORUS POISONING:

Phosphorus, the active ingredient of various roach and rat poisons, is also found in matches and fireworks. The clinical signs of phosphorus poisoning are vomiting and diarrhea with considerable abdominal distress. After the initial recovery, liver degeneration and hemorrhage can occur.

The treatment is *gastric lavage* with a .4% copper sulfate solution. *Activated charcoal* will help absorb the phosphorus. Mineral oil can be given as a cathartic. Intravenous dextrose will help to spare the liver and protect it from the affects of phosphorus. DO NOT give vegetable oil! Also, remove all fats from the diet. The prognosis is fair to guarded depending on the amount of liver pathology.

PLANT POISONING, LISTING:

Aconite (Wild)	Cherry Seed
Alocasia	Chrysanthemum
Arum Plant Family	Crow Foot Family
Bird of Paradise	Dieffenbachia
Buckeye	Finger Cherry
Caladium	Holly

Hydrangea	Mushroom
Indian Tobacco	Oleander
Iris	Peas
Jessamine	Philodendron
Laurel	Poinsettia
Lily	Primrose
Lupine	Privet
Manchineel	Rayless Goldenrod
Marijuana	Rhubarb
Mistletoe	Wisteria
	Yew

The plants listed can cause toxic reactions when parts or all of the plant are consumed by a dog. Each listed plant is discussed separately in this chapter.

POINSETTIA PLANT POISONING:

The ornamental holiday season plant, the poinsettia (Euphorbia pulcherrima) can cause both skin and gastrointestinal irritation. The sap, leaves, and stems all contain irritating material capable of producing clinical signs. If the skin is exposed to sap, blistering and redness occur. The blisters break resulting in ulcerated areas. If the leaves or sap are eaten, irritation to the mucous membranes of the gastrointestinal tract will result. Clinical signs are vomiting and diarrhea.

The treatment of poinsettia ingestion is to remove any remaining plant from the digestive tract by giving an emetic (vomit inducer). Any remaining sap on the skin can be removed with soap and water. Additional treatment with protectants and demulcents like milk soothe the irritated membranes. The prognosis is good with proper treatment.

POISON CONTROL CENTER:

The number for the Poison Control Center or Poison Center in your area is listed in the front of your telephone book. In large metropolitan areas, most Poison Centers are located in Children's Hospitals. While their focus is primarily as a service to human poisoning, they are also very helpful in cases of dog poisoning. Do not hesitate to call the number of the Poison Center nearest you when confronted with poisoning. You must provide as much information as possible about the kind, name, and amount of the poison consumed. The Poison Control Center and the *Animal Toxicology Hotline* telephone numbers should be posted by your telephone.

POISON NEUTRALIZATION, PRINCIPLES OF:

The following guidelines are general and will only supplement the specific instruction given by Hotline personnel or your veterinarian.

ON THE DISCOVERY OF A POSSIBLE POISONING, calmly carry out the following steps:

1. Write down the brand name, active ingredient(s), and approximate amount missing.

2. Look for clinical signs of toxicity: red or blistered skin, salivation, vomiting, depression, garlic or almond odor to breath, diarrhea, muscle tremors, seizures, labored breathing, cardiorespiratory collapse, unusual tongue color (blue, white, gray, brick red, pink), altered consciousness (agitated or stupor).

3. Call Animal Toxicology Hotline at **(217) 333-3611** or the Poison Center listed in the front of your phone book.

4. Call your veterinarian for immediate instructions and to advise of the emergency nature of your visit.

5. Give home antidote as per instructions from Animal Toxicology Hotline and your veterinarian. Do not waste time! TRANSPORT IMMEDIATELY!

Any external poison should immediately be washed away with copious amounts of water. DO NOT TOUCH the poisoned area with bare flesh. Wear rubber gloves if you must touch red blistered areas.

DO NOT ATTEMPT TO STIMULATE VOMITING IN ANY OF THE FOLLOW-ING SITUATIONS:

- If the dog is unconscious or severely depressed.
- If petroleum distillates (e.g. gasoline) have been ingested.
- If acids have been ingested.
- If alkalis have been ingested.
- If tranquilizers or other antiemetics (vomit prevention) has been consumed
- If the poison was ingested more than 90 minutes earlier.

Many emetics (vomit inducers) may be relatively ineffective and can actually cause more harm than good. When in doubt, give up to one pint of milk with 4 beaten egg whites. *Activated charcoal,* an important part of poison treatment, should be given by your veterinarian as part of the *gastric lavage* procedure.

Mineral oil is an excellent cathartic (bowel evacuator). Because it has no taste, mineral oil does not stimulate a swallow reflex so requires care with its use. Mineral oil is helpful in fat soluble poisons. Vegetable oils like olive oil can be used but will be absorbed to some degree. If the poison is soluble in oil or fat, it may aggravate the situation. Approximately 30 minutes after oil is given, a saline (salt) laxative should be given to stimulate emptying of the bowel.

Treatment of poisons must be done quickly and expertly. If you follow the instructions outlined in this section, the prognosis may improve due to your rapid, intelligent action.

PRIMROSE PLANT POISONING:

Primrose leaves and stems contain a contact irritant which makes skin red and blistered. This stimulates the dog to scratch, sometimes resulting in the self-mutilation of the involved skin surface. Since this plant is so irritating, the toxic affects are limited to topical application. The irritating substance is removed with soap and water. The inflamed area may be soothed with rubbing alcohol. Following treatment, the prognosis for complete recovery is good.

PRINCIPLES OF POISON NEUTRALIZATION:

Refer to *POISON NEUTRALIZATION, PRINCIPLES OF.*

PRIVET PLANT POISONING:

The toxic substance contained in the leaves and berries of the privet plant (Ligustrum vulgare) can cause gastrointestinal irritation. Later, signs of kidney damage occur if the toxic substance has been absorbed in any quantity. The treatment consists of removing the privet by stimulating emesis (vomiting) and following this with *gastric lavage. Kidney function tests* and *urinalysis* should be performed for two to four days after apparent recovery to ascertain any damage to the kidneys. The prognosis is fair to good depending on the absorption of the toxin and subsequent kidney compromise.

RAYLESS GOLDENROD PLANT POISONING:

All parts of rayless goldenrod (Happlopappus heterophyllus) contain the toxic chemical tremetol which causes gastrointestinal upsets followed by liver and kidney damage. The clinical signs are those of liver damage: jaundice, ascites, and a shutdown of urine production associated with kidney damage. In treatment, the liver and kidney function must be supported. The recovery and prognosis depend on the amount of damage done to these organs. The prognosis is guarded.

RHUBARB PLANT POISONING:

Rhubarb leaves are rich in oxalic acid. For further discussion, refer to *OXALIC ACID POISONING.*

RODENTICIDES, LISTING OF:

ANTU®	Thallium
Arsenic	Vacor
Fluoroacetate (1080)	Warfarin
Red Squill	Zinc phosphide
Strychnine	

Many of the items on this list are currently or have been previously used in rat poisons. Some are so toxic that they are not now available (e.g. thallium) or are only available to professional exterminators. Refer to each topic individually within the chapter for further discussion.

SALICYLATE POISONING:

Refer to *ASPIRIN INTOXICATION.*

SKIN IRRITATION, POISONS CAUSING:

Acids	Gasoline (Petroleum Distillates)
Alkalis	Gila Monster Bite
Black Widow Spider	Manchineel
Bleaches	Phenol & Creosote
Brown Recluse Spider	Poinsettia
Chrysanthemum	Primrose
Creosote Poisoning	Snake Bites
Fire Ant Bites	Tarantula Bite
Formaldehyde	

SNAKE BITE:

The coral snake is the only poisonous snake related to the cobra family in the United States. All snakes in the cobra family produce a neurotoxin. Further treatment principles are discussed under *CORAL SNAKE BITE.*

All other poisonous snakes in the United States belong to the pit viper family including the copperhead, the cotton-mouthed water moccasin, and all species of rattlesnakes. These snakes produce a hematoxic venom. Soon after a bite, the bite site swells causing small blood vessels to rupture as tissue destruction continues. Systemic signs like bloody stool, bloody urine, vomiting, convulsions, and death follow. Antivenin-polyvalent produced by Fort Dodge Laboratories, Fort Dodge, Iowa can be used to neutralize pit viper family venom. If treatment is postponed for longer than three to four hours, the prognosis for recovery is very poor.

SPIDER BITES:

The bites of four spiders are considered toxic or poisonous: the black widow spider, the brown recluse, the common brown spider, and the tarantula. The docile tarantula is not apt to bite unless seriously provoked. Refer to each spider individually for further discussion.

STAPH ENTEROTOXIN:

Refer to *GARBAGE TOXINS.*

STOMACH PUMPING PROCEDURE (GASTRIC LAVAGE):

The removal of toxic substances by gastric lavage (stomach pumping) should only be done by your veterinarian. This procedure is very effective for the removal of some poisons before they are absorbed into the body. To be successful, however, gastric lavage should be done within an hour of the consumption of the poison. The administration of *activated charcoal* is a useful complement to gastric lavage. Extra care must be taken if the stomach wall has been weakened from caustic material. Remember, a veterinarian must perform this procedure because anesthesia is required. The procedure is accomplished with the affected dog under light anesthesia or if the dog is otherwise unconscious. A cuffed endotracheal catheter is inserted in the windpipe to prevent aspiration of the lavage solution. A stomach tube about the same diameter as the endotracheal catheter is passed to the level of the last rib. The lavage solution is administered at the rate of 5 ml (teaspoon) per pound of body weight (a little more than 1/2 pint for a mature Doberman Pinscher). Extreme pressure should be avoided in placing the lavage solution in the stomach since it could be forced into the small intestine. The lavage solution is then removed from the stomach with bulb suction syringe. The procedure is repeated up to 15 times or until the solution returns clear. A slurry of activated charcoal is included in the last two to four lavage procedures.

STRYCHNINE POISONING:

Strychnine is a substance found in some *rodenticide* and predator baits. Most of the commercial baits contain several times more strychnine than is needed to kill an average-sized Doberman Pinscher.

Clinical signs of toxicity occur as quickly as 15 minutes after ingestion or as long as two hours after. Early signs are nervousness and agitation. These signs rapidly change into seizures and extreme muscle rigidity with the legs extended out in "saw horse" fashion. The head and neck are thrown back at an extreme angle. In a characteristic appearance, the ears and lips are drawn back. When *seizures* begin, periods of relaxation will occur. As the poison circulates, the muscular rigidity becomes almost continual. This depresses respiration, leading to an elevated body temperature. Characteristic strychnine seizures may be initiated by sound or touch, differentiating them from toxaphene insecticide seizures which are not initiated by external stimuli.

The use of *gas or barbiturate anesthesia* controls the seizures while the poison is being removed from the stomach by *gastric lavage* and *activated charcoal* and while it is being metabolized by the liver. Between six and twelve hours of intensive care are required to metabolize the strychnine absorbed and to stop the seizures. Watching for respiratory depression during this period is very important.

The prognosis is somewhat dependent on when treatment is initiated and the amount of strychnine ingested. If lavage and intensive care are started within an hour of ingestion of the poison, the prognosis is guarded to good. The prognosis would be less favorable if severe *tetanic seizures* had already begun.

TARANTULA SPIDER BITE:

The tarantula (Eurytelma) is capable of a venomous bite. However, most are not very aggressive and do not seem to become agitated easily. Because the principles for managing a tarantula bite are similar to those for other spiders, refer to *BLACK WIDOW SPIDER BITES* or *BROWN RECLUSE and COMMON BROWN SPIDER BITES* for further discussion.

TAR REMOVAL FROM HAIR COAT:

Some people want to use petroleum distillates or gasoline on the hair coat and skin of a dog to remove road tar. UNDER NO CIRCUMSTANCES SHOULD PETROLEUM PRODUCTS BE USED TO REMOVE TAR!!!! Instead, the following procedure should be followed.

- Cut away any tar on the hair, without cutting the skin.
- Saturate the area covered with tar in vegetable or mineral oil. The area should be covered with the oil for 24 hours.
- After 24 hours, wipe away as much tar as possible using several towels.
- Bathe the hair coat and skin in a mild detergent to remove the final traces of tar.
- Observe the skin for 24 hours for signs of redness and irritation. If irritation occurs, it may be treated with steroid creams and ointments.

THALLIUM POISONING:

Because ant, rat, and roach baits are more strictly regulated today, thallium poisoning is not as common as in the past. However, old baits placed on farms over the years can serve as a source for current intoxications. Thallium can either kill very quickly or be chronic, taking months to cause death.

Early clinical signs are salivation and very severe stomach pains. The gait becomes weak and wobbly, followed by paralysis, coma, and death. This whole syndrome can occur in one or two days. If the dog lingers, hemorrhages on its gums and skin are observed. *Pneumonia* frequently develops. The chronic form most commonly affects the skin and mucous membranes. The skin becomes inflamed and ulcerated causing most of the hair to fall out. Ulcerated areas are also seen around the anus, mouth, eyelids, and under the front legs.

Treatment must be aggressive but with the realization that chances for recovery are slim. Following repeated gastric lavages with activated charcoal, Prussian blue is given orally three times daily to bind thallium and carry it out of the GI tract. The prognosis is poor to fair depending on whether the case is acute or chronic.

TOXINS:

The following toxins are discussed in detail within this chapter under each individual heading.

Botulism Toxin
Garbage Toxin
Lethal Staph Toxin

TRANQUILIZER POISONING:

Tranquilizer poisoning usually results from the dog gaining access to a prescription drug. The two clinical signs seen most frequently are extreme depression and a coma with very low blood pressure. If the dog is seen before the depression starts, gastric lavage is indicated. If depression has begun, do not attempt *gastric lavage.* If supportive care treatment can be maintained while the drug is metabolized, the prognosis is good.

UNKNOWN POISON - ANTIDOTE:

In the case where poisoning is suspected but the cause is unknown, the best home antidote is large quantities of milk (1 pint) with 3 beaten egg whites for an adult Dobe. This procedure is helpful in nearly all cases of poisoning. The use of activated charcoal in gelatin capsules can also be very helpful where poisoning is suspected. A cathartic or an emetic (vomit inducer) should follow. Even if these measures are taken, they do not eliminate the need for professional care. In most types of poisoning, supportive care is needed until the poison that has been absorbed is metabolized.

VACOR POISONING:

Vacor, a *rodenticide* available as a bait or as a powder, is classified as a nicotinamide, vitamin B antagonist. Clinical signs are vomiting, abdominal discomfort, muscle quivering, dilated pupils followed by collapse, coma, and death. Treatment is gastric lavage followed by intramuscular injections of the B vitamin, *nicotinamide,* for about two weeks after the early clinical signs have ceased. Other forms of supportive treatment are used as needed. The prognosis, which is somewhat dose related, is guarded to good.

VOMITING, INDUCTION OF:

In many kinds of poisoning, the stimulation of emesis (vomiting) is a very important part of the treatment. However, in cases where strong caustics like acids and alkalis have been ingested, vomiting should NOT be stimulated since the caustic will burn on the way up as it did on the way down. Petroleum products should not be forcefully vomited. Also unconscious or very depressed dogs should not be stimulated to vomit. As a rule of thumb, induction of vomiting is worthwhile up to 90 minutes after a poison has been ingested.

The products available at home that may be used to induce vomiting are 2-3 teaspoons of hydrogen peroxide, copper sulfate, warm salty water, and syrup of ipecac. Syrup of ipecac is a gastric irritant that is effective at the rate of 1 ounce (2 Tablespoons) per 30 pounds of body weight. If activated charcoal is to be used as part of the treatment regimen, syrup of ipecac should not be used because it reduces the effective absorption of activated charcoal. Your veterinarian may have apomorphine available which is an excellent emetic (vomit inducer).

WARFARIN POISONING:

Warfarin, the most common over-the-counter rat poison, contains coumadin which interferes with the production of *vitamin K* in the liver. Vitamin K is essential for proper blood clotting. Toxic signs include hemorrhaging which occurs almost anywhere in the body. Other clinical signs such as labored breathing, lameness, or central nervous system signs are related to the hemorrhagic tendencies. Treatment is fresh, whole blood transfused when *anemia* becomes life threatening. Intramuscular and oral use of vitamin K is also necessary for five to seven days. Any other signs must be treated by supportive therapy. The prognosis is very good to excellent in most cases if treatment is initiated before blood loss becomes critical.

WILD ACONITE PLANT POISONING:

Refer to *ACONITE (WILD) PLANT POISONING.*

WISTERIA PLANT POISONING:

All parts of the wisteria plant can produce toxic consequences. The usual signs are digestive upset and vomiting. Treatment is symptomatic and supportive in nature. Early treatment will usually insure a satisfactory outcome.

YEW PLANT POISONING:

The yew is one of several species of ornamental trees that can cause poisoning. The wood, bark, leaves, and seeds contain the toxic substance, taxine, which causes intestinal irritation and upset and later, cardiovascular disturbances. Initially, the dog appears nauseous and has abdominal cramps. Vomiting and dilated pupils then occur. As the cardiovascular system becomes involved, weakness, shock-like signs, and irregular heart beat, and death result. Treatment for yew tree poisoning is similar to the treatment for *DIGITALIS POISONING.* The prognosis is guarded.

ZINC PHOSPHIDE POISONING:

Zinc phosphide is a highly toxic *rodenticide.* The early signs are severe gastrointestinal upset with pain, vomiting, and diarrhea. The next phase of toxicity is fluid accumulation in the lungs and great difficulty breathing. Further affects are in the central nervous system with extreme restlessness, convulsions, coma, and death. The treatment is supportive and generally not effective. Oxygen is given to assist breathing difficulties. *Seizures* must also be controlled. The prognosis is poor to fair.

Chapter 10

SENSORY SYSTEMS

Eyes, Ears, Nose

ACUTE ANTERIOR UVEITIS:

Acute anterior uveitis is an eye emergency that a veterinarian should see immediately. As an owner, look for severe pain, excessive tearing, redness, excessive blinking, and pupil constriction. Other emergency eye problems may also present similar signs. However, the most important thing to remember is that veterinary attention is absolutely necessary. With acute anterior uveitis, the area around the iris (the colored part of the eye around the pupil) and the tissue that supports the iris become inflamed.

Causes of anterior uveitis include trauma to the eye, either internal or external infections, *systemic fungal diseases,* and *heartworm infestation.* This may also occur after a *hepatitis vaccination* or be associated with *toxoplasmosis.* Acute anterior uveitis may also come as a sequelae to intraocular *(cataract)* surgery, as part of *canine brucellosis,* or as a result of *infectious canine hepatitis.*

The usual ophthalmic tests *(tonometry, fluorescein dye test,* an ophthalmoscopic exam), and a complete systemic work-up *(CBC, chest x-rays, biochemical serum tests,* lymph node aspiration) may be necessary for an accurate diagnosis. Anterior uveitis may be a symptom of a systemic disease or of some form of cancer.

Treatment is dependent on whether or not a systemic cause is found. Appropriate action must be initiated quickly since vision will be lost if treatment is delayed. Generally, *atropine* helps to dilate the eyes. Then either *aspirin* or *steroids* are used to minimize inflammation. If an infection is suspected, appropriate antibiotics are utilized. The systemic problem must be resolved for uveitis therapy to be successful. With quick action, the prognosis is good to excellent for complete recovery.

ACUTE BLINDNESS:

True acute blindness is an optic emergency requiring early diagnosis and treatment by a veterinarian for any chance of visual recovery. If you suspect that your Dobe is not seeing, observe it in unfamiliar surroundings. With bilateral (in both eyes) blindness, the dog will have difficulty moving around without running into furnishings. Do not assume that pupils which are responsive to light indicate a sighted dog! Some forms of blindness occur at higher levels in the brain.

Provide your veterinarian with an accurate history of the dog's past seven to fourteen days. Recent vaccination history, excessive tearing, continual blinking, and *red eyes* are important facts. Neurological signs like *circling* and *head tilt* are also significant. Signs attributed to generalized illness such as fever, excessive water consumption, and digestive upset may provide clues as to the cause of acute blindness.

Optic neuritis and *retinal detachment* are the two most common causes of acute blindness. The underlying causes of these conditions are discussed fully under each individual topic.

Use of *steroids* in treating some forms of acute blindness can result in the return of sight providing the medication was initiated at the proper dosage level early enough. If steroids are effective, improvement is seen within two weeks. If absolute blindness is still present after two weeks of therapy, no return of vision should be anticipated.

The cause of visual loss, the proper use of medication, the length of time between blindness and the start of therapy are all relevant factors. Prognosis for recovery of vision is guarded.

ACUTE CORNEAL ULCER:

The clear window through which we see, the cornea, has five layers. Normally the cornea is devoid of a blood supply but does have a generous network of nerves. Because of the nerve supply, ulceration of the cornea causes signs of a painful eye such as excess tearing, rubbing, redness, and blinking.

The rapid ulceration of the corneal tissue by enzymes cause it to dissolve resulting in a very serious eye emergency. A grayish mucoid exudate is present on and around the cornea when the enzymes are digesting the tissue. These proteolytic enzymes are produced by bacteria like *Pseudomonas*. In a matter of HOURS, these potent enzymes erode the entire five layers of the cornea causing perforation of the eye with subsequent infection of inner structures of the eye. The usual signs of eye pain are present. IMMEDIATE treatment is mandatory!

The treatment of this acute ulcerative process must occur HOURLY until the enzymatic degeneration is brought under control. This may take from six hours to two or three days. *Gentamycin* and *tobramycin* are the two most effective antibiotic ophthalmic medications for this condition. In addition to this treatment, 10% Mucomyst® drops should be administered every two hours to deactivate the enzymes. *Atropine* drops are also needed to keep the eye dilated. Systemic antibiotics are given to help support internal eye structures during this battle. If the battle is lost and perforation of the eye occurs, vision in that eye will probably be lost.

Immediate diagnosis and intensive care are necessary to keep this eye condition from becoming a disaster. While cultures from an eye ulcer are usually taken, treatment must begin before those results are received. The choice of antibiotics can be modified when culture results are known. The prognosis is guarded.

AMERICAN COLLEGE OF VETERINARY OPHTHALMOLOGISTS:

The American College of Veterinary Ophthalmologists (ACVO), established approximately 20 years ago, currently includes about 90 members. The five objectives of the ACVO are: 1) To encourage education, training, and research in veterinary ophthalmology, 2) to establish standards for training and experience in the field, 3) to aid in the development of methods of residency graduate training in veterinary ophthalmology, 4) to recognize qualified individuals with certification, and 5) to advise veterinarians desiring certification and training in the field.

Members of the ACVO are recognized as experts in the diagnosis, treatment, and surgery of veterinary eye problems. If a perplexing canine eye problem arises, your local veterinarian can refer you to the nearest member of the ACVO. While most members are in academic situations, some also maintain private referral practices in ophthalmology.

ANTERIOR LENS LUXATION:

The anterior luxation of the lens of the eye is a true eye emergency. The lens, after coming out of its normal place, pushes forward blocking the normal drain openings for the liquid within the eye (aqueous humor). This blockage causes the eye to swell with a secondary *glaucoma.*

Clinical signs are a painful eye that appears cloudy and red. The only effective treatment for this condition is the surgical removal of the misplaced lens. Because the lens is in an abnormal location, the performing surgeon should have above average expertise in dealing with eye problems. The prognosis for retaining vision is guarded, depending on how long secondary glaucoma was present before the lens was removed.

APPLANATION:

Applanation is a method of *tonometry* which measures the intraocular pressure of the eye. At lower pressures, this technique is more accurate than *Schiotz's tonometry.* Specialized equipment and some degree of expertise in interpreting the results are required for this procedure.

AURAL HEMATOMA:

The presence of free blood between the skin and the cartilage of the external ear, an aural hematoma, is more common in uncropped Doberman Pinschers than in those with cropped ears. The ear flap (uncropped) or the pointed ear (cropped) appear swollen and spongy. The dog shakes its head because of an unbalanced feeling created by the swollen ear.

In most cases, an underlying cause exists for the capillary blood vessel rupture that fills the ear with blood. Violent head shaking from an ear canal infection, a clotting defect such as *Von Willebrand's Disease*, or a liver deficiency that prolongs the clotting time could all contribute.

Treatment is directed at removing the blood and clots from the subcutaneous tissue compartment. Stapling or gluing the skin to the cartilage eliminates the compartment. Some techniques utilize Silastic tubes placed under the skin to drain off any further blood as healing progresses. With any procedure, the underlying cause must be treated when possible. An uncropped, treated ear should be taped to the side of the head to keep it from being shaken while undergoing healing.

The prognosis for recovery is excellent. The amount of scar tissue (thickening) in the healed ear is usually related to the surgeon's expertise. Some increase in thickness of the ear should be anticipated.

BLINDNESS:

Blindness is described as an inability to see. In dogs, assessing partial loss of sight is impossible. When a dog is placed in a familiar environment, it can move around with no trouble even though totally blind. Loss of sight can happen for many reasons. Some causes of blindness are hereditary. The blindness may be permanent or correctable with treatment.

Sensory impulses normally occur in the retina at the back of the eye then travel the optic nerve to register in the brain. However, if the clear cornea is covered or cloudy or if the lens is cloudy or out of position, sensory impulses are not perceived making the dog blind. If blindness is suspected, the dog should be thoroughly examined by a veterinary ophthalmologist since some cases can be corrected.

BLOOD IN THE EYE:

The presence of red blood cells in the anterior chamber between the lens and the cornea is termed *hyphema*. While the presence of blood in the eye is a debatable ocular emergency, a serious traumatic or systemic condition is indicated. Early veterinary attention should be received. Blood in the anterior chamber of the eye comes from the iris, its associated ciliary body, or the vascular layer under the retina. The causes of hyphema include trauma to the eye, *detached retina, bleeding disorders,* cancer, infections, and some of undetermined origin.

The cause usually dictates the treatment. If the blood is from an *anterior uveitis, atropine* and *steroids* are used. If anterior uveitis is not a problem, *pilocarpine* drops are used to increase the emptying of the fluid from the anterior chamber of the eye. Therefore, in the presence of an identifiable clotting disorder, clotting therapy should be instituted. After the hyphema has lessened, atropine and steroids can be used. The use of *vitamin K* is of questionable value. An important adjunct to treatment is very quiet, confined rest for 10 to 14 days. If hyphema recurs, a tumor somewhere in the eye should be suspected.

BLOODY NOSE:

A bloody nose *(epistaxis)* is the loss of blood from one or both nostrils. The history is important in determining the cause of the nasal hemorrhage. A traumatic blow to the muzzle can cause capillary hemorrhage. Violent sneezing may produce clots of blood. Certain systemic diseases and poisons have been known to cause epistaxis. Nasal cavity tumors which are more common in long-nosed dogs can cause nosebleeds from one or both sides. Persistent nasal hemorrhage with no traumatic history requires a thorough diagnostic work-up including radiographs of the nasal cavity, cultures, and serum lab tests. The treatment and prognosis depend on the cause. Early identification of any cause improves the chances for successful treatment.

BLUE EYE:

"Blue Eye" is the common name given to the presence of a hazy, gray-blue opacity which usually appears in only one eye. In a severely affected eye, the iris color is not visible. This phenomena is most frequently a reaction to *canine hepatitis virus* - either after an infection or a vaccination. The time between exposure and development of the ocular lesion is seven to ten days. This ocular reaction has not been found after vaccination with *adenovirus-2*. Canine hepatitis is *adenovirus-1*.

In actuality, the developing eye problem is an *anterior uveitis*. The blue color is due to the accumulation of fluid between the layers of the cornea. The eye tears excessively, is sensitive, and may also appear inflamed as the blue color develops.

Treatment is controversial. Some advocate no treatment while others recommend anterior uveitis therapy. Most cases will resolve satisfactorily within two weeks. However, a small percentage may sustain permanent blindness.

BULGING EYE:

The bulging eye is unilaterally swollen. In comparison to the other eye, the swollen eye appears larger, redder, and may appear to be looking in a different direction. Pain often accompanies a bulging eye early in its development.

Increased intraocular fluid pressure *(glaucoma)* increases the size of the eyeball causing a bulging eye. *Tonometry* and an ophthalmic examination will diagnose this condition. Early glaucoma treatment will save the sight in the affected eye.

Traumatic proptosis (popping out of the eyeball) causes the affected eye to appear larger than the normally placed eye. This is an optic emergency! Early replacement of the eye is essential for the sight to be saved.

A third cause of bulging eyes is a retrobulbar lesion, usually in the form of an abscess or a tumor. The lesion located behind the eye pushes the eye outward giving the eyeball an enlarged appearance. A *retrobulbar abscess* causes pain and reluctance to open the mouth. A tumor, however, is slow growing with no pain sensation.

The cause dictates the treatment for bulging eyes. A diagnostic work-up is necessary to determine the feasibility of treatment and the prognosis.

CANINE EYE REGISTRATION FOUNDATION:

Refer to *CERF*.

CATARACTS:

A cataract is a partial or total opacity of the lens and capsule within an eye occurring in one or both eyes. Cataracts are grouped by their cause, by the age at occurrence, and by the location within the lens. By age, congenital cataracts can be present at birth. Developmental cataracts are found in dogs between the ages of one and five years. Old dogs or any dog past five years of age can develop senile cataracts. *Nuclear sclerosis* is a normal phenomena of the aging process which changes the opacity of the lens protein. Even though the lenses appear cloudy, sight is not impaired with nuclear sclerosis. Cataracts can also form as the result of other disease processes or from traumatic injury to the lens or capsule. *Diabetes mellitus* and some infectious diseases can initiate the mechanisms that cause cataracts to form. In some breeds of dogs, cataract formation is present with other serious eye disorders (e.g. *retinal atrophy, retinal dysplasia).*

A variety of cataract medical treatments have been tried. No universal cure or treatment for cataracts, short of surgical removal of the lens, exists. Consider three factors when contemplating cataract surgery: 1) the ability of the owner to treat and control the cataract patient, 2) the age and general health of the dog, and 3) the possibility of the presence of concurrent blindness from another cause resulting in surgical failure to provide vision.

With dense cataracts, evaluating the retina behind the lens is impossible. If significant retinal degeneration is present, cataract surgery is not indicated. Cataract surgery is expensive. Only after discussing all of the pros and cons with you should an experienced ophthalmologist perform the surgery. Possible post-operative complications to cataract surgery include severe *anterior uveitis, secondary glaucoma,* adhesions of the iris to the lens capsule, and persistent cloudiness to the cornea from surgical trauma. Occasionally, *retinal detachments* may occur post-operatively. Consider all aspects before making the decision for cataract surgery.

CERF:

The Canine Eye Registration Foundation (CERF) was founded in 1974 to function as a registry for clear-eyed dogs of all breeds. The examination of eyes for CERF certification must be performed by a member of the *American College of Veterinary Ophthalmologists (ACVO)*. Within 15 minutes after dilating the eyes with drops, they are examined with a slit lamp for corneal and lens abnormalities. An *indirect ophthalmoscope* is then used to examine the retina and associated structures. The examined dog is classified into one of three groups: 1) clear of hereditary eye disease at the time of examination, 2) affected with hereditary eye disease, or 3) suspicious or cannot judge properly. If a suspicious rating is given, the dog should be re-examined in six months.

American and English Cockers and Afghan Hounds are examined at 24 months of age. All other breeds are checked after 12 months of age. A CERF certification is good for 12 months for an initial registration fee of $5.00. Recertification may then be obtained following a subsequent examination for a $3.00 fee. For more information about CERF, write to Dolly Trauner, Canine Eye Registration Foundation, Inc., P.O. Box 15095, Station A, San Francisco, CA 94115.

CHEMICAL KERATITIS:

Chemical keratitis is a true ocular emergency! A foreign substance has irritated the cornea causing it to become inflamed *(keratitis)*. Shampoo from bathing the dog is the most common cause of chemical keratitis. To guard against this problem, place a small amount of eye ointment, petroleum jelly, or mineral oil in each eye prior to a bath. More serious sequela result from strong acids or alkalis. Acids are not as severe a problem as alkalis because acids are neutralized on contact. Alkalis stimulate the migration of *neutrophilic blood cells* to the damaged area resulting in severe *corneal ulceration* with possible corneal penetration.

Immediately after exposure to a strong chemical, the eye should be irrigated with tap water for 30 minutes. The dog should then be transported directly to your veterinarian for follow-up treatment. While the prognosis for recovery from soap in the eye is excellent, it is guarded following alkali damage.

CHERRY EYE:

"Cherry eye" is characterized by the presence of a red mass at the inner lower edge of the upper and lower eyelid junction. Excessive tearing and conjunctival inflammation accompany this condition. A prolapse of the glandular structure located on the inside of the membrane nictitans (third eyelid) causes this problem. A hereditary weakness in the fibrous tissue keeps the gland from being hidden under the third eyelid.

In the past, the accepted form of treatment has been to surgically remove the gland. Recently, a connection between the development of *"dry eye" (keratoconjunctivitis sicca)* and the removal of the third eyelid gland was discovered. Dogs having *Schirmer tear* levels below 18 mm. should not have this form of surgery. A new surgical technique preserves the gland, replacing it in a cosmetically acceptable method. Before surgery, ask the veterinarian which technique will be performed to correct the gland prolapse. This procedure may either be done as a one day or overnight stay in the hospital. Prognosis is excellent for normal recovery.

CLOUDY EYE:

A cloudy eye, one which has a bluish or gray colored cornea, signifies an eye problem involving at least the cornea. If the entire cornea is involved, the iris or any of the internal eye structures can not be seen. Cloudy eyes are associated with a number of more complex eye problems such as *glaucoma, descemetocele, corneal laceration,* and *anterior uveitis.* The "blue eye" syndrome following exposure to *canine hepatitis virus* is another example of a cloudy eye.

The layers of the cornea take on fluid disrupting the normal cell continuity of the cornea. As the eye condition returns to normal, the corneal fluid level diminishes and the tissue clears. However, if edema (fluid) remains in the cornea, permanent blindness results.

CONJUNCTIVITIS:

Conjunctivitis is inflammation of the mucous membranes which attach to the cornea on the eyeball and to the membranes inside both eyelids including both surfaces of the third eyelid. Conjunctivitis is the most common eye problem in dogs.

A myriad of causes exist for conjunctivitis. Irritants such as dust and pollen can result in an irritant conjunctivitis. *Staph* and other bacteria are capable of creating an infectious conjunctivitis. *Canine distemper, adenovirus (canine hepatitis),* and other viral diseases can cause viral conjunctivitis.

The clinical signs vary. Some dogs show very little reaction while others exhibit a thick mucopurulent discharge from the eyes. Swelling of the affected mucous membranes is common. Little or no pain is felt with pure conjunctivitis. However, if a concurrent *corneal ulcer* is present, much pain will be exhibited.

The preferred treatment is the application of a wide spectrum antibacterial ointment three or four times daily for 7 to 10 days. Unless the case is complicated, it should be under control within that period. Complicated cases may require bacterial culture and antibiotic sensitivity tests because resistant *Staphylococcus* can be a therapeutic nightmare. The prognosis is generally good to excellent.

CONTACT LENSES:

The use of soft hydrophilic contact lenses can be helpful in cases of chronic *corneal ulcers*. All forms of medical and surgical therapy appear to be fruitless in such cases. Soft contact lenses provide protection for diseased corneal tissue. They do not correct vision problems. Vifilcon-A hydrophilic contact lenses can be obtained from American Optical Corporation, Framingham, MA 01701.

The major problem in the use of soft contact lenses in dogs is that the lenses are lost so require frequent replacement. However, in cases where the lens remained in place for 10 days, healing occurred in 92% of the dogs. The loss of the contact lens is generally attributed to either the movement of the third eyelid, a poor fit, or the presence of a bulging eye as seen in some short-nosed breeds.

CORNEAL DISEASES:

The cornea can be affected as a primary disease or secondarily to other conditions such as acute *corneal ulcer, corneal dystrophy* and *pannus*. Changes in the transparency of the cornea with pain manifested by squinting, excess tearing, and closed eyelids are the most consistent signs of corneal disease. Application of a topical anesthetic like *Ophthaine®* can eliminate pain related to the cornea helping to differentiate corneal pain from *glaucoma* and uveitis pain. Because of the loss of transparency of the cornea, a decrease in sight occurs in dogs. Total blindness, however, is not a result of corneal disease.

Keratitis is the inflammation of the cornea. Pannus is an unusual nonulcerous form of keratitis. Acute corneal ulcers *(ulcerative keratitis)* are discussed earlier in the chapter. Assorted organisms are the cause of infectious types of keratitis with the most common fungal types being *Aspergillus* and *Candida*, a yeast.

Several **congenital conditions** such as *microcornea* (smaller than normal cornea), *megalocornea*, (larger than normal cornea), and *corneal dermoids*, affect the cornea. A dermoid is the presence of a piece of tissue containing hair, an eyelash, or other epithelial elements on the normally clear cornea. The cornea can be partly occluded by a *persistent pupillary membrane* which adhered to the inner surface of the cornea and did not degenerate at birth.

Other corneal diseases include *corneal dystrophy* and *corneal degeneration*. Corneal degenerations are associated with an inflammatory process affecting only one eye. They are often part of a systemic disease process which must also be treated.

An accurate diagnosis is necessary for proper treatment of corneal disorders. Many can have a good prognosis with early and accurate therapy. Also refer to *CORNEAL DYSTROPHY, PANNUS,* and *ACUTE CORNEAL ULCER.*

CORNEAL DYSTROPHY:

By definition, corneal dystrophy is a deficiency in the growth and nutrition of the cornea. A number of dystrophies have been observed in purebred dogs and even some mixed breeds. Both eyes are equally affected with corneal dystrophy. The condition, which is not part of any systemic disease, is not inflammatory nor progressive in its development. Because corneal dystrophy is frequently seen in young puppies, there may be some hereditary basis.

An ophthalmologist with special lighting equipment should examine the eyes. The axis of the cornea will show some steamy opacities which interfere only slightly with vision. These opacities in the subepithelial portion of the cornea are not painful. No treatment is indicated since corneal dystrophy does not interfere with sight and in most cases, does not progress from its early appearance.

CORNEAL LACERATION:

A corneal laceration (tear) is an ocular emergency! If a traumatic injury to the eye is apparent, veterinary care must be found immediately. Initially, moist pressure bandages control hemorrhaging from a protruding, bleeding iris. The moist bandage also prevents self-trauma to the eye. Each corneal laceration must be evaluated independently. The faster competent surgical repair can be accomplished, the more satisfactory the results.

CORNEAL ULCER:

Refer to *ACUTE CORNEAL ULCER.*

CROPPING:

Refer to *EAR TRIMMING.*

DEAFNESS:

Deafness, which may be partial or complete, is the inability to hear. Since the normal hearing range for dogs is different than humans, evaluation of partial hearing loss is difficult. Deafness can be congenital (present at birth) or acquired. Congenital deafness may or may not be hereditary. Since deafness is not treatable, dogs deaf from birth present special problems in adapting to their environment. Maintaining a deaf dog and small children in the same household is difficult.

Acquired deafness may be due to either external or middle ear disease resulting in a nonfunctional ear drum (tympanic membrane). If the hearing loss is due to a traumatic *rupture of the ear drum,* hearing will return after the ear drum has repaired itself. However, if the ear drum is permanently damaged by infection or proliferative tissue, hearing ability may remain impaired.

Aging causes fusion of the small bones that carry sound to the inner ear resulting in acquired deafness. With senility (old age) comes a decrease in the sound carrying ability of three small bones that vibrate and transmit sound waves to the inner ear. This loss in the ability to perceive sound occurs gradually. It is both irreversible and untreatable in dogs.

DESCEMETOCELE:

A descemetocele is an eye emergency which requires immediate veterinary care! This *corneal ulcer* has eroded down to the level of the elastic Descemet's membrane. The pressure of the aqueous humor fluid in the eye causes the elastic membrane to protrude through the ulcer and bulge above the outer level of the corneal surface. A descemetocele is one layer away from having the eyeball rupture!

Vigorous aggressive medical treatment is necessary to reverse the ulcerative process present in a descemetocele. The dog must be hospitalized for the application of timely medication and the administration of any other care necessary to keep the eyeball from rupturing. If medical therapy fails to reverse the process, surgical intervention is necessary. Post-operatively, the eye is treated with *atropine* and antibiotics until healing is complete. With aggressive treatment and timely surgery, the prognosis is excellent for saving the sight in the eye.

DIRECT OPHTHALMOSCOPY:

The direct ophthalmoscope is the most common piece of eye examination equipment present in veterinary clinics. The cornea, iris, lens, vitreous, and retina can be examined with a hand held direct ophthalmoscope. This kind of ophthalmoscope has a moderate cost, is easy to use, gives great magnification of the retina, and allows one to determine the size of lesions found in the eye. However, the depth of the eye field seen is very small as is the area examined. Dilating the eyes of a dog is usually necessary to perform a thorough examination of all of the components of the eye.

DISTICHIASIS:

Distichiasis, a source of eye irritation and excessive tearing, is hereditary. An affected dog should not be used for breeding. Distichiasis is rarely found in the Doberman Pinscher.

If present for a long period of time, corneal damage and ulceration results. Pigment is produced to protect the irritated area of the cornea. Clinically, this condition is due to cilia (fine hairs) or eyelashes abnormally located along the eyelid edge. Normally, the hairs are directed outward away from the eye itself. In distichiasis, the hairs are directed toward the corneal surface.

Recommended treatment depends on the number of hairs causing the problem. If a small number are misdirected, electroepilation is the most efficient method of treatment. Repeat electroepilation may be necessary if the entire hair follicle is not destroyed the first time. While this method can cause scarring on the eyelid, the scarring is not serious if only a few hairs are treated. However, if a large number of hairs are involved, delicate surgery on the eyelid will give the best results. This surgery requires above average ophthalmologic surgery skills and is best handled by a specialist.

DRY EYE:

"Dry eye" is the common name for *keratoconjunctivitis sicca (KCS)*. The Doberman Pinscher has less chance of developing KCS than a number of other breeds. Dogs seven years and older of either sex are most commonly affected. Although the exact cause is unknown, KCS can be part of the following systemic disease complexes: *hypothyroidism, Cushing's disease, diabetes mellitus, demodectic mange, canine distemper, systemic lupus erythematosus,* and occasionally, *vitamin A deficiency*. In some cases, KCS will occur while dogs are receiving sulfa drugs *(dapsone, sulfadiazine, Azulfidine®*) or *atropine* eye drops. Dogs that have had their third eyelid glands removed have a greater chance of developing "dry eye."

"Dry eye" is commonly misdiagnosed as chronic recurring *corneal ulcers* with allergic or bacterial *conjunctivitis*. Early in the course of the condition, the white tissue around the eye (the conjunctiva) becomes inflamed. Corneal ulceration follows from lack of lubricating tears. Ulceration causes pain indicated by blinking and pawing at the face. In cases that become chronic, the cornea becomes thickened, pigmented, misshapen, and covered with stringy mucus.

The diagnosis is made by the *Schirmer tear test*. A normal Schirmer reading is between 15 mm. and 25 mm./minute. Any dog under 10 mm./minute has a positive for "dry eye" diagnosis. Most will be under 5 mm./minute.

Treatment lubricates the cornea and conjunctiva so that the eyelid movement friction doesn't damage the epithelial tissue surface. Among the medical means used to increase the lubrication effects, artificial tears are the best. They must be applied every two or three hours to be effective. The minimum application rate would be four times daily. Some artificial tear ointments can be used in conjunction with drops for overnight application when more frequent applications are not possible.

If any residual tear secreting gland is present, *pilocarpine* drops can be used orally to stimulate tear formation. Some dogs do not tolerate pilocarpine well and will vomit, salivate, and develop diarrhea. However, if pilocarpine is tolerated satisfactorily, it is an excellent alternative to frequent artificial tear administration. If all else fails, a surgical procedure may help selected individuals. The parotid salivary gland duct is transplanted from its normal opening in the cheek to the outer corner of the eye. This procedure requires above average surgical skill and could be expected to approach a 90% success rate. With any form of treatment, use of antibiotics is occasionally necessary to minimize infection. The overall prognosis ranges from fair to good.

EAR CULTURE:

The ear culture is important in the battle against chronic ear infections. Because the technique is not difficult, your veterinarian can routinely perform this procedure. If a culture is anticipated, the ear should be left "as is." No medication or ear cleaner should be used to make it look better for your veterinarian. In 24 to 48 hours, a culture can grow both yeast and bacteria for results. Once the organism causing the infection is identified, an *antibiotic sensitivity test* should be done.

EAR DISCHARGE:

The exudate (discharge) present in the ear of a Doberman Pinscher is important in determining the origin of an ear infection. In observing the quantity and kind of exudate, knowing what is normal is important. The normal ceruminous material is a yellow-brown color, shiny, and reasonably devoid of odor. Each dog has its own rate of cerumen (ear wax) accumulation. Until the interval for wax removal is determined, inspect the ears weekly.

The presence of abnormal ear wax is indicative of a pathological process. Your veterinarian should diagnose and treat this condition immediately. Black-brown, dry, gritty wax is characteristic of *ear mite infestation.* With a magnifying glass and good light, ear mites appear in the gritty wax as gray-white dots which move in the heat from the light. A yellow, moist, and foul smelling ear discharge indicates a purulent infection. These discharges are very ulcerative to the ears and can cause a great degree of pain.

EAR MITES:

Ear mites *(Otodectes cynotis)* can contribute to inflamed ear canals. This parasite burrows into the epidermal layer of the external ear canal resulting in inflammation and infection. A characteristic gritty dark wax is present in most cases. Ear mites are contagious to other dogs and cats and will also cause itchy red "bites" on people.

Treatment is necessary to prevent its spread and keep human lesions to a minimum. With a life cycle of three weeks, treatment for the affected ears must be at least that long to break the life cycle. Today, the most effective treatments are *Tresaderm®* drops twice daily for 10 days and once daily for 20 days or *Xenodine®* drops once weekly for five weeks. The prognosis for recovery is excellent if treatment is maintained long enough.

EAR TRIMMING:

Ear trimming (cropping) is done on the Doberman Pinscher to improve the cosmetic appearance. Some foreign countries do not allow ear cropping on any breeds. This surgical procedure is usually performed at six or seven weeks of age. A pleasing, proper ear trim is both an art and a science. Most satisfactory ear trims are customized to fit the characteristics of the head and body. Shorter, broader heads will look better with shorter ears. Long delicate heads require longer ears.

Because of several idiosyncrasies in the Doberman Pinscher, the following recommendations should be considered. Before subjecting the puppy to surgery, test it for *Von Willebrand's Disease.* Early vaccination against *parvovirus* is recommended since the Doberman is more susceptible to this disease.

The ear crop surgery requires *general anesthesia, sterile surgical technique,* and attention to hemostasis (blood clotting). The cut ears contain sutures which are removed in a week to minimize the formation of scar tissue. Various methods are used to support the ears as healing and growth take place over the next several months. Usually if the ears won't stand by the end of teething at six to seven months, they will never stand unaided. Generally, several veterinarians within an area will have a reputation for doing a great Doberman ear crop. Ask around and go to the best. Nothing is more disconcerting than looking at a beautiful dog with a poor ear crop!

ECTROPION:

Ectropion is the outward rolling or drooping of the eyelid usually present only in the lower lid. Sometimes this will be present in the middle of the lid when both ends of the lower lid are turned inward *(entropion).* Because the cornea and lower conjunctival tissue around the eye are exposed to more debris and dust, chronic irritation occurs.

Mildly irritated eyes are managed with cortisone-antibiotic ophthalmic ointments as needed. Dusty places should be avoided. Severely affected eyes require surgery. Some eyes require more than one surgical procedure because of the complexity of the involvement of the eyelids. While the prognosis following surgery is excellent, any dog with this problem should not be used for breeding purposes unless the ectropion was due to a traumatic injury to the eyelid.

ENTROPION:

Entropion is much more common in the Doberman Pinscher than *ectropion.* With entropion, all or part of the upper or lower eyelid turns inward. The cilia and eyelashes touch the cornea or, in extreme cases, the eyelids may touch the cornea. Irritation to the cornea elicits tearing, squinting, and the formation of *corneal ulcers.*

The presence of an entropion should be treated medically first. Some are due to the spastic contraction of eyelid muscles which cause the lid to turn inward. If the spasm can be eliminated with medication, the entropion will disappear. Other entropions disappear as puppy head's mature. However, a severe entropion can rapidly ulcerate an eye so must be watched closely. Surgery may be the only means of correcting a major entropion. The surgeon will determine which technique should be utilized after the extent of the problem is determined. The prognosis for normal sight is very good unless serious corneal scarring occurs. Many entropions are hereditary and breeding should be discouraged.

ENUCLEATION OF EYES:

Enucleation of the eye is the surgical removal of the entire globe of the eye. Reasons for eye enucleation include congenital sightless small eye, an infection within the eye that has not responded to medical treatment in which sight has been lost, conditions of non-responsive inflammatory changes with blindness, a tumor within the eye that cannot be removed, severe irreparable damage to the globe of the eye, and prolapse of the eye with permanent muscle, optic nerve, and blood vessel damage.

Several surgical techniques can be used at the discretion of the surgeon. Early post-operative complications include hemorrhage and infection. If the tear duct apparatus is not removed, a draining wound may develop several months after the surgery. Also, inadvertent damage to the zygomatic salivary gland may be apparent several months post-operatively. After the surgery, bloody serum drainage may be present for a few days but will resolve itself.

This surgery, which is performed for any of the mentioned reasons, is probably done more frequently than necessary. Owners must be aware that the surgery involves suturing the eyelids closed which results in an obvious indentation where the eyeball had been. Sometimes this is not cosmetically acceptable. Dog owners should be aware of the alternate solution, having a prosthetic eyeball placed in the globe for cosmetic reasons. A more complete discussion of the FALSE EYE (prosthesis) is found within the chapter.

EPISTAXIS:

Refer to BLOODY NOSE.

EVERSION OF THIRD EYELID:

The third eyelid (nictitating membrane) contains a cartilaginous form that can roll forward or backward causing irritation to the eye structures. A cosmetically unacceptable appearance results. Eversion can occur in one or both eyes. Swelling appears in the inner corner of the eye accompanied by excessive tearing or a mucoid discharge from the irritation.

The treatment of choice is surgical removal of the curled cartilage without removing the third eyelid. Aftercare is instillation of antibiotic ointment during the week of healing. This defect, seen in young dogs, is genetically transmitted as a simple recessive gene. Affected dogs should not be used for breeding purposes.

EYE COLOR:

Eye color is derived from the pigmentary cells present in the iris surrounding the black pupil opening. Eye color is hereditary and related to the color of the coat. The eye color in blue and isabella (fawn) colored Doberman Pinschers is lighter than the eye colors found in blacks or reds. A yellow iris color has a tendency to occur with a blue coat. Yellow eye color is one step away from blue or walleye color. Blue eyes are one step removed from pink eyes which occur in true albinos. No visual deficit is related to any of the various iris colors. However, strong sunlight is avoided when albinism is present. *Heterochromia* is the presence of two or more colors either in the same iris or in the same dog. In the Doberman Pinscher, this is undesirable and selection should be away from this condition. Occasionally, pigment spots or iris freckles are seen. They cause no problem and need no treatment but may be cosmetically objectionable.

EYE EMERGENCIES:

A number of conditions are considered to be true eye emergencies. They are listed here but discussed individually. All of these situations require the immediate treatment by a competent veterinarian. DO NOT "LET THEM GO OVERNIGHT OR THROUGH THE WEEKEND!" If your veterinarian is not available, find someone else to provide the needed help.

Acute Anterior Uveitis	Chemical Keratitis
Acute Corneal Ulcer	Corneal Laceration
Acute Blindness	Descemetocele
Anterior Lens Luxation	Eye Foreign Body
Blood in Eye	Glaucoma
Bulging Eye	Optic Neuritis
	Traumatic Proptosis

EYE PAIN, SIGNS OF:

Since our dogs are unable to tell us if and where it hurts, we must be aware of clinical signs which indicate eye pain. Behavioral changes such as agitation or even snapping may be observed if pain is intense. The apparent signs in acute eye pain are excessive tearing, the presence of increased redness, and increased blinking or closing of the eye. Many painful eyes will appear sunken in the eye orbit and may also be partially covered by the third eyelid.

EYE TESTS:

To determine the cause of eye abnormalities, various eye tests are necessary. Each test is discussed individually within the chapter. Since specialists have other types of equipment and tests available, this list includes tests available in most well-equipped veterinary clinics.

Applanation - tonometry test	Indirect ophthalmoscopy
Direct ophthalmoscopy	Rose Bengal test
Fluorescein dye test	Schirmer tear test
Gonioscopy test	Schiotz tonometry

EYE TUMORS:

Eye tumors can be grouped by the affected tissues. Your veterinarian must determine if the tumor is a primary eye tumor or one that has spread to the eye from somewhere else.

Tumors of the eyelids have a very low malignancy potential. Most involve the various glandular structures of the eyelids causing irritation to the eye. The *sebaceous gland adenoma* is the most common tumor. Depending on the extent of the tumor, eyelid tumors can be treated by excision, cryosurgery, or observation. Tumors of the third eyelid are relatively uncommon but must be differentiated from "cherry eye."

Tumors of the tissues around the orbit of the eye present special problems. Most of these tumors are malignant. Their location makes them very difficult to remove surgically. The prognosis is guarded, at best. Although tumors occurring within the eye as a primary neoplasm are rather rare, when they do occur, they cause a number of signs of ocular disease. In depth examination of an eye suspected of having a tumor requires a specialist with sophisticated diagnostic aids. Clinical signs of primary and secondary tumors of the eye are similar making it necessary to perform a complete work-up for the entire body to determine the chances of metastasis (spreading). A chest radiograph should be included. The *uveal melanoma* which grows as a black mass from the iris is one of the more common intraocular tumors in dogs. This neoplasm, more common in young dogs, is a rather benign type of tumor. A *melanoma* found in an older dog's eyes is more invasive causing deterioration of multiple tissues within the eye.

EYELASH ABNORMALITIES:

In dogs, most eyelash abnormalities are congenital and possibly hereditary in nature. *Distichiasis* and *trichiasis* are two types of eyelash abnormalities which are discussed within the chapter under their own heading. *Ectopic cilia,* the least important kind of abnormality, are fine hairs that are directed through the eyelid toward the surface of the cornea. Their abnormal location causes a great degree of irritation with signs of epiphora (excess *tearing*), blinking, and redness. Ectopic cilia can be diagnosed by a veterinarian through magnification with strong light. Surgical removal of the tissue containing the cilia is the most effective treatment. One week of antibiotic-steroid ointment follows.

EYELID ABNORMALITIES:

The two eyelid abnormalities which occur in the dog are *ectropion* and *entropion.* Both conditions may be hereditary. Breeding affected dogs is not advised.

FALSE EYES:

False (prosthetic) eyes are more widely accepted than *enucleation* of the eye. In a sightless eye in which the disease process is not progressive like a tumor or infection, the installation of a false eye should be considered. The results are more cosmetically acceptable. The degree of surgical skill needed for this procedure is not much greater than that needed to remove the globe of the eye completely. However, special instrumentation and implants are required. These inert silicon implants are well tolerated by the dog after the initial surgical recovery period. Post-operatively, some swelling and irritation may exist for two to three days. Warm compresses, analgesics, and possibly topical antibiotics can relieve this condition. Within two weeks of the surgery, the eye has usually healed giving pleasing results to both patient and owner.

Implants are available from Jardon Plastics Research Corporation, Southfield, MI 48076. The special instrumentation can be obtained from Storz Instruments, St. Louis, MO.

FLUORESCEIN DYE TEST:

Fluorescein dye has several uses in eye-related conditions. Instillation into both eyes determines patency of the lacrimal (tear) ducts. The tear ducts drain from the inner corner of each eye through a small tube under the skin which empties at the opening in the nose. If the ducts are open, dye placed in the eye should be evident at the end of the nose within one to five minutes.

The primary usage of fluorescein dye is in the detection of corneal ulcers. Normal corneal epithelium (covering) is resistant to the yellow-orange stain. However, when the epithelial lining is ulcerated, the stain enters the corneal tissue and colors it green indicating *corneal ulceration.*

FOREIGN BODY - EAR, EYE, NOSE:

A foreign body is the abnormal presence of a material in its current location. The body reacts vigorously trying to wall off or remove anything that does not belong. This inflammatory response is marked by swelling, redness, fever, and the presence of *white blood cells.*

The presence of a foreign body in the ear can cause acute violent head shaking. The head is generally tilted to one side. The affected ear canal is inflamed and very sensitive. Foreign bodies take the form of dirt, plant material, kid's toys, or even medication that has dried in the ear canal. In areas like California, the plant awn of the foxtail is a major source of ear foreign bodies. Usually deep *sedation* or *anesthesia* is required to examine and treat one of these painful ears. The prognosis for recovery is excellent providing the problem is not chronic.

The presence of a foreign body in the eye is an emergency requiring immediate veterinary attention. These are classified as penetrating or non-penetrating depending on their location in the eye tissue. A foreign body that penetrates the cornea will cause intense pain. The presence of pain makes anesthesia necessary in order to perform a thorough examination of the eye. Each foreign body wound in the eye must be evaluated on its own merit to determine if removal is feasible, needed, and in the best interest of the patient. Antibiotics are used to prevent infection and surgery can be anticipated. The prognosis is guarded to good depending on the kind of foreign body, the location of the lesion, and the damage done. The presence of a foreign body in the nasal cavity is manifested by the existence of a one-sided nasal discharge. The discharge contains pus and some blood. An affected dog paws at his nose and exhibits signs of discomfort in other ways. Anesthesia is necessary to examine and diagnose this condition. Occasionally, *bacterial cultures and antibiotic sensitivity tests* are needed to diagnose concurrent infections. The use of radiographs may be necessary to differentiate foreign bodies from tumors or *fungal infections* of the nasal cavity. Since removal may be difficult or may require a major surgical procedure, the prognosis is fair to good for recovery.

FOREIGN SUBSTANCE IN EYE:

This category differentiates between foreign bodies that have been traumatically introduced into the eye and the presence of foreign substances that are not normal in a healthy eye. Some of the foreign substances which occur within the eye are blood, pus, tumors, *persistent pupillary membrane,* hyaloid remnants, asteroid hyalosis, and the *Thelazia worm.* Some of these require treatment and removal. Others do not need any attention because vision is not appreciably affected.

GLAND OF THIRD EYELID HYPERTROPHY:

Refer to *"CHERRY EYE".*

GLAUCOMA:

Glaucoma is a disease of the orbit of the eye in which the intraocular (within) pressure has greatly increased causing many structures within the eye to degenerate. Hereditary glaucoma has not currently been reported in the Doberman Pinscher. Secondary glaucoma can affect any dog.

Among the several methods for the classification of glaucoma, the most practical is based on the stage of the disease. The four levels that are considered are: Class I - enlarged, blind eye, Class II - normal-sized eye, blind, Class III - recent attack of congestive glaucoma, and Class IV - very early glaucoma.

The only treatment for Class I is to eliminate the pain of increased pressure. Since the eye is blind, implanting a *prosthesis,* using cyclocryosurgery to lower the pressure, or *enucleation of the eye* are the only available choices. Class II treatment options include intense medical therapy, cyclocryosurgery, and the implant of a prosthesis. The blindness is probably permanent even in Class II.

In both Class III and IV, intense medical therapy has a chance to save the vision. Long term control with medications is unlikely in the dog. The surgical procedures that should be considered are designed to either decrease intraocular fluid production or to increase the outflow of the intraocular fluid. In any case, these surgical procedures coupled with appropriate medical therapy may be successful in controlling the intraocular pressure in one or both eyes. Be aware that early, aggressive treatment is essential to save an eye with increased intraocular pressure.

Acute glaucoma is considered an ocular emergency which requires immediate veterinary attention! The clinical signs of acute glaucoma include a hazy bluish cornea, a reddened eye, a pupil which may or may not be responsive to light, a slightly enlarged eye, and eye pain.

GONIOSCOPY:

Gonioscopy is an eye test used to measure the angle of filtration for the removal of fluid from within the eye. This test requires specialized equipment, magnification, and a light source. The special lens also allows one to see if the iris is adhering to the eye lens. A veterinary ophthalmologist will generally perform this test.

HEMERALOPIA:

The hereditary condition of hemeralopia (day blindness) is passed on by a simple autosomal recessive gene. At three or four months of age, this condition becomes apparent. Night vision remains normal. No ophthalmologic lesions are visible on examination. To date, day blindness has only been found in Alaskan Malamutes and miniature poodles.

HYPHEMA:

Refer to *BLOOD IN EYE.*

HYPOPYON:

Hypopyon is an accumulation of pus in the anterior chamber of the eye, the area between the lens and the cornea. This is fairly uncommon and is usually a sequelae to very severe corneal disease. Aggressive antibiotic therapy and surgical drainage occasionally are required to resolve the problem.

INDIRECT OPHTHALMOSCOPY:

Because a larger area of the eye is visible, an indirect ophthalmoscope gives the ophthalmologist a great deal of information in a short period of time. The stronger light used in this ocular test is also able to penetrate a diseased cornea. The drawbacks encountered in this type of eye examination are that the room must be dark, the pupils must be dilated, the image is magnified one-third of the amount of the direct ophthalmoscopy image, and all of the observed images are upside down.

This instrumentation is available in either monocular or binocular models. The technique is not easy to learn but once learned, indirect ophthalmoscopy provides valuable information quickly. This equipment is usually found in a referral practice or in a veterinary clinic with a special interest in eyes.

INNER EAR INFECTION:

The inner ear is part of the *vestibular system.* The brain stem is connected to the vestibular function by the inner ear. Infections involving the inner ear must be treated aggressively. Clinical signs of an inner ear infection include *head tilt, circling,* loss of balance, fever, and sometimes other neurological dysfunctions.

The diagnosis is made with radiographs which may show lesions in the middle ear if the problem is an extension from that region. With the aid of an otoscope, blood can sometimes be observed through a *broken ear drum.* Inner ear infections are treated with systemic antibiotics for extended periods. If the middle ear is seriously involved, surgical drainage is required on occasion. If caught early, the prognosis is fair.

IRIS ATROPHY:

The most common sign of iris atrophy is an irregular shape to the pupil of the eye. Closer inspection shows that fragments of the iris are present. Iris atrophy occurs in old dogs as a senile aging change. No treatment is necessary because sight is not affected.

KCS:

Refer to *DRY EYE.*

KERATITIS, CHEMICAL:

Refer to *CHEMICAL KERATITIS.*

KERATOCONJUNCTIVITIS SICCA (KCS):

Refer to *DRY EYE.*

MIDDLE EAR INFECTION:

A middle ear infection originates from either a broken ear drum or via the blood stream. Many times the infection settles in the bony bullae just inside the ear drum. Systemic antibiotics are used for two weeks. If control is not achieved, the dog is placed under anesthesia and the middle ear is gently flushed until the fluid is clear. Generally, one flushing session is sufficient. However, in rare instances, an additional flushing session is needed if the ear has not healed. If the bony bullae are infected, surgical drainage is possible. The prognosis for recovery is fair to good.

NASAL DISCHARGE:

The presence of a nasal discharge can either mean that any of a number of disease processes are underway or that the tear ducts are open and draining properly. Characterizing the kind of discharge present is important. Observe to determine if the discharge is serous (clear and watery), mucus, bloody, or a combination. Is the discharge from one or both nostrils? Attempt also to determine the amount of the drainage present.

Following is a list of many of the causes for different kinds of nasal discharges. Nasal discharges must be diagnosed as accurately as possible since the prognosis and treatment possibilities are so variable.

SEROUS DISCHARGE (Clear)
Viral infection
Normal tear drainage
Early tumor (in old dogs)
Extension of dental disease to nasal sinus
Nasal mites, Pneumonyssus
Nasal worm, Linguatula

MUCOPURULENT DISCHARGE	BLOODY NOSE
Chronic nasal infection	Clotting defect
Cryptococcus infection	Warfarin poisoning
Aspergillus infection	Tumor
Mature tumor	Nasal worm
Foreign body	Aspergillus infection
Trauma to sinuses	
Foreign body	

NASAL SWELLING:

Nasal swelling can occur in conjunction with nasal discharge, sneezing, pawing at the face, and with systemic signs like fever and depression. The cause should be determined as accurately as possible. *Radiographs, fungal cultures, bacterial cultures, serology tests,* and other blood tests are often necessary to establish the exact cause of nasal swelling. The location of the swelling on the nose also helps to focus on the cause. For instance, a swelling located just below the eye in the presence of a broken upper fourth premolar tooth is good evidence of a bacterial sinusitis. This case should respond to tooth extraction and antibiotic therapy.

Early diagnosis is important if treatment is to be successful. The prognosis in nasal swelling is related to cause and length of time the swelling has been present.

NOSE BLEED:

Refer to *BLOODY NOSE.*

NOSE DEPIGMENTATION:

The causes of nasal depigmentation are generally idiopathic (unknown). In Chapter 11, *PROGRESSIVE HYPOPIGMENTATION*, a problem specific to the Doberman Pinscher, will be discussed in detail. Progressive hypopigmentation occurs on the nose "leather" and lips after having developed normal pigmentation as a young puppy.

Some plastic food bowls cause depigmentation of the lips and nose. *"Snow nose"* is the fading of the pigment in the winter. The lack of sunlight and cold temperatures may contribute to this fading of nasal pigmentation. Another syndrome that causes nasal hypopigmentation is similar to *Vogt-Koyanagi-Harada syndrome*. Additional information on the V-K-H syndrome is found in Chapter 11 on the skin. Other proposed causes of nasal depigmentation are immune mediated diseases like *discoid lupus erythematosus*, trauma to the nose "leather," and nutritional mineral deficiencies.

OPTIC NEURITIS:

Optic neuritis is the inflammation of the optic nerve. If inflammation is located where the nerve enters the retina, it can be seen on eye examination. Otherwise, the eye exam shows nothing but a dilated blind eye. While it can occur in just one eye, normally both eyes are affected.

Optic neuritis has a number of both known and unknown causes. Brain tumors, *systemic fungi, canine distemper virus,* toxic chemicals, trauma to the eye, and reticulosis are among the known causes. Determining the cause is important. Without infection, the treatment of choice is *cortisone* which prevents demyelination of the optic nerve. If cortisone therapy is effective, improvement is seen within one week. If no sight has been restored in 14 days, further therapy is futile.

Early treatment is important to prevent permanent damage to the optic nerve. However, relapses can occur when treatment is discontinued. The prognosis for return of sight is guarded to fair.

OTODECTES CYNOTIS:

Refer to *EAR MITES.*

PANNUS:

Pannus is a severe *immune-mediated* degenerative condition of the cornea. The upper outer edge of the cornea is first affected. If untreated, the entire eye, third eyelid, and cornea become covered with pigmented, fibrous tissue. The only effective treatment is topical and/or systemic *cortisone* drugs. This is control, not cure. Surgery is occasionally recommended to remove the thickened pigmented tissue covering the cornea. However, surgery is probably not necessary if compliance with steroids is good. Most common in German Shepherds, the condition does occur in other breeds.

PERSISTENT HYPERPLASTIC PRIMARY VITREOUS (PHPV):

In the Doberman Pinscher, persistent hyperplastic primary vitreous (PHPV) is one part of a dysplastic disease process of the lens and posterior lens capsule of the eye. *Persistent hyperplastic tunica vasculosa lentis (PHTVL)* is also an integral part of this syndrome. The condition is referred to as *PHTVL/PHPV.*

PHTVL/PHPV is an ocular defect in the Doberman Pinscher, inherited through an incomplete dominant gene. To date, almost all cases in Dobes have been restricted to the Netherlands. Both eyes are usually affected. In most cases, it becomes progressively more severe. PHTVL/PHPV begins during the 25th to 35th day of fetal development, occurring equally in both sexes. A defect in the formation of the covering of the lens in the eye is followed by a failure in the regression of fetal eye lens blood vessels.

The severity is graded from 1 to 6. Grade 1 is very slight and consists of a slight posterior lens capsule cataract with small pigmented dots in the same region. At the other end of the scale, grade 6 consists of a combination of findings present in lower grades including severe degeneration of the lens, the presence of a great deal of pigment on the lens, and the presence of fetal vascular structures around the lens. Dobes having grade 1 PHTVL/PHPV are able to see well. Those affected with grades 3 to 6 have increasingly poor vision sometimes manifested by increased aggressiveness. As vision decreases, fear of being out of control causes increased reactions to stimuli.

Generally specialized ophthalmic examination equipment is required to assess the degree of involvement. The clinical signs are only apparent to the naked eye when the eyes are severely affected. The pupil of the eye looks white and the eye itself may be smaller than normal. In some Dobes, the presence of a *cataract* keeps the ophthalmologist from seeing the pigmented dots on the posterior lens capsule (covering). In most dogs, the degree of blindness is progressive. Only those dogs with Grade 1 and very slight cataract involvement may not progress with age.

The white pupil associated with PHTVL/PHPV must be distinguished from intraocular cancers, *congenital cataracts, retinal dysplasia,* and *retinal detachment.* If treatment is attempted, the lens must be removed. In cases where the lens was removed, other problems related to the lens removal have appeared several months later.

Since PHTVL/PHPV is a hereditary eye defect in the Doberman Pinscher, affected stock should not be used for breeding. Carriers with no visible defects do occur and should also be eliminated from breeding programs. All possibly affected Dobes should be examined by a competent veterinary ophthalmologist any time after four weeks of age.

PERSISTENT PUPILLARY MEMBRANE:

Before birth, the pupil of the fetal eyes are covered with a thin membrane. Just prior to birth, this membranous tissue and associated blood vessels are absorbed. Within ten days after birth, the eyes can react to light and movement. Occasionally, part of the pupillary membrane is not absorbed creating a "cobweb" appearance when a light is shined into the eye. This persistent pupillary membrane does not interfere with vision. The condition may be hereditary in development. No treatment is necessary.

PHOTOPHOBIA:

Photophobia, an abnormal intolerance of light, is a sign present in some systemic diseases like canine distemper. Signaling ocular disease, the signs include blinking and attempting to shield the eyes from bright light.

PHTVL/PHPV:

Refer to *PERSISTENT HYPERPLASTIC PRIMARY VITREOUS.*

PROSTHETIC EYE:

Refer to *FALSE EYE.*

RED EYE:

Redness in one or both eyes is a clinical sign of ocular disease. The location of the "redness" is important in isolating the affected parts of the eye. The eyes will look red if the normal blood vessels are unusually prominent, if the blood vessels on the normally white sclera are congested, if new blood vessels are growing out on the cornea, and if solid red masses are on or around the eye. In a healthy situation, a prominent blood vessel lies on the top of the white of the eye, appearing to approach the cornea. This large blood vessel is normal!

Causes for "red eye" include *anterior uveitis, acute glaucoma, ulcerative keratitis, dry eye,* hemorrhage around the eye, and *retrobulbar abscess* or tumor. Because some of these conditions are considered emergencies, seek veterinary care immediately when you see a "red eye" to determine its urgency.

Some of the tests used to ascertain the cause of the "red eye" are the *Schirmer Tear Test, fluorescein dye test, tonometry,* and *direct or indirect ophthalmoscopy.* The prognosis depends on the cause and available treatment. Having a "red eye" diagnosed early improves the chance of resolving the problem satisfactorily.

RETINAL ATROPHY:

Retinal atrophy is a gradual deterioration of the retina's ability to carry images to the optic nerve and the brain. While a large number of breeds are affected by retinal atrophy, the Doberman Pinscher appears to be free from the condition. The hereditary aspects are of great concern to breeders because it may not show up in some breeds until five or six years of age, long after they have sired or borne puppies.

Two types of retinal atrophy are diagnosed. *Progressive retinal atrophy (PRA)* is characterized by progressive night blindness and increased reflectivity of the retina. Both eyes are involved resulting in blindness. No treatment is currently available. *Central retinal atrophy (CRA)* occurs in a number of breeds as a hereditary disease. Day vision is the first sight affected, followed by the inability to see stationary objects. Increased pigmentation in the retina is evident, followed late in the disease by retinal hyper-reflectivity. Blindness is the end result. No treatment exists.

RETINAL DETACHMENT:

Causes for retinal detachment are grouped into three categories. The first group includes detachments due to pushing the retina away from the reflective part of the eye. This type of detachment generally is caused by infections, parasitic worms, and tumors. The second group of detachments occurs when the retina is pulled forward away from its attachments. A blood clot within the eye is the principle cause of this type. As the clot shrinks, the retina is pulled away from the wall of the eyeball. The third group of detachments occurs when the semi-solid mass in the center of the eyeball (the vitreous body) is lost. Without support of the vitreous material, the retina can detach from the eyeball wall. This can occur after intraocular surgery or from a penetrating injury.

Small retinal detachments are not noticed because the eye is not yet blind. Only massive detachments that cause sudden blindness are apparent to owners. A detached retina can be observed with the use of a pen-light. A veil-like structure appears behind the lens. In many cases, only one eye is involved. A comparison may alert one to an abnormality. Some detached retinas can be treated effectively with *steroids* and antibiotic therapy for a period of 30 days. The prognosis is guarded to fair depending on the origin of the retinal detachment. Lasers are used in humans to reattach some detached retinas.

RETINAL DYSPLASIA:

When puppies are three to five weeks of age, the congenital condition of retinal dysplasia becomes evident. In this condition, the eyes are slightly smaller than normal. The retina is detached making the puppy totally blind. No treatment is available. Retinal dysplasia is felt to be hereditary.

RETROBULBAR ABSCESS AND TUMOR:

Retrobulbar abscesses and tumors clinically appear very similar. Because the space behind the globe of the eye becomes occupied, it displaces the eye causing redness, third eyelid protrusion, and bulging. In the majority of cases, only one eye is involved. The cause of this eyeball protrusion may be an abscess (cellulitis) behind the eye, a space occupying tumor, or the presence of a foreign body that has penetrated the roof of the mouth near the back teeth.

A *general anesthetic* is usually necessary in order to open the mouth enough to inspect the area behind the molar teeth for a foreign body or abscess. While abscesses develop quickly and are painful, tumors develop more slowly and are not painful. The use of *blood counts* and skull radiographs may be necessary as aids in the diagnosis of the cause. Fine needle aspirations will help with tumor prognosis.

Abscesses and foreign body removal are generally treated through the mouth. They respond quickly to drainage, removal, and antibiotic therapy resulting in a good prognosis. Tumor treatment prognosis is guarded depending on the type of neoplasia (tumor) present.

ROSE BENGAL TEST:

The rose bengal test is a red stain instilled in the eye to color diseased and dying cells on the cornea and conjunctiva. The test is well-suited for use in the diagnosis of *"dry eye" (KCS)*. Because rose bengal dye 1% is irritating to the eye, the stain is better tolerated if a drop of *topical anesthesia* is placed in the eye before beginning the dye test. Excess dye should be removed with a saline or artificial tear wash.

ROUTINE EAR CLEANING:

Ear wax is normally produced in varying amounts in all dogs. Breeds and individuals will differ in the amount of wax that forms in the external ear canal. Until you learn how often ear wax needs to be removed from your own Doberman, inspect the ears weekly. A few dogs will accumulate a significant amount of wax on a weekly basis. Most Dobes will require wax removal at monthly or semi-annual intervals. Normal wax is a yellow-brown glistening material located in the external ear canal. If the wax in the ear canals is present with no redness and no offensive odor, the ears can be safely cleaned without veterinary supervision.

Rubbing alcohol and cotton balls are needed to clean normal Doberman Pinscher ears. Do not use baby oil, peroxide, or mineral oil! Do not place cotton-tipped applicators in the ear canal!

The cleaning procedure is quick and simple. Saturate a cotton ball with rubbing alcohol, squeezing it as it is placed in the ear canal. With your other hand, massage the base of the ear to work the alcohol into all "nooks and crannies" of the external ear canal. Using clean dry cotton balls, remove the alcohol and the loosened wax from the ear canal. The procedure is repeated until the cotton ball comes out clean with no yellow-brown wax on it. Repeat the procedure in the other ear. If you fail to remove all of the alcohol, it will evaporate causing no further problem.

NOTE: DO NOT use alcohol in an inflamed ear! Seek veterinary help in treating all ear infections!

RUPTURED EAR DRUM:

A ruptured ear drum (tympanic membrane) will not cause permanent deafness. Ruptured ear drums can be caused from the introduction of foreign objects (cotton applicators, fox tails) into the horizontal external ear canal. *Middle ear infections* that create pressure on the tympanic membrane causing it to break and over zealous flushing of the ear canal are also reasons that ruptured ear drums occur. If infection is not present, the ear drum can heal in seven to ten days. Scar tissue does form. If hearing was diminished, it will return. If infection is present in the middle ear, antibiotic medication and flushes are necessary.

SCHIOTZ TONOMETRY:

The Schiotz tonometer is the most common indirect tonometric method for determining intraocular pressure. This instrument is used to diagnose *glaucoma*. A small, weighted plunger is placed on the cornea measuring the degree of indentation on a numerical scale. The normal values for the dog are lower than 25 mm. Hg. The instrument is designed for the human eye so a built-in error exists when used on dogs. Calibrations for compensating for this error are available in the 1976 Proceedings of the *American College of Veterinary Ophthalmologists*, pages 47-73.

SCHIRMER TEAR TEST:

The amount of tear formation from the dog's eye can be measured by the Schirmer tear test. Both eyes are tested individually without placing any drops or anesthesia in the eyes topically. A piece of filter paper is placed in the lower eyelid for one minute. The amount of tear formation found on the paper is measured in millimeters. The normal tear flow for a dog is at least 10 to 15 mm. in one minute. Any reading under 10 mm. is very suspicious of "dry eye" (KCS).

SNEEZING:

Sneezing is a sign of acute or chronic nasal passage irritation. As a reflex act, it occurs from irritation of the fine hairs (cilia) that line the nose. Since this clinical sign may indicate a more serious problem, a diagnostic work-up is needed to determine the cause. Allergies, the presence of a *foreign body,* an infectious disease, parasites, or an injury to the nasal passages can all cause sneezing.

SWELLING OF EAR CANAL:

In ears that have been infected or inflamed for a long time, the tissue lining the external ear canal will swell. This tissue swelling may be so extensive that the ear canal cannot be seen by normal methods. Since the ear canal is occluded, medicating the diseased canal is very difficult. This hyperplastic tissue can be treated by two methods. The medical use of *cortisone* and *dimethyl sulfoxide* in a topical mixture will shrink the swollen ear canals over a period of time. A surgical procedure removing the lateral (outer wall) of the ear canal allows deeper involved tissues to be medicated with appropriate antibiotics. Either procedure is effective and can be part of any ongoing treatment for chronic ear problems.

SWOLLEN EYES:

Swollen eyes are actually swollen eyelids. The eyes are very puffy with the tissue around the eye appearing red and swollen. The eye itself may be difficult to see. Swollen eyelids should be seen by your veterinarian to determine what treatment should be initiated.

The cause of swollen eyelids varies. In newborn puppies, a serious infection called *ophthalmia neonatorum* occurs before the eyelids have opened. If this condition is diagnosed, the eyelids must be quickly opened and wide spectrum antibiotic ophthalmic ointment instilled frequently. Trauma can cause eyelids to swell. Cold packs minimize any damage in these cases. *Insect bites* and some *food allergies* can cause *angioneurotic edema* (fluid accumulation in the eyelids). The use of *cortisone* parenterally will control this problem. The prognosis with treatment is good.

TEAR DUCT BLOCKAGE:

Tear duct blockage occurs either from congenital causes or from infection later in life. An absence of a lower opening in the tear duct can cause tear duct blockage. Also, a malalignment of the lower opening so that drainage does not naturally occur presents similar problems. Because the Doberman Pinscher is a tight-eyed breed, this latter type is more common. Tears overflow and stain the side of the face with both congenital causes.

The most common acquired type of blockage is due to infection in the tear duct canal causing accumulation of debris, ductal swelling, and canal occlusion. After the cause is determined, the veterinarian can use medical or surgical procedures to correct the problem. If the blockage recurs, a Silastic tube may be inserted in the tear duct for three or four weeks while antibiotic drops are administered.

TEARING:

Epiphora, an excessive amount of tearing, is evidenced by moisture and debris extending from the eye down the side of the face. In light haired dogs, the fur is stained with a reddish discoloration from the excess moisture. A specific cause of epiphora should be determined. Some of the conditions that cause excessive tearing are pain within the eye like *glaucoma,* pain from irritation or ulceration of the cornea, inflammation of the tear gland, defects in the lacrimal duct system, an abnormal number or placement of eyelashes or cilia, and turned in eyelids (entropion). A complete eye examination with ancillary tests may be needed to ascertain the cause of epiphora. The prognosis for recovery is excellent if a cause can be found.

TRAUMATIC PROPTOSIS:

Traumatic proptosis is an ocular emergency! In this condition, the eyeball protrudes or hangs outside of the eyelids. In dogs with normally bulging eyes, this is common after a fight or a car accident. The problem is very rare in the Doberman Pinscher because of the relatively deep set almond-shaped eye. It is a genuine emergency! Immediately, place a cold compress over the exposed eye and call for veterinary service!

The veterinarian will attempt to replace the eyeball in its socket. This procedure may require *general anesthesia*. Before any anesthesia is given, he will determine whether the cornea is ulcerated and whether the pupil responds to light. Having a constricted pupil is a better sign than one that is widely dilated or normal in size but unresponsive.

The healing from traumatic proptosis can take four to six weeks. During that period, several surgical procedures may be necessary. If the eyeball is hanging or has collapsed, *enucleation* is recommended. The prognosis depends on the degree of damage and the length of time before veterinary care is obtained. At best, it is guarded.

TRICHIASIS:

Trichiasis is an eyelash abnormality in which the hairs arise from normal follicles coming in contact with either the cornea or the conjunctiva (white part of the eyeball). These hairs act as an irritant causing the dog to blink and tear excessively. This congenital condition is usually a hereditary defect which is secondary to another underlying cause such as *entropion* or a *dermoid growth*.

Temporary relief can be obtained by protecting the eye with an eye ointment. The only permanent cure is to remove the cause of the irritant usually through surgery. The prognosis with treatment is good. However, the breeding of affected individuals should be discouraged.

ULCERATIVE KERATITIS:

Refer to *ACUTE CORNEAL ULCER.*

YEAST INFECTION IN EAR:

A great deal of controversy exists as to the role that yeasts play in otitis externa (external ear canal infections). The two yeasts found in infections of the ear canal are *Candida* and *Malassezia (Pityrosporum)*. What complicates the situation is the presence of Malassezia or Pityrosporum in about 40% of the normal ears. Some investigators feel that dogs that frequently get water in the ear canals are more prone to yeast infections. If severe overgrowth of yeast occurs in a diseased ear canal, the veterinarian should be suspicious of an *immune deficiency* or a possible *diabetes* complication.

A culture of stubborn ear infections is absolutely necessary since most antibiotics are not effective against yeasts. From the results, other forms of medication can be prescribed to bring the otitis under control. With proper therapy, the prognosis is fair to good if no complicating immune deficiencies exist.

Chapter 11

SKIN AND RELATED STRUCTURES

Skin, Hair, Nails, Anal Sacs

ACANTHOSIS NIGRICANS:

Acanthosis nigricans is an uncommon skin disorder which occurs more frequently in the Dachshund than in any other breed. The characteristic skin lesions are manifested as a thickened blackening of the skin in both armpits (axillae). In chronic cases, the ears and even inner surface of the rear legs are involved. The cause is unknown but some think that the hormone regulation of the melanin pigmentation is disrupted. Acanthosis nigricans can occur secondarily due to rubbing the legs against the chest, to hormone disruptions, or as a response to allergies. In secondary forms of the disease, resolution occurs when the underlying cause is treated.

The prognosis depends on the cause. In primary acanthosis nigricans, control rather than cure is sought. Treatments include the use of *melatonin,* a pineal gland hormone available from Rickards Research Foundation, 18235 Euclid Avenue, Cleveland, OH 44112. *Cortisone* and antibiotics combined with weight reduction programs are also helpful.

ACNE:

Canine acne is a very common problem in the Doberman Pinscher. The bumps, pustules, and blackheads (comedones) appear on the chin and lips most commonly between three and twelve months of age. Many cases clear up at sexual maturity (about 12 months of age). Some cases, however, continue into adulthood and are difficult to handle. The usual treatment is the daily application of benzoyl peroxide gel with twice weekly benzoyl peroxide shampoo baths. Bathing will control all but the most stubborn cases. In cases of follicle infection, the use of anti-staphylococcus antibiotics are indicated. The prognosis is guarded since the condition can recur over a long period of time. Acute flare-ups should be treated because permanent scarring can result.

ACRAL LICK:

The acral lick, also incorrectly called *lick granuloma,* is classified as a *psychogenic dermatosis.* Emotional high-strung Doberman Pinschers have a high incidence of this condition. Reasons ranging from lack of human companionship to stressful or boring life-styles can be the cause. Many of the dogs that develop acral licks are shy and/or nervous. Dobes over five years of age and males more than females seem to be affected.

Clinically, the lesion appears on the front leg near the carpus (wrist) or on the rear leg near the hock joint. The skin lesion is round, raised, thickened, hairless, and darker than normal. In most cases, only one lesion is apparent. On occasion, the skin lesion looks like a slow healing ulcer.

The treatment is complex. The dog's routine must be changed by exercising it at a different time, feeding it differently, and giving it new toys. Anything that gives the dog something else to think about helps. The lesion should be covered for 30 days while the life-style is altered, providing the Dobe will leave a bandage on. Breaking the itch-lick cycle is the most important part of the treatment. Recently, a combination of *Synotic®* and *Banamine®* applied daily for three weeks has shown much promise. The prognosis depends on the success of changing the life-style and on the appropriate use of medication to break the itch-lick cycle. Recurrences are common if the life-style is not varied from time to time.

ACUTE MOIST DERMATITIS:

Moist eczema, pyotraumatic dermatitis, and *"hot spots"* are among the names given to acute moist dermatitis. Pyotraumatic dermatitis is the most accurate because this skin problem occurs secondary to a primary irritation. "Hot spots" are more common in medium-coated and long-coated breeds than in the Doberman. The condition is more common in the summer. Inciting causes can be *anal sac infections,* ear infections, a dirty dead hair-coat, and pain in the area where *hip dysplasia* lesions are found. The development of lesions is very rapid. What may appear as a small oozing, hairless, red, ulcerated lesion will grow to an area three to four times as large in less than two hours.

To minimize the dog's discomfort, vigorous treatment is necessary early in the course of this condition. Often, *sedation* (anesthesia) is necessary in order to clip hair from around the lesion to initially treat the oozing painful dermatitis. An excellent astringent for this problem is 5% tannic acid, 5% salicylic acid, and 70% alcohol. This solution is applied two to three times daily until the skin starts to crust. The use of *cortisone* is necessary in some cases. In all cases, the primary cause should be treated or eliminated. Prognosis for recovery is excellent. The more aggressive the therapy, the earlier the recovery. The missing hair will grow back because the hair follicles are not destroyed.

ALLERGY:

A dog may develop allergies to many of his surroundings. Doberman Pinschers are more prone to *bacterial hypersensitivity* than many other breeds but are less susceptible to inhalant and food allergies. The following allergies are discussed individually within this chapter.

Atopy (inhalant allergies)	Food allergy
Bacterial hypersensitivity	Hives
Drug allergy	Hormone hypersensitivity
	Irritant contact dermatitis

ALLERGY TESTING:

An alternative to cortisone for *atopy (inhalant allergy)* is the use of skin testing and *immunotherapy (hyposensitization)* to desensitize the body to the inhalant allergens. The best results in allergy testing are achieved when individual antigens are used. These antigens should be regionalized to your area of the United States. The veterinarian who performs the test should have a good deal of experience in reading test results since some interpretation is required.

An area of skin is prepared for the test by shaving and marking a spot where each intradermal injection is to be made. The dog may or may not be sedated for the test procedure. Normally 40 to 60 antigens are tested at one time, including a positive and negative control. The test results are read after 15 minutes and after one hour to determine allergic skin reactions. A number of factors can alter the test results. Prior to the allergy test, dogs should be free from orally administered *cortisone* for three to four weeks and from injectable cortisone for seven to eight weeks. Some allergens test more strongly at certain times of the year. For example, ragweed is a late summer and early fall allergen. Its skin reaction will be stronger then than in the spring of the year. Allergy testing and treatment are 60% to 80% successful in the hands of a competent veterinary dermatologist.

ALOPECIA:

Alopecia (hair loss) can be normal or due to a wide number of disease processes. Hair grows in a cyclic pattern. During anagen (the growth period), hair grows in length by mitosis (dividing of cells). At the end of anagen, the hair bulb where growth occurs constricts causing the area above the hair bulb to thicken. This transitional period is called catagen. After a variable length of time, telogen (the resting period) is begun. Weeks or months later, the whole cycle begins again.

The Doberman Pinscher has a short-hair coat. Short-hair coats have the highest number of hair follicles per unit area of any kind of hair coat. This is not, however, true in the blue and fawn varieties. These coat color variations have a deficient number of healthy hair follicles. Refer to *COLOR MUTANT ALOPECIA (BLUE DOBERMAN SYNDROME)*.

ALOPECIA, CONGENITAL:

Refer to *CONGENITAL ALOPECIA.*

ALOPECIA, ENDOCRINE:

Refer to *ENDOCRINE ALOPECIA.*

ANA TEST:

The ANA (antinuclear antibody) test is done when *immune mediated skin diseases are suspected. The ANA test is most useful when systemic lupus erythematosus* is suspected. Accurate test results can be obtained on dogs receiving *cortisone,* however, many drugs and diseases can create positive ANA tests. The test is done on a serum sample. The titer and staining pattern are the most important factors in interpreting the test results.

ANAL SAC DISEASES:

The anal sacs are located at 8 o'clock and 4 o'clock from the anal opening. These sacs open to the outside through small ducts at the junction of the anal tissue and the skin. Impaction, acute infection or abscess formation, and chronic infection are the three disease processes which occur within the anal sacs.

   Anal sac impaction is a chronic process in which the sacs are filled with a black, dry odorless material. This substance is difficult to express from the sacs either with a bowel movement or by digital expression. After removal of the impacted material, the sacs are filled with an antibiotic ointment.

   Acute anal sac infection is a very active process in which the infected sac enlarges and ruptures through the skin. This infection responds to antibiotic therapy administered both locally and systemically. In the acute infection, the thin, bloody discharge is accompanied with some pus and a fetid odor.

   Chronic anal sac infections produce a thicker reddish paste which has a fetid odor. After the sacs are expressed, antibiotic ointment is placed in the sacs daily for a period of time.

ANAL SAC INFECTION:

Refer to *ANAL SAC DISEASES.*

ANGIOEDEMA:

Refer to *HIVES.*

ATOPY:

Canine atopy *(allergic inhalant dermatitis)* is a common itch-causing dermatitis which occurs from inhaling environmental allergens. Most commonly the first occurrence is between one and three years of age, most frequently from spring to fall. More females than males are affected. Atopy does have a genetic predisposition. The clinical signs are generalized itching initially without the presence of skin lesions. In chronic cases, the skin becomes very flaky, blackened, and thickened. Affected dogs lick their feet and rub their faces. Diagnosed is made by the clinical signs present, time of year, and conclusively, by intradermal skin testing.

The treatment can involve a combination of any or all of three forms of therapy. First, avoidance of the allergen will stop the clinical signs. This, however, is sometimes impossible. Second, the use of systemic *cortisone* will stop the itching. When the length of time that the offending allergens are in the air is relatively short, this is an excellent means of control. However, if the allergy season is longer than one month or the dog is very sensitive to cortisone, the third method of treatment should be considered. *Hyposensitization (immunotherapy)* is the administration of increasingly larger doses of the allergen over a period of time with the hope that the body will become desensitized to the allergen. Dogs do not respond as humans do to antihistamine therapy for inhalant allergies.

Atopy can be controlled when the offending allergens are identified. Occasionally, the use of both cortisone and immunotherapy are necessary to provide relief from pruritus (itching).

AUTOIMMUNE SKIN DISEASES:

Autoimmune skin diseases are uncommon skin disorders characterized by blistering and ulceration of the skin and mucous membranes. A variable amount of pruritus (itching) is present.

Four varieties of *pemphigus* are diagnosed in the dog. The most common, pemphigus foliaceus, involves general ulceration over the body. Often the foot pads become hardened and thickened. Thought to be a more benign form of pemphigus foliaceus is pemphigus erythematosus. The most virulent form is pemphigus vulgaris which usually produces lesions involving the skin, the oral cavity, and other mucous membranes. Its benign counterpart is pemphigus vegetans. *Bullous pemphigoid* is a closely related disorder. The diagnosis, clinical signs, and treatment are similar for all of the pemphigus diseases.

Two other autoimmune diseases seen in the dog are *systemic lupus erythematosus* and *discoid lupus erythematosus*. Systemic lupus is a very complex disease that involves multiple organ systems such as the skin, kidneys, joints, and heart. Discoid lupus is always limited to skin lesions on the nose, face, and ears.

The diagnosis of autoimmune skin disease requires *biopsies, direct immunofluorescence testing, ANA tests, and* direct smears from lesions. These, coupled with history and clinical signs, formulate a diagnosis. All of these diseases are treated with very high levels of cortisone, anticancer drugs like *azathioprine* and *cyclophosphamide,* and gold salt therapy. Some cases require long courses of treatment with flare-ups being common. With the exceptions of discoid lupus and pemphigus erythematosus, the prognosis for these skin diseases is guarded for long term control.

BACTERIAL HYPERSENSITIVITY:

Bacterial hypersensitivity is a very pruritic (itchy) skin disorder caused by a hypersensitivity to the antigens of the *Staph bacteria*. Clinically, the swollen red pustules are very itchy. Many dogs with bacterial hypersensitivity are also *hypothyroid, atopic*, or allergic to some foods. The disease can be diagnosed by reading an intradermal skin test 24 to 72 hours after the test injection.

Management of this skin problem requires a combination of antibiotic therapy and injections of increasing amounts of Staph antigens. The most commonly used antigen products are Staphoid A & B® and Staphage Lysate® . Good control can be obtained if the owner is diligent in the treatment of bacterial hypersensitivity.

BASAL CELL CARCINOMA:

The basal cell carcinoma, more correctly termed basal cell tumor, is one of the most common benign tumors of the skin. This tumor is an ulcerated solitary nodule. Generally, this occurs after the age of seven years on the dog's head and neck. Basal cell tumors are managed by any number of surgical removal methods. Since the tumor is benign, the prognosis is excellent.

BIOPSY, SKIN:

The biopsy of skin aids in the understanding of skin diseases. A punch provides a circular 6 mm. sample of the skin. In the case of a tumor, an excisional biopsy removes the entire growth. After the sample is removed, it is fixed in a preservative for further processing. Samples are prepared for routine microscopic examinations with formalin. Michel's media or freezing are used for *direct immunofluorescence testing*.

While biopsies may or may not provide definitive answers to the cause or diagnosis of skin disease, they do provide the clinician with an assessment of the current status of the skin. Biopsies can be taken by freezing the skin with a *local anesthetic*. However, samples from the nose and mouth require *general anesthesia*.

BLUE DOBERMAN SYNDROME:

Refer to *COLOR MUTANT ALOPECIA*.

BULLOUS PEMPHIGOID:

Refer to *AUTOIMMUNE SKIN DISEASES*.

BURNS:

Both full thickness and partial thickness burns occur in the dog. In a partial thickness burn, the entire thickness of the skin has not been destroyed making healing faster and complications less likely. Full thickness burns also destroy the underlying nerves and connective tissue. The underlying tissues are subject to massive bacterial infections. The major secondary problems from full thickness burns include infection, *kidney failure,* respiratory difficulty, shock, and *anemia.* Even when the complications are successfully managed, healing is a long painful process. The amount of nursing care for a burn patient is tremendous. Extensive burns require costly, time-consuming periods of healing.

The prognosis for full thickness burns covering 25% or more of the body is poor to fair. Partial thickness burns have a better prognosis and depend to some degree on the amount of burned tissue present.

CALCINOSIS CUTIS:

Calcinosis cutis is a rare skin disorder usually associated with too much circulating *cortisone* or *diabetes mellitus.* The causes can, however, range from cancer to kidney disease. Clinically, inflamed bumps in the skin appear which feel gritty. Some infection may be evident around the gritty plaques. These raised areas are calcium salts that have been mistakenly deposited in the skin tissues. Calcinosis cutis can be reversed when the underlying cause is controlled or eliminated. Two to four months are required for the calcium plaques to be resorbed. Refer to *CUSHING'S DISEASE* and *CALCINOSIS CUTIS* in Chapter 4.

CALLUS:

Callus formation is a normal body reaction to trauma over pressure points. The most common areas for this kind of trauma are the elbows, hocks, and breast bone. Doberman Pinschers will develop chest calluses with some frequency. If trauma continues, the callus becomes infected as the thickened tissue cracks and ulcerates.

Treatment involves removing the hard surface which is causing the trauma. Cushions, water beds, and padded chest and elbow wraps are important in correcting callus build-ups. In rare instances, surgery is needed to remove the callus. Many potential complications to this surgical technique include hemorrhaging, sutures that don't hold well, and difficulty in immobilizing the affected area slowing down healing.

CHEYLETIELLA MANGE (WALKING DANDRUFF):

Dogs, cats, humans, and rabbits are all affected by cheyletiella mange, caused by a large mite. Because owners may also complain of red, itching welts, this condition is of public health significance. The mite does not burrow through the skin layers but lives on the dead skin surface keratin. Puppies will exhibit a yellow scurf over the entire length of the back with variable degrees of itching. This mite can live its entire life on one dog and remain alive off the host for three or four days.

The condition is diagnosed by clinical signs and finding the mite on superficial *skin scrapings* from the dog. This form of mange is easily treated with three weekly insecticide shampoo baths. During the bathing process, the environment should also be treated to remove any free living mites. Prognosis for recovery is excellent.

CHIGGERS:

About twenty species of chigger mites are capable of causing dermatologic disease. In most cases, they are a seasonal problem of late summer and fall. These mites are orange-brown in color and can be seen by the naked eye. The affected areas are very itchy with raised red bumps.

Treatment consists of the use of various insecticide products over a two or three week period. The dog should not be returned to the environment from which the chigger infestation was obtained until later in the fall season. On occasion, *cortisone* is used for several days to minimize the itching during insecticide treatment. Prognosis for a full recovery is excellent.

COLOR MUTANT ALOPECIA:

In the Doberman Pinscher, black and red hair coats are the normal hair colors. The blue and fawn (isabella) colors and some red coats are called color mutants. All blue and fawn Dobes are born with normal hair coats. Most dogs with color mutant alopecia are apparent by four to six months of age. However, some blues do not become moth-eaten and scaly until they are three years old. Because the color mutant hair coat has a genetic basis, breeding is to be discouraged.

The condition of the skin is related to the color mutant hair coat. Color mutant dogs have abnormal skin and hair coats. The skin over the trunk has patchy, moth-eaten areas where the hair is missing. The skin feels scaly and rough with papules and pustules throughout the body surface. The existing hair is brittle, dry, and lacks the shine associated with a normal healthy hair coat.

There is no cure for the condition. Treatment is designed to alleviate some of the clinical signs. The most effective therapy is total body immersion in warm water to fully hydrate the skin followed by benzoyl peroxide shampooing to remove the scale and flush the hair follicles. If secondary hair follicle infections are present, antibiotics must be used. *Hypothyroidism* can occur in color mutant alopecia. Thyroid replacement therapy will not alleviate color mutant alopecia and skin disease. Control is the best hope for managing the color mutant alopecia condition although the hair coat will never again be normal because the follicles are devoid of hair.

CONGENITAL ALOPECIA:

Congenital alopecia is hair loss at birth or shortly after birth. Color mutant alopecia is part of this group of hair loss conditions. Occasionally in puppies, balding patterns are related to hair color. In dogs with black and white hair coats, the black hair becomes sparse while the skin becomes scaly. With the exception of the Blue Doberman syndrome, these unusual conditions are of no major importance to Doberman Pinscher fanciers.

CULTURE, BACTERIAL AND FUNGAL:

Obtaining bacterial and fungal cultures is part of any thorough dermatologic case work-up. Bacterial cultures are taken with sterile swabs from pustules and from under crusts or other lesions. The swab is either placed in a transport media or streaked on appropriate culture media. After the sample is incubated, any growth is identified. An *antibiotic sensitivity test* is then prepared from the culture growth. The time necessary to do a bacterial culture and antibiotic sensitivity test ranges from 36 to 72 hours. Most bacteria grow out in 18 to 36 hours. Reculturing is necessary for the antibiotic sensitivity test portion.

Fungal cultures are taken from diseased hair and scale near the edge of a skin lesion. They are inoculated in an appropriate media and incubated at room temperature for a period of up to four weeks. Most of the common *dermatophytes* start to grow in four to seven days, but since some uncommon varieties have a longer incubation period, the culture is routinely kept for four weeks.

CUTANEOUS LEISHMANIASIS:

Cutaneous leishmaniasis is common in the temperate Mediterranean region and in Africa. A rare disease in the United States, it has been diagnosed in Florida and Oklahoma. A *protozoan parasite* spreads the disease to susceptible dogs by an insect bite. The clinical lesions are itchy, red, or ulcerated nodules commonly on the abdomen, inner thighs, head, and ears. The diagnosis is made from a *skin biopsy* and a *serological* blood test. The standard treatment for leishmaniasis is an *antimony* compound given intramuscularly. Because these drugs are not routinely used in the United States, they must be ordered through the Parasitic Diseases Drug Service of the Center for Disease Control in Atlanta, GA (404/329-3670). Treatment periods of six weeks are not uncommon. The prognosis for a cure is good if the disease is diagnosed early in its development.

CUTANEOUS LYMPHOSARCOMA:

Cutaneous lymphosarcoma is a rare form of fatal skin cancer usually in older dogs of either sex. Some breed predilection has been found but the Doberman is not included. Cutaneous lymphosarcoma may consist of a solitary nodule or, more commonly, as multicentric lesions with generalized red, scaly, itchy skin. While some cases advance rapidly, others become more chronic in nature. In either case, a fatal outcome will result unless an individual nodule can be successfully removed.

Cutaneous lymphosarcoma is usually diagnosed by repeated *skin biopsies.* **Mycosis fungoides,** one form of the disease, requires multiple biopsies to diagnose. While no treatment will cure the cancer, nitrogen mustard has been used to prolong life. If this compound is used, gloves must be worn by the owner when handling the dog. The prognosis for long term recovery is poor.

DANDRUFF:

Refer to *SEBORRHEA.*

DEMODICOSIS (RED MANGE):

Demodicosis is an inflammatory skin disease characterized by an *immune deficiency* condition and a larger than usual number of *Demodex mange mites* on the skin. A few demodectic mites are found on normal skin. One of the two types of demodicosis is localized involving a small, scaly, hairless area of skin which does not seem to itch very much. These lesions are commonly found on the legs or face. Clinical features of localized mange are circumscribed, scaly, red areas that may or may not itch. The majority of these cases will regress once any stress is over. However, a small percentage will become generalized if not treated. For this reason, all cases must be treated even if spontaneous regression is anticipated.

Generalized demodicosis has three subtypes: juvenile onset (3 to 12 months), adult onset, and chronic pododemodicosis (foot mange). Most adult onset generalized cases of mange have either cancer or a serious systemic disease as a predisposing factor. The Doberman Pinscher is one of the breeds predisposed to generalized demodectic mange. These dogs are genetically predisposed. Because these dogs have a specific genetic *T-cell deficiency,* they should not be used in breeding programs.

Generalized demodicosis is a very severe inflammatory skin disease which results in much *hair loss, pyoderma,* severe crusting on the skin, and deep infections in the hair follicles. The most severe lesions appear on the head and neck. Because of the tremendous inflammatory feature of this disease, many owners choose euthanasia.

The disease is diagnosed by *skin scrapings.* All cases of *seborrhea* and generalized skin disease should have a number of skin scrapings done to determine if demodicosis is present. All swollen foot lesions should be scraped.

The treatment and prognosis depend on the form of the disease. Most local cases will respond to Goodwinol® ointment applied daily to the lesions for several weeks. The prognosis is excellent if no new lesions are observed during treatment. Generalized demodicosis is treated with antibiotics for the secondary pyoderma and either weekly *Mitaban®* dips or the use of Scott's solution over a long period of time. Some generalized cases can only be controlled and not cured. If diligent treatment over a four month period has not resulted in a clinical cure, the Demodex will only be controlled in that individual. In those cases of stubborn Demodex infection involving the feet, Mitaban® should be added to mineral oil submersing the feet in the mineral oil-Mitaban® mix daily for 30 days. Recently, a report from Brazil indicated that 5,000 international units of *vitamin E* daily resulted in total cures of generalized demodicosis. Vitamin E therapy is unproven in the United States. Because the dogs are already immunosuppressed, under no circumstances should any kind of *cortisone* be given to dogs with generalized demodicosis! The prognosis for demodicosis has improved with the advent of Mitaban® (amitraz), but much supportive care is needed in seriously infected generalized cases.

DERMATITIS:

Dermatitis itself actually means inflammation of the skin. A word that is widely misused, in order to use the word properly, dermatitis must be modified with a descriptive term.

DERMATOPHYTOSIS:

Dermatophytosis is a fungus infection of skin cells, nails, or hair caused by fungi of the species *Microsporum, Trichophyton,* or *Epidermophyton*. The term dermatomycosis is sometimes incorrectly used interchangeably with dermatophytosis. Dermatomycosis are caused by fungi that are not members of the mentioned species of fungi.

The clinical appearance of a superficial fungus infection is extremely variable. Some forms of the dermatophytes (fungi) cause inflammation, hair loss, crusting, and scaling of the skin. In other cases, only a mild "breaking" of hairs and slight balding are observed. The term "ring worm" was so named because the fungus would attack the hair causing it to fall out as the fungus spread to the periphery of the circle. After a period of time, the hair in the center would start to grow in giving the appearance of a ring.

The superficial fungal diseases are best diagnosed by *fungal culture* and occasionally by direct observation of diseased hair under the microscope. Since fungi grow slowly, all fungal cultures are maintained for 28 days before being discarded as negative. A few dermatophytes fluoresce under the UV light of the Wood's lamp. However, less than 50% of the *Microsporum canis* species do this. A negative Wood's lamp reading is not reason enough for rejecting a diagnosis of superficial fungus infection.

If only a few small circumscribed areas are present on the Doberman Pinscher, treatment of superficial fungus infections can be topical. Effective topical fungicidal agents include *miconazole nitrate, clotrimazole,* 1:20 Captan dips, and Weladol® shampoo. If a generalized fungus infection is present, oral systemic medication is needed to eliminate the dermatophytosis. The drug of choice is *griseofulvin* in the microcrystalline form. Griseofulvin should not be given to pregnant dogs under any circumstances because it will cause fetal abnormalities. Since over two weeks are required for this drug to reach the hair shaft, quick cures are not possible. The length of time for a clinical cure can vary from four weeks to nine months. The drug should always be given for two weeks longer than clinically deemed necessary. The gut absorption of the griseofulvin is enhanced with a high fat meal. *Ketoconazole* is a new antifungal drug found to be effective against dermatophytes. Because of its expense, it use is limited to cases where griseofulvin is found to be ineffective.

With the exception of fungus infections of the claw, the prognosis for curing superficial infections is good. *Nail bed infections* may require systemic griseofulvin for as long as a year to effect a cure. In rare cases, the surgical removal of the claw is necessary to cure the fungus infection.

DIRECT IMMUNOFLUORESCENCE TESTING:

Direct immunofluorescence testing is done on skin biopsy samples to determine if an *autoimmune skin disease* is present. Biopsy samples are submitted in Michel's media. A positive DIT will reinforce the diagnosis of an autoimmune skin disease. This very complicated test is currently done in only a few testing labs.

DISCOID LUPUS ERYTHEMATOSUS (DLE):

Lesions of discoid lupus erythematosus are confined to the face, most commonly involving the nose. Many dogs previously diagnosed as having *"Collie nose"* are probably discoid lupus cases. Scarring is common. Ultraviolet light rays aggravate the condition.

Solar screens are helpful in the treatment. *Vitamin E* oil has also been used successfully. *Cortisone* preparations help to control the condition. The response to treatment is good but therapy must be maintained for as long as a lifetime. Also refer to *AUTOIMMUNE SKIN DISEASE.*

DRUG ALLERGY:

A drug allergy can also be termed a *drug idiosyncrasy.* Individual dogs react to *penicillin* in an allergic manner requiring prompt treatment. Some breeds show increased sensitivity to certain drugs. The Doberman Pinscher should NOT be given the drugs *Tribrissen®* or *Bactrim®* . Many members of this breed develop an *immune complex polyarthropathy* and ocular hypersensitivity to these drugs.

ECZEMA:

The word "eczema" has been misused for a long time by referring to any deviation from normal skin as eczema. The actual definition of eczema is an inflammatory, superficial skin disease that, in its early stages, is red, swollen, oozing, and crusting, and later becomes scaly, red-purple, thickened, and possibly pigmented.

ENDOCRINE ALOPECIA:

The hormone (endocrine) system in the body has a profound affect on skin and hair coat health. Most hormone disturbances affect the skin by causing a symmetrical baldness. Usually, the remaining haircoat becomes dry and brittle and is easily pulled out. The clipped coat will not regrow in an affected dog. Generally, increased pigment is observed in the bald areas on the skin. Most hormone skin disturbances are not itchy. However, exceptions do occur when other factors complicate the clinical signs.

ENDOCRINE DERMATOPATHIES:

The following is a list of endocrine dermatopathies (skin diseases). Each is discussed individually within the text of the book.

Cushing's disease (hyperadrenocorticism)
Diabetes mellitus	Ovarian imbalance, type I & type II
Growth hormone responsive dermatosis	Pituitary dwarfism
Hypothyroidism	Sertoli cell tumor
Male feminizing syndrome	Testosterone - responsive dermatosis

ERYTHEMA:

Erythema is a redness of the skin produced by congested capillaries.

EXTERNAL PARASITES OF THE SKIN:

The following is a list of the external parasites of the skin. Each is discussed within the chapter unless otherwise indicated.

Cheyletiella mange	Hookworm dermatitis
Chiggers	Lice
Demodicosis	Pelodera Strongyloides
Ear mite otitis - Refer to Chapter 10	Scabies
Fleas	Spiders - Refer to Chapter 9
Flies	Ticks - Also refer to Chapter 7

FATTY ACID DEFICIENCY:

The signs of a fatty acid deficiency are most common in dogs fed only "people foods" and those exclusively on a dry dog food diet. While most dog foods have the proper amount of essential fatty acids present at the time of manufacture, the product can deteriorate in storage. The food must be stored in a cool area to prevent rapid oxidation of the added fat. Long term storage, however, can cause the fat coating of dry dog food to diminish.

The presence of antioxidants like *vitamin E* are important to prevent rancidity. Within six months from time of production, the fat coating is no longer nutritious.

Several months of low essential fatty acid intake will cause dermatological changes. The hair coat becomes dry and dull and the hair falls out. The skin becomes thicker with evidence of itching and scaling. Fatty acid deficient dogs have a greater tendency to develop *"hot spots."* The skin and ears become greasy, filling with wax more frequently. Because the normal lipid film on the skin changes, a dog deficient in essential fatty acids is more prone to the development of *pyoderma.*

Providing *essential fatty acids* is important to good skin health. The dog can convert linoleic acid into all of the fatty acids needed. At 70%, safflower oil provides the greatest amount of unsaturated essential fatty acids. Other fats provide the following percentages: corn oil, 59%; pork fat, 30%; chicken fat, 24%; and beef tallow or butter, 3%. Petab FA with zinc® - liquid and EFA-Z Plus® are the two superior commercial products. Both products are better balanced than vegetable and animal fats alone. Each can be obtained from veterinarians. Three weeks to three months of essential fatty acid supplementation are required before a change is seen in the skin. The prognosis is excellent with continued supplementation. Also refer to Chapter 8 on Nutritional Management.

FLANK SUCKER SYNDROME:

A common psychogenic dermatosis in the Doberman Pinscher is the flank sucker *(side sucker)* syndrome. Dogs exhibiting this condition seem to be obsessed with sucking and licking the flank region of one side, or both sides rarely. Because of the constant moisture and mouth stimulation, the hair coat is thin in the area. The skin may be reddened or thickened. In fawns (isabella), the hair around the area shows a reddish discoloration.

The cause of flank sucking is not known. Several causes that are most frequently mentioned are *whipworm* and a form of psychomotor *epilepsy.* Treatment is individualized for each affected Dobe. *Phenobarbital* and *primidone* can be helpful in adjusting the behavior. *Methylprednisolone* is helpful in breaking the itch-lick cycle.

FLEA COLLAR DERMATITIS:

The most common cause of flea collar dermatitis is the tightness of the collar around the neck. A minimum of a two fingers distance must be between the collar and the skin. This type of dermatosis is more common in very short-coated breeds. Some dogs are very sensitive to the polyvinyl plastic collars while others are irritated by the insecticide chemical impregnated in the collar.

The clinical signs appear near or under the collar. These red, raised, ulcerated areas initially become thickened and crusty in chronic cases. The lesions can spread over the entire body.

The treatment involves removing the flea collar and treating any signs of insecticide toxicity. Refer to *INSECTICIDE POISONING* in Chapter 9. The acute skin lesions are treated with wet dressings or astringents. Use of *cortisone* ointments is helpful. In severe cases, hospitalization and intensive therapy are required. Recovery is usually complete although occasional scarring can be evident in Doberman Pinschers. Other forms of flea control are more reliable.

FLEAS:

Fleas are small wingless insects that live for up to a year in an optimum environment consisting of a suitable host (the dog) and high temperature with humidity. The higher the temperature and humidity, the more efficient the flea life cycle becomes, completing itself in as little as two weeks. The flea is incriminated in the transmission of a *tapeworm* in the dog. Fleas do not live in altitudes over 5,000 feet above sea level.

The flea also causes *flea bite dermatitis* (hypersensitivity), the most common skin problem observed in dogs. A dog not sensitive to the flea saliva will not acknowledge the presence of fleas. No irritation or itching is present until the dog becomes sensitized to the flea saliva. The hypersensitive state usually develops between three and six years of age, but with proper exposure, can occur as early as one year of age. At that time, a hypersensitive state is produced in which the dog reacts with severe itching. A raised, crusty skin lesion most commonly found on the posterior part of the back near the tail, on the back part of the thighs, and belly is seen. This intense *pruritus* (itching) also initiates *acute moist dermatitis (hot spots)* with hair loss and scaling. Flea allergy dermatitis is seasonal in climates with cold winters and on outside dogs. Dogs from warm climates and those that live in the house exhibit the problem through the entire year.

The diagnosis of the flea bite allergy is made from the location and appearance of the skin lesions and by finding evidence of fleas. This evidence may be an actual flea or the presence of "flea dirt." Flea dirt is actually flea excrement (dried blood) that appears on the skin as a black, gritty material. An easy test for flea dirt is the placement of several particles of black grit on a white piece of paper. Add a small drop of water and rub with a toothpick. Since it is actually dried blood, genuine "flea dirt" turns the water red. Once the diagnosis of flea bite dermatitis (allergy) is made, the treatment is directed toward eliminating the fleas from the environment and the dog. Since fleas spend about 10% of their life on the dog feeding, the environmental treatment is very important. While the flea population is being brought under control, use of *cortisone* may be necessary to relieve the allergic signs present in the dog. Some dermatologists and veterinary allergists have good luck desensitizing dogs to flea antigen. Most, however, don't feel the hyposensitization therapy works well in flea allergy.

Flea control must be individualized to each dog and environmental situation. The following are general observations about various flea control products and procedures. Flea shampoos are generally worthless because there is no residual activity. The residual activity of some flea dips is rapidly lost if the dog gets wet. *Brewer's yeast* and *vitamin B₁* are not effective in flea control. Generally, *flea collars* are ineffective on most dogs. *Spotton®* is used in the Southern United States for flea control. Most effective at a concentration of 20%, it is dangerous and is not cleared for use on dogs. Humans may have toxic reactions to the treatment. *Pro-Spot®* , the counterpart of Spotton® , is cleared for use in dogs. The concentration in Pro-Spot® is much lower making it less effective.

The most effective management of fleas involves the usage of premise sprays and foggers at timely intervals coupled with the use of a good insecticide spray on the dog EACH time it goes outside. Many flea sprays contain pyrethrins which are effective flea killers. Pyrethrin is derived from the chrysanthemum, a member of the ragweed family. Some dogs have *inhalant allergies* to ragweed that will cross react with pyrethrin flea products causing increased itching and redness.

FLY BITE DERMATITIS:

Several types of dermatological problems occur from fly bites. A problem common in late summer in young puppies is the presence of a circular hole surrounded by a swollen area beneath the skin. This *Cuterebra fly larva* can be seen moving through the skin opening. The hole is enlarged to remove the larva with a forceps without crushing it. Serious inflammatory reactions can occur as a result of crushed larva.

More common are stable fly bites on the nose and ear tips. The inflamed crusted areas on the ear tips are usually seen in the summer. The flies can be seen landing on the ears or nose. The lesions are treated with an anti-inflammatory cream or ointment. A repelling insecticide gel like Pet Guard® gel is applied as needed during the fly season.

FLY STRIKE (MAGGOT INFESTATION):

Fly strike (maggot infestation), a disease of negligence, is much more common in long-haired dogs that have soiled the area under their tails with stool and urine. This damp dark area is an ideal environment for flies to lay eggs which hatch into larvae (maggots) that feed on the skin. The skin has a punched out appearance as the maggots quickly proliferate. The dog becomes systemically ill from the degenerating toxic skin products poisoning their system.

Treatment requires veterinary care for complete removal of all maggots, clipping the hair from the affected area, and topical and systemic treatment of the severely diseased skin. Prognosis for recovery is good if treatment is started early and maggot removal is complete.

FOLLICULITIS:

The Doberman Pinscher is commonly affected by a type of folliculitis called *pruritic superficial folliculitis.* Folliculitis is an inflammation within the hair follicle. The pruritic superficial form has a very itchy yet superficial clinical feature. This pruritic form is very common in a number of short-coated breeds including the Doberman Pinscher. Long-coated breeds like the Golden Retriever, Irish Setter, Sheltie, and German Shepherd are also commonly affected.

The clinical features of this itchy disease are the presence of pustules with hair growing out of the pustule. The region of the lesion can be severely inflamed. As the lesion ages, a 'target' or 'bull's-eye' pattern is formed. The outer circle is red with a scaly inner region and a darkly pigmented center.

The exact cause of this disease varies from *bacterial hypersensitivity* or nutritional deficiency to hormone imbalances like *hypothyroidism.* The diagnostic test work-up includes *skin biopsies*, staphylococcal antigen skin testing, *skin scrapings*, and bacterial and *fungal cultures.*

The management of folliculitis can be troublesome because of its tendency to recur. If bacterial allergy is found, hyposensitization or elimination of the bacterial cause should be attempted. *Cortisone* is contraindicated because it cuts down on sebum (skin oil) production further aggravating the condition. Antibiotic therapy is used at full dosage for one to two months. Weekly bathing with a good quality follicle-flushing shampoo is done during treatment. If relapses occur following the cessation of antibiotic therapy, hyposensitization for the Staph antigens should be considered. Prognosis for complete recovery is guarded. Many cases will require occasional bathing, nutritional supplementation, and antibiotic therapy.

FOOD ALLERGY:

Food allergy (hypersensitivity) is an uncommon problem causing nonseasonal itching in any aged dog. Puppies as young as six months of age are affected. More commonly, these allergies are seen in dogs that have been on the same diet for over two years. A food allergic reaction can develop to any kind of meat, milk, eggs, cereal grains, fish, potatoes, rice, and soybean. The dog must have had previous exposure to the offending food in order to develop hypersensitivity to it.

The diagnosis for this cause of itching skin is made by placing the dog on a *"hypoallergenic diet."* This is a single form of food to which the dog has had little or no previous exposure. This diet must be strictly maintained for three weeks. Only distilled water is given to drink. The whole diagnostic procedure may yield faster results if three cleansing enemas are administered during the 48 hour fast at the beginning of the three week diet. A commercially prepared hypoallergenic diet called **"DD"** diet or a homemade lamb or mutton and rice mixture can be used to feed the affected dog. During the test period, no supplements, vitamins, or heartworm chewable tablets are given. Results (less itching) are observed in five to seven days in many cases. However, in some cases, up to fourteen days may pass before a significant decrease in itching and red skin lesions is noticed. If at the end of the three week feed trial there is a significant decrease in itching, individual food items are added back one week at a time. For instance, Wheat Chex® could be added to the hypoallergenic diet as a source of wheat. After one week with no increase in itching, Cheerios® could be added as a source of oats. Each addition is tested for one week. By following this procedure, a list of nutrients that do not cause food hypersensitivity can be compiled and used in an every day diet.

The prognosis for controlling food allergy is good providing the offending allergen can be identified. Many food allergy problems are poorly responsive to cortisone. Because *prednisolone* does not control an itchy food allergy dog very well, identifying the cause of the hypersensitive state is more effective.

FOOT DISEASES:

Diseases involving the feet, foot pads, and nails are very difficult to control or cure. If a well thought out treatment program is to be undertaken, making a definite diagnosis is important. The following conditions involve the feet, interdigital (between the toes) areas, and the foot pads: *atopy,* contact *dermatitis, demodicosis, dermatophytosis, hookworm dermatitis,* interdigital foreign bodies, *rhabditic larvae dermatitis, pemphigus,* and *pododermatitis.* Refer to each topic individually for a complete discussion.

FROST BITE:

Because of its very short hair coat and standing ears which may have poor blood circulation to the tip area, the Doberman Pinscher is prone to frost bite on its ear tips. Dobes that are either not acclimated to a very cold climate or have been left outside for several hours in sub-zero temperatures are most likely to suffer frost bite.

The signs of frost bite vary. A mild case is evidenced by a very light redness and scaling. Total death of the cells at the ear tips results in necrotic sloughing of the tissue and very slow healing. Hair near the affected areas can turn white in response to extreme cold.

If the ear tips are pale and cold to the touch, they should be gently bathed in warm water to return the tissues to a normal temperature as quickly as possible. Severe loss of tissue may necessitate the surgical removal of dead flesh and plastic repair of unsightly defects. Surgery should not be done too quickly because more tissue may be saved than originally anticipated.

FUNGUS INFECTIONS:

Fungus infections of the skin are classified as *dermatophytosis* (superficial fungal infections) and *deep fungal infections.* Deep fungal infections are primary infections of other body organs, secondarily involving the skin. These primary infections include *blastomycosis, cryptococcosis, mycetoma, sporotrichosis,* and *phaeohyphomycosis.* A more complete discussion of most of these conditions can be found within the book.

GENERIC DOG FOOD SKIN DISEASE:

With the advent of generic dog foods, a specific skin disease related to nutritionally deficient generic food has been observed. Clinical signs of the disease are similar to *zinc deficiency skin disease.* A bilateral symmetrical loss of hair with crusting on the nose, pressure points (elbows), and on the feet becomes apparent. Severely affected dogs run a fever and have swollen lymph nodes. A rapid clinical response is seen when the dog is fed a good quality dog food instead of the generic dry food. Changes are observed within one week. The prognosis for recovery is excellent providing the good quality food is continued.

GROOMING:

Grooming of a short-haired breed like the Doberman Pinscher can be achieved with a hound glove and an occasional bath. If the dog has a tendency toward dandruff formation, a soaking, submerged bath with a hypoallergenic shampoo is an excellent method of hydrating the skin. Rubbing the coat with a hound glove will remove any dead hair, leaving the coat shiny.

GROWTH HORMONE SKIN DISEASE:

Growth hormone responsive skin disease has not been observed in the Doberman Pinscher. However, the Poodle, Keeshond, Chow, and Pomeranian have all been diagnosed with this problem.

The signs are typical of a hormonal skin problem with bilateral hair loss, generally no itching, soft skin, and hair left on the head and legs. The condition can be diagnosed by *growth hormone stimulation tests* using the drug *xylazine* to stimulate growth hormone release from the pituitary gland.

Treatment is growth hormone replacement which is in short supply today. However, growth hormone replacement is being genetically engineered and will be more readily available within five years. Treatment is usually for life with periodic injections.

HAIR DISEASE:

Signs of diseases involving the hair coat can exhibit any of the following four clinical changes: 1) change in the color of the hair, 2) broken hair shafts, 3) easily removed hair (can be pulled out of skin with no effort), and 4) loss of sheen to the hair shaft. Certain nutritional deficiencies alter the color of the hair coat or can change the type and consistency of the protein in the hair.

HAIR LOSS:

Refer to *ALOPECIA.*

HISTIOCYTOMA:

The histiocytoma is a rapidly growing benign tumor of the skin of young adult dogs. It appears as an orange button-like growth on the head, ears, and legs. If this tumor is examined by a "human" pathologist, a malignant diagnosis is given. Veterinary pathologists know that in spite of the malignant appearance of the tumor cells, it is a benign growth that will regress and disappear with no treatment.

Treatment is surgical removal or waiting approximately four to six months for it to completely disappear on its own. There is no scar if allowed to regress on its own.

HIVES (ANGIOEDEMA):

Hives (urticarial angioedema) is an uncommon hypersensitive reaction which can occur in dogs. Swelling within the skin layers can occur in the muzzle, ears, area around the eyes, or on the body and extremities. While some of these wheals (swellings) are very itchy, others exude serum or blood. If the respiratory system is involved, the larynx and trachea can swell closed causing death from asphyxiation.

The causes of hives are varied. A partial list includes some antibiotics, various kinds of food, stings from insects and arachnids (spiders), sunlight, *Staph* infections, excessive heat or cold, *vaccines,* and *blood transfusions.* The hive reaction can be controlled with either *epinephrine* or *cortisone* injections. In severe cases, the dog should be hospitalized to watch for respiratory embarrassment. Antihistamines do not have any effect on this type of hypersensitive reaction. The prognosis for complete recovery is usually excellent with treatment and observation. Determining the cause of hives is hard. Consequently, avoiding the causative agent is equally difficult.

HOOKWORM DERMATITIS:

Hookworm dermatitis is usually a disease of poor sanitation and a dirty environment. The third stage larva, especially of the *Uncinaria hookworm* species, can penetrate the hairless areas of the belly and groin region of the dog. These larva also penetrate the feet and elbows causing small, red skin lesions. The dog's chewing or licking of its feet indicates some itching is present.

The diagnosis is made by finding hookworm eggs in the feces and determining that the kennel sanitary measures are lacking. Treatment involves hookworm control both in the dog and in the environment to eliminate the infective larvae. VIP Hookworm Concentrate® or Borax® at the rate of 10 pounds per 100 square feet of ground will kill hookworm larva. Borax® also kills vegetation.

HORMONE HYPERSENSITIVITY:

Hormone hypersensitivity is a rare itchy skin condition in which the intact dog has become reactive to its own sex hormones. While most cases occur in unspayed bitches, the unneutered male can also be affected. *Testosterone, progesterone,* and *estrogen* are possible causes of the skin lesions.

Clinical lesions are bilateral hair loss on the lower abdomen and groin area. This hair loss can extend up the backside of the rear legs. In chronic cases, the feet, face, and ears appear crusty and inflamed. Bitches usually exhibit enlarged nipples and vulva.

The diagnosis is made by clinical signs and skin testing the dog for sex hormones. The reaction is either immediate or delayed for 24 hours. Treatment produces dramatic improvement within seven to ten days after *castration* or *ovariohysterectomy*. The prognosis with treatment is excellent for complete recovery.

HORMONE SKIN DISEASE:

A large number of hormones affect the skin and related structures. The hormones listed here are discussed individually in this chapter and in Chapter 4 on the ENDOCRINE SYSTEM.

While hormones have different functions and different target organs and cells, the clinical signs of hormone caused skin disease are similar. The first sign of hormone skin disease is a bilateral *alopecia* (hair loss). This hair loss is symmetrical (the same on both the left and right side of the body). A disturbance in pigment production in the skin generally is present in the form of *hyperpigmentation* or an increase to the skin layers. Increased skin pigmentation is noticeable in areas where the hair has fallen out.

The hair coat in hormone skin disease is very dull and unhealthy in appearance. The hair can be easily epilated (pulled out). In cases where the coat has been clipped, the hair does not regrow or, at best, regrows very slowly. Generally speaking, hormone skin disease is not itchy. However, in chronic cases, *seborrhea* (dandruff) can be present producing pruritus (itching) from excessive flaking and secondary bacterial infections which occur on seborrheic skin.

Hormones that can be associated with skin disease are *thyroid, glucocorticoids, growth hormone,* and *sex hormones.* Discussion of each of the individual hormones can be found within the book.

"HOT SPOT":

Refer to *ACUTE MOIST DERMATITIS.*

HYGROMA:

A hygroma *(pressure point granuloma)* is the body's response to continued irritation to the skin and underlying tissue at the point of a bony prominence in the body. The problem is more common in short-haired dogs like the Doberman that do not have long hair to cushion the bony points from environmental irritation. The most common areas for hygroma development are the elbows, hocks, and chest (keel bone).

The condition begins as a fluid-filled swelling under red, irritated skin at a bony prominence. A false sac (bursa) fills with fluid in an attempt to cushion the trauma area. Continued irritation causes the swelling to grow in size as the tissue thickens. If the inflammatory swelling grows large enough, joint function is impaired.

Early in the course of the disease, only padding the elbow and providing soft bedding are needed to eliminate the inflammatory reaction. However, as the condition becomes chronic, the use of surgical drains, antibiotics, and cortisone are necessary to bring this problem under control. Surgical drains can be very effective in the treatment of chronic large hygromas. The prognosis for resolution of the problem is fair to good depending on how well the hard environmental surfaces can be managed.

HYPERKERATOSIS:

Hyperkeratosis, one sign of skin disease, is defined as an increased thickness in the cornified (horny) outer layer of the skin.

HYPERPIGMENTATION:

Hyperpigmentation, a sign of skin disease, is an increase or excessive amount of *melanin* pigment in the epidermis layers of the skin. The presence of pigment is not diagnostic in chronic skin disease and hormonal imbalances. However, determining the normal level of skin pigmentation in your Doberman is important. This information will help you establish whether or not an increase in pigmentation has occurred.

HYPOPIGMENTATION:

As a sign of skin disease, hypopigmentation is a decreased amount of *melanin* in the epidermal layer of the skin. Causes of hypopigmentation can be congenital, due to chemicals in plastics and rubber bowls, due to hormone disorders, or due to pigmentary disturbances in *immune-mediated skin diseases.*

HYPOTHYROIDISM:

Hypothyroidism can affect most body systems. A number of clinical signs are associated with hypothyroidism affecting the skin and related structures. Hypothyroidism signs of skin disease include bilateral hair loss, thickened cool skin, *hyperpigmentation,* itch or no itch, *seborrhea,* external ear infection, and hypertrichosis (retained hair so thick that it feels like a mat), and dull, dead, easily epilated (pulled out) hair coat.

The Doberman Pinscher is at higher risk than the general canine public when it comes to developing a thyroid deficiency. Thyroid deficiencies take many forms and the physiology of these are complex. The two most important causes are lymphocytic thyroiditis (an autoimmune disease) and idiopathic thyroid atrophy.

The diagnosis of hypothyroidism requires blood tests. In many instances, the T_3 and T_4 serum values will confirm suspicions about clinical signs. On occasion, however, *TSH stimulation tests* must be performed and reverse T_3 and T_4 checked. Some veterinarians prefer to run therapeutic trials rather than blood tests. This is effective only if one can afford to wait up to six weeks to see changes in the skin.

Treatment is effective in over 90% of cases with *L-thyroxine* replacement (T_4). Treatment is administered once or twice daily for the life of the dog. *L-triiodothyronine* (T_3) is more expensive, less effective, and must be given three times a day. The prognosis for revitalizing a hypothyroid hair coat is excellent with appropriate therapy and patience.

ICTHYOSIS:

Icthyosis is a congenital skin disease characterized by greatly increased *hyperkeratosis* which can involve all or part of the skin, nose, and foot pads. The life-long treatment must be done daily to keep the thickened skin hydrated and soft. Soaking baths are very therapeutic. The use of Humilac® is very beneficial because of the presence of lactic acid in a water base. Because there is no cure, controlling the symptoms is the best one can hope for with canine icthyosis.

IMMUNE-MEDIATED SKIN DISORDERS:

A list of immune-mediated diseases follows. Because most are rare, only *TOXIC EPIDERMAL NECROLYSIS* is discussed in this chapter. Other skin diseases in this group include vasculitis, erythema multiforme, linear IgA dermatosis, and alopecia areata. The triggering mechanisms of these diseases vary from drugs like antibiotics to *Staph folliculitis.* Some immune-mediated skin disorders have mild skin lesions while others like *TEN (toxic epidermal necrolysis)* can have a fatal outcome.

IMMUNOLOGIC SKIN DISEASES:

An increasingly large number of immunologic skin disorders have been recognized in the dog. Those of importance are discussed separately and under *AUTOIMMUNE SKIN DISEASES* in this chapter. A complete list follows.

Bullous pemphigoid	Graft-versus host disease
Cold agglutinin disease	Pemphigus group
Dermatitis herpetiformis	Systemic lupus erythematosus
Discoid lupus erythematosus	

IMPETIGO:

True impetigo is a superficial pustular dermatitis of young puppies most frequently affecting the skin on the abdomen. The hair follicles are not involved. The underlying predisposing causes vary from immune depression to parasitism, a dirty environment, and poor nutrition. Impetigo is usually caused by a *Staphylococcus* bacteria.

Treatment is necessary if pustular skin lesions have not spontaneously regressed within a week. A shampoo like Pyoben® or Sebalyt® used two or three times over two weeks will eliminate the infection. However, in rare instances, oral antibiotic therapy is necessary. *Culture* and *sensitivity testing* can be utilized to determine the underlying causes. If they are eliminated, the prognosis for complete recovery is excellent.

IMPRESSION SMEAR:

The impression smear is a valuable aid in the diagnosis of skin disease. In this simple technique, the smear is stained with any Giemsa or Wright's stain. The smear demonstrates tumor cells, bacteria, fungi, and parasites. On rare occasions, immunologic diseases like *pemphigus* and *pemphigoid* are diagnosed by impression smears.

INTERDIGITAL CYSTS:

The term interdigital cyst is an incorrect term since none of the problems which occur between and within the toes and foot pads are cystic. Refer to *FOOT DISEASES* for a complete list of individual foot problems. Also refer to *PODODERMATITIS.*

INTRACUTANEOUS CORNIFYING EPITHELIOMA:

Refer to *KERATOACANTHOMA.*

IRRITANT CONTACT DERMATOSES:

For a Doberman to react to a contact irritant, the offending material must have directly contacted a hairless or sparsely haired region of the body. These easily accessible areas are the abdomen and groin region, the axillae (armpits), and between the toes and foot pads. Since the Dobe is a very short-coated breed, they are more prone to various environmental contact irritants.

The following compounds can cause dermal irritation from casual or long-term skin contact: *acid* and *alkali,* soap and detergents, *flea collars, weed sprays,* and *fertilizers.* A more complete discussion of these compounds is found in Chapter 9 on POISONING.

The initial treatment of contact dermatitis is to remove the offending irritant from contact with the skin. After all residual irritant material is washed away with water, the extent of skin inflammation and damage can be determined. Treatment with Burrow's solution and steroid creams is continued until the skin has returned to normal.

KELOID:

Keloid means a nontumorous growth of fibrous scar tissue, a term taken from human dermatology. However, in the dog, a keloid can occur following removal of skin tissue.

KERATOACANTHOMA:

Keratoacanthoma (intracutaneous cornifying epithelioma) is a skin tumor common in younger adult dogs, primarily occurring in males under five years of age. Found mostly in breeds with the coat length of a German Shepherd or a Norwegian Elkhound, it has not yet been reported in the Doberman Pinscher. Clinically, a claw or a nail appears to be growing out of a mass on the neck, shoulders, or back of the dog. This benign growth is generally removed surgically for cosmetic reasons. Once a dog has a keratoacanthoma, additional growths will probably appear throughout its life.

LICE:

Refer to *PEDICULOSIS* and *PARASITIC SKIN DISEASE.*

LICK GRANULOMA:

Refer to *ACRAL LICK.*

LIPOMA:

Lipomas are common, benign skin tumors of older dogs. Obese females over eight years of age have the greatest incidence of lipomas. Many of these masses of fat are found over the thorax. Although they are benign, they can become large enough to mechanically restrict muscle movement.

Small growths are not removed. Most large growths peel out very well surgically. A new nonsurgical treatment involves the injection of a sclerosing calcium salt into the fatty tumor causing the fat cells to die and disintegrate. This may become an alternative to surgery. The prognosis from surgical removal or weight reduction is excellent.

LUPUS:

Refer to *DISCOID LUPUS, SYSTEMIC LUPUS,* and AUTOIMMUNE SKIN DISEASE.

MAGGOTS:

Refer to *FLY STRIKE.*

MALIGNANT MELANOMA:

Malignant melanomas are highly malignant, occurring most frequently in male dogs over nine years of age. They have been reported in a large number of breeds. These tumors appear as black growths on the skin or mucous membranes. The only treatment for malignant melanoma is wide surgical excision. The malignant melanomas on the tongue are especially malignant making early radical surgical excision necessary. Even with surgical intervention, the long term survival rate is very low.

MAMMARY GLAND TUMORS:

Mammary gland tumors are not technically neoplasms of the skin and related structures. Statistically, 60% of dog mammary gland tumors are malignant, meaning they will spread (metastasize) to the lymph nodes and the lungs. Mammary gland tumors are made up of different tumor elements with some so-called mixed tumors containing bone or cartilaginous tissue.

The tumor growth is either a slow, solitary nodule or a rapidly spreading mass not limited to one mammary gland. Most tumors spread only within the glands connected by the blood supply on one side of the body. When tumors are found across from each other, the disease has probably spread to other areas in the body. The incidence of mammary tumors in bitches spayed before their first heat is practically zero. Some mammary tumors are responsive to the *estrogen* hormone associated with heat. These tumors grow rapidly after the *heat period* is over.

Treatment of mammary tumors is surgical. Surgery varies from a "lumpectomy" to radical excision of the diseased mammary glands. The lungs should be radiographed before surgery to establish that no metastasis has taken place to the chest. The prognosis following surgery varies from excellent to poor depending on the amount of malignant tumor activity demonstrated by the neoplasm.

MANGE:

A discussion of each of the following forms of mange can be found in either this chapter or Chapter 10.

> Cheyletiella mange (Walking dandruff)
> Demodicosis (Demodectic or red mange)
> Otodectic mange - Refer to *EAR MITES* in Chapter 10.
> Scabies (Sarcoptic mange)

MAST CELL TUMOR:

Mast cell tumors are generally solitary nodules of varying sizes which ulcerate early in their growth. The nodular growth is poorly defined because of the difficulty deciding where the tumor ends in the subcutaneous tissues. Many short-haired breeds of dogs have an increased risk to the mast cell tumor. Because mast cells produce the anticoagulant heparin, mast cell tumors are associated with poor blood clotting. In some cases, the diagnosis of a mast cell tumor is made from an appropriately stained impression smear. The methods for handling each mast cell tumor depend on the clinical and microscopic appearance of the tumor. Consider all mast cell tumors as potentially malignant! Early surgical removal is recommended. However, even with wide excision, about one-third of the tumors recur.

Four stages occur in the growth of mast cell tumors. Stage I has no evidence of spread to lymph nodes, only requiring surgical excision. In stage II, lymph nodes are also involved requiring both surgical removal of the tumor and radiation therapy. Stage III consists of infiltrating large multiple mast cell tumors. These are treated with *steroids* injected into the tumors and *cimetidine* to bind the mast cell histamine. The last stage, stage IV, has evidence of a spreading tumor to distant parts of the body requiring systemic *cortisone* (steroids) and cimetidine.

The prognosis for mast cell tumors is guarded because many are malignant. The elaboration of histamine and heparin by the tumor cells causes additional problems.

NAIL DISEASES:

Bacterial or fungal organisms can affect the toenails. Paronychia is inflammation of the tissue around the nail bed, usually caused by bacteria. However, systemic diseases like *pemphigus, systemic lupus,* and *demodicosis* can also involve the nail beds. Diagnosis of the cause of paronychia requires *fungal* and *bacterial cultures, biopsies,* and *skin scrapings.*

Several conditions involve the nail itself. In **onychomadesis,** the hard nail is separated from the underlying nail bed. Infections, trauma, and immune diseases like *lupus* and *pemphigus* can contribute to this.

Onychorrhexis is the tendency for nails to break. The cause of the brittle nail problem is difficult to determine. If the problem becomes recurrent, the surgical removal of the defective nail may be necessary.

Onychomycosis is a *fungal infection* of the nail material. These infections are very difficult to clear up, requiring months of *griseofulvin* therapy to eliminate the fungus completely. If the condition recurs, surgical removal of the nail should be considered.

NODULAR PANNICULITIS:

Nodular panniculitis is an uncommon subcutaneous skin condition. Multiple lumps are found over the back and sides. These lumps are more noticeable in short-coated breeds like the Doberman Pinscher. As the condition progresses, the lumps first ulcerate and then heal by scarring. Generally, the affected dog feels sick, has a fever, has no appetite, and is lethargic.

The diagnosis is made by *biopsy*. Treatment is systemic *cortisone* or in some cases, *vitamin E* therapy. Once the lesions are gone, therapy is halted since most dogs will have a long-term remission.

NUTRITION RELATED SKIN DISEASE:

Each of the following nutrition related skin disease subjects is discussed separately within the chapter.

Fatty acid deficiency
Food allergy
Generic dog food skin disease
Vitamin A deficiency skin disease
Zinc responsive skin disease

OTODECTIC MANGE:

Refer to *EAR MITES, Chapter 10.*

PAPILLOMA:

Refer to *WARTS.*

PARASITES, EXTERNAL, OF THE SKIN:

Refer to *EXTERNAL PARASITES OF THE SKIN.*

PARASITIC SKIN DISEASE:

Each parasitic skin condition is discussed separately within this chapter.

Chiggers
Cutaneous leishmaniasis
Fleas
Fly bite dermatitis
Fly strike (maggot infestation)
Hookworm dermatitis
Pediculosis (Lice infestation)
Rhabditic larvae dermatitis
Ticks

Mange:
Cheyletiella (Walking dandruff)
Demodicosis (Demodectic or red mange)
Otodectic mange - Refer to *EAR MITES* in Chapter 10.
Scabies (Sarcoptic mange)

PEDICULOSIS (LICE INFESTATION):

Two kinds of lice parasitize the dog. Both biting and sucking lice have a life cycle of two to three weeks and spend their entire life cycles on the dog. They can also transmit *tapeworm* to a dog.

Clinical signs of pediculosis (lice infestation) vary from none to severe agitation and itching. In rare cases, severe *anemia* occurs. Generally, the condition is easily diagnosed. This condition is becoming rather uncommon because most dogs are bathed routinely in insecticide shampoos. Treatment is the use of either insecticide dips or shampoos twice two weeks apart. Reinfestation can be prevented by improving sanitation in the dog's environment.

PEMPHIGUS:

Refer to *AUTOIMMUNE SKIN DISEASE.*

PERIANAL ADENOMA:

The perianal adenoma is a tumor of the circumanal glands and related structures in old male dogs. These nodular growths can be either individual or multiple. While most are benign, some do grow large enough to mechanically block the rectum, making defecation difficult. When exposed to constant trauma from sitting, they tend to ulcerate. Because the tumor is very sensitive to male androgen hormone levels, the treatment of choice is *castration*. Over 95% of the tumors disappear within two months after castration.

PHOTODERMATITIS:

Photodermatitis *(solar dermatitis)* is hypersensitivity to light. This condition is more common in regions with long days of intense sunlight. The nasal region is the most common area on the body to develop lesions. Early signs of solar dermatitis are redness and loss of hair. This progresses into crusting and scaling. Unattended, these lesions can develop into a *squamous cell carcinoma* form of cancer. The diagnosis must differentiate this problem from autoimmune diseases like *discoid lupus* and *pemphigus.*

The management of solar dermatitis involves protection from the sun. Keeping the dog out of the sun between 10 a.m. and 4 p.m. and using sunscreens on the skin protect the sensitive tissues from intense sunlight. Tattooing or magic marker application also provide protection. The prognosis is good if attention is paid to solar protection. Otherwise, after squamous cell carcinoma develops, the prognosis is poor.

PIGMENTATION DEFECTS:

Hyperpigmentation and *hypopigmentation* are discussed earlier in this chapter. **Acquired nasal depigmentation** occurs in the Doberman Pinscher. Affected dogs are normal at birth, but with age, the nose "leather" fades from black to brown and even to a whitish color. The cause of this abnormality in pigmentation is not known. To date, no treatment has been found effective. The depigmentation on the nose can also spread to include all or part of the lips.

A rare combination ocular and skin pigmentation disorder, *Vogt-Koyanagi-Harada-like syndrome,* has been found in dogs. The same disease with the same name is found in man. This is thought to be a response to a viral infection or an *autoimmune disorder.* The eye lesions and skin lesions are progressive and usually result in euthanasia. In some cases, early treatment with *cortisone* will stop the eye lesions and may cause reversal of the depigmentation process over a period of months. The prognosis is guarded even with an early, accurate diagnosis.

PODODERMATITIS:

Pododermatitis is an inflammatory disease of the feet which can be caused by many agents. Because the cause of recurrent pododermatitis is not well understood, a diligent attempt must be made to discover the cause. *Skin scrapings, bacterial* and *fungal cultures, direct immunofluorescence, thyroid function tests, skin biopsies,* and *allergy testing* are necessary to discover the cause of pododermatitis. If a foreign body is suspected, a radiograph is also needed.

Inflammatory lesions on the feet are seen in short-haired breeds like the Doberman and appear to be more common in young males. Pododermatitis treatment includes antibacterial therapy with whirlpool treatments containing antibacterial solutions. The feet are occasionally treated with topical antibacterial preparations and bandaging. If *demodicosis* is a problem, the mites must be eliminated before the feet will clear up.

The prognosis for effective treatment is guarded to poor unless the cause can be determined. If a specific cause is determined, the prognosis improves to fair to good. However, treatment may be for prolonged periods.

POST PARTUM HAIR LOSS:

Refer to *TELOGEN EFFLUVIUM.*

PRESSURE POINT GRANULOMA:

Refer to *HYGROMA.*

PROGRESSIVE HYPOPIGMENTATION:

Refer to *PIGMENTATION DEFECTS* (acquired nasal depigmentation).

PRURITUS:

Pruritus, one of the signs of skin disease, is defined as itching. The following is a list of skin diseases causing pruritus

Allergy reactions	Insect bites
Foreign bodies	Parasites
Infections	Psychogenic factors
Inflammation	Ulcerative disease

PSYCHOGENIC DERMATOSES:

Refer to *ACRAL LICK* and *FLANK SUCKER.*

PYODERMA:

Deep and superficial pyodermas are bacterial infections of the skin and associated structures. The superficial pyodermas, like *impetigo* and *folliculitis*, involve the skin and hair follicle. Deep pyoderma affects layers beneath the skin including the subcutaneous tissues and deep sebaceous glands. A localized deep pyoderma is usually associated with a foreign body (foxtails, awns) penetration of the tissues. Generalized deep pyodermas are secondary to systemic problems such as cancer, immune deficiencies, *hypothyroidism, hyperadrenocorticism (Cushing's disease)*, or *demodicosis*.

Superficial pyodermas are treated with an appropriate antibiotic and medicated shampoo. In general, the antibiotic should be continued for three to four weeks. Treatment of deep pyodermas must be directed toward correcting the underlying problem and utilization of aggressive antibiotic therapy based on culture and sensitivity results for a minimum of six to eight weeks.

The prognosis for superficial pyodermas is good if therapy is continued long enough. Depending on the underlying cause and the type of bacteria causing the infection, the treatment of deep pyodermas has a guarded to good prognosis.

RED MANGE:

Refer to *DEMODICOSIS*.

RHABDITIC LARVAE DERMATITIS:

Rhabditic larvae dermatitis, also called *pelodera dermatitis,* is due to an invasion of the skin by a larva of the worm, <u>Pelodera strongyloides.</u> These parasites are found in marsh hay, straw, and rice hulls used for bedding. If a dog has direct contact with infested ground or bedding, red, raised, very itchy lesions on the abdomen develop. The hair follicles are inflamed. The lesions will become crusty from a secondary bacterial infection.

With a history of nonseasonal itching, rhabditic larvae dermatitis is diagnosed by *skin scrapings* and sometimes *biopsies.* An insecticidal dip and removal of the infected bedding results in a rapid recovery. Usually two weekly dips cure the dermatitis. The prognosis is excellent with appropriate treatment.

SARCOPTIC MANGE:

Refer to *SCABIES*.

SCABIES:

Scabies is a highly contagious, extremely itchy skin disease caused by the mite, <u>Sarcoptes scabiei.</u> This mite lives on the skin, burrows into the skin layers, lays eggs in these burrows, and hatches out. This life cycle is complete in three weeks. Because the mite prefers areas of the body that are somewhat devoid of hair, early infestations are seen on the elbows, hocks, abdomen, and ears. However, as the entire dog becomes parasitized, red papules (bumps) and scaly lesions with hair loss become generalized. This mite will temporarily infest people! Many times the diagnosis is made because itchy, red bumps are found at the beltline of the owner or at other areas where clothing is tight. Dogs with scabies are extremely pruritic (itchy). Even *cortisone* has little effect at alleviating the scratching.

The diagnosis is made by *skin scrapings* although many dogs with negative skin scrapings still have scabies. The history of an intense, nonseasonal, cortisone unresponsive itch, and human skin lesions make the diagnosis possible. Weekly insecticide dips for four to twelve weeks or for two weeks past the presence of any clinical signs compose the treatment for scabies. Although not cleared for use in scabies, *amitraz* (Mitaban®) is effective when done weekly or every two weeks for three dips. The safest treatment is lime-sulfur dipping. The odor is terrible but the dip is very safe. Little mite resistance has been observed. *Ivermectin* by injection is a new and effective treatment. Although not cleared for dog use, one injection is reported to cure scabies. Remember, a complete treatment can take several months until all of the mites are dead and the life cycle is broken. All animals in contact with the infected dog should be treated and the kennel environment should be cleaned thoroughly. Prognosis is good to excellent with adequate treatment.

SCALING:

Refer to *SEBORRHEA* and *SIGNS OF SKIN DISEASE.*

SEBACEOUS CYST:

Sebaceous (epidermal) cysts, most frequently found on the head, body, forelegs, and neck, are solitary skin growths containing a white cheesy material. If a cyst ruptures beneath the skin surface, a secondary infection and localized inflammatory reaction occurs. Treatment of these cysts is by surgical removal. Antibiotics are used if secondary infection is present. The prognosis is excellent after removal of an individual cyst. However, recurrence in other locations is the rule.

SEBORRHEA:

Seborrhea is a very important skin disorder in the Doberman Pinscher. This chronic skin disease is characterized by a defect in the maturing process of skin cells. Excess scaliness is observed. It is sometimes greasy. Infections in the skin can result from the excess sebaceous gland activity.

The three forms of the disease are classified by appearance: 1) seborrhea sicca (the dry, scaling form), 2) seborrhea oleosa (the greasy, waxy form), and 3) seborrheic dermatitis (both scales and greasiness are present with infections in the skin). The Doberman Pinscher is most commonly affected by seborrhea sicca.

After the disease is classified by cause, two general forms, primary seborrhea and secondary seborrhea, are distinguished. Primary seborrhea is a result of hormonal dysfunctions, defects in fat metabolism, or unknown causes. Secondary seborrhea occurs after infestations with *external parasites* (anything from mange to fleas), or from *fungus infections,* cancer, *allergies, drug* or *bacterial hypersensitivity,* and *autoimmune diseases.*
Identifying whether the problem is a primary or a secondary seborrhea is important. Many Dobe seborrhea problems are due to a *thyroid hormone* dysfunction. If the underlying cause can be determined and corrected, seborrhea can be controlled. Blue, fawn, and to some degree, red Dobermans have seborrhea associated with the *color mutant alopecia* syndrome. This type of seborrhea is very difficult to control.
While normal skin has a turnover rate of twenty days, seborrheic skin cells turn over every three to four days. Seborrheic skin has a very high amount of free fatty acids on the surface. Normal skin has a protective covering of waxes, esters, sterols, and cholesterol, but virtually no free fatty acids. Normal skin has few bacteria, while many pathogenic *Staph* are present on seborrheic skin.
Seborrhea therapy should include the use of medicated shampoos, nutritional supplements, treatment of seborrheic dermatitis infections with appropriate antibiotics, and possibly the use of certain hormones to decrease sebaceous gland activity. Medicated shampoos containing tar and sulfur will help remove scale and debris from the skin. These shampoos also decrease the amount of oil present on the surface. A bathing interval of three days to two weeks helps control seborrhea.
Unless a primary cause of seborrhea is determined and eliminated, symptomatic treatment must be maintained throughout the life of the dog. Prognosis for a cure is guarded. Prognosis for control is fair to excellent.

SIGNS OF SKIN DISEASE:

The following list of changes in the skin are signs of skin disease. Each is discussed separately within the chapter.

Acute moist dermatitis ("hot spot")   Hypopigmentation
Alopecia (Hair loss)   Icthyosis
Erythema   Pruritus
Folliculitis   Scaling (Refer to SEBORRHEA and
Hives (Angioedema)   SIGNS OF SKIN DISEASE)
Hyperkeratosis   Seborrhea (Dandruff)
Hyperpigmentation

SKIN SCRAPING:

Skin scraping testing is used by the veterinarian to determine the cause of some dermatoses, especially the identification of certain types of mange. *Demodex mange* mites are easily seen while *sarcoptic mange* mites can be extremely difficult to scrape because they burrow and tunnel in the skin layers. Skin scrapings are also useful in some tumor identifications. Cutaneous *mast cell tumors* can be identified in this manner. Scraping hair and scale is also helpful in identifying fungi that cause skin disease.

SKIN TESTS:

A number of skin tests are helpful in diagnosing the cause of skin disease. While general tests like *complete blood counts, urinalysis,* and *chem screen blood panels* help determine causes, specific skin tests may be necessary. Those listed below are discussed individually within the chapter.

Allergy testing	Direct immunofluorescence testing
ANA test	Impression smear
Biopsy, skin	Skin scraping
Culture, bacterial and fungal	

SKIN TUMORS:

Many tumors are related to the skin and associated structures. Below is a list of those discussed in this text.

Basal cell carcinoma	Malignant melanoma
Cutaneous lymphosarcoma	Mast cell tumor
Histiocytoma	Mammary gland tumors
Keloid	Perianal adenoma
Keratoacanthoma	Sebaceous cyst
Lipoma	Warts (Papilloma)

SOLAR DERMATITIS:

Refer to *PHOTODERMATITIS.*

SYSTEMIC LUPUS ERYTHEMATOSUS (SLE):

Approximately one-third of systemic lupus cases involve the skin. The type of skin involvement varies greatly. Excessive scaling *(seborrhea),* foot pad ulcers, *hyperkeratosis,* and ulceration at the lip-skin junction are common dermatologic signs of SLE. The diagnosis of lupus requires *ANA testing, biopsies,* and other lab data which must be compatible. Treatment is discussed in other chapters. Each treatment must be designed to fit the individual case. The prognosis is guarded to fair depending on the response to therapy. Refer to Chapter 6.

TELOGEN EFFLUVIUM (POST PARTUM HAIR LOSS):

The phenomenon of hair loss after the birth of puppies occurs in the bitch. Telogen effluvium is not a diseased state of the hair coat. The loss is due to the action of programming hormones which causes most individual hair shafts to pass into telogen (the resting phase of hair growth). Normally, each hair shaft does this individually. The synchronized telogen hair stage causes most of the coat to fall out in a large group simultaneously. The reason most dogs have a more magnificent hair coat after puppies is because all of their hair follicles become active while growing back in a synchronized manner.

TICKS:

The mouth of the tick attaches itself to dogs. They commonly are found in the ear, under the front leg (armpit), and between the toes. Ticks can cause hypersensitive skin reactions, produce *tick paralysis,* and be carriers of a number of viral and rickettsial diseases. Normally, ticks require three different hosts to complete their life cycle. However, the brown dog tick can complete its life cycle on the same dog making it difficult to break the life cycle of that species.

Ticks can be removed by first saturating the attached tick with rubbing alcohol and then using a tweezer or forceps to grasp the body of the tick. Steady traction will pull it out. The alcohol makes the tick release its hold as well as disinfecting the bite location. Insecticidal dips are effective in killing large numbers that can parasitize a dog during "tick seasons" in various parts of the country. Do not use kerosene, gasoline, or lighted cigarettes to remove ticks!

TOENAIL CUTTING:

A proper, tight foot can be maintained by frequent toenail cutting or grinding. If nails are allowed to grow long, the toes spread and the foot looses its strength. Nails can be shortened by weekly cutting to the tip of the quick. This causes the quick to recede, allowing further cutting of the nails. Eventually the desired length is achieved. Radically cutting the nails causing the quick to bleed profusely is unwise since infection is a frequent sequelae. Nail infections can be very difficult to eliminate. The Dremel® hobby grinding tool can easily be used to grind the nails down to the quick. Weekly grinding takes less than five minutes after the desired length of nail has been achieved.

TOXIC EPIDERMAL NECROLYSIS:

Toxic epidermal necrolysis (TEN) or Lyell's disease is a rare, painful ulcerative skin disease of dogs. An immune mediated response to drugs, cancer, infections, and other systemic disorders is the primary cause. The skin is painful. The dog is depressed with no appetite. While the initial actual lesion is a fluid filled pocket, ulceration of the skin is the first observed clinical defect. A *skin biopsy* is necessary for the diagnosis of TEN. Large doses of *cortisone* and other supportive therapy are the recommended treatment. Recovery takes two to three weeks. The prognosis for recovery is guarded to fair. A death rate approaching 25% to 30% occurs.

276 SKIN AND RELATED STRUCTURES

TREATMENT OF SKIN DISORDERS:

A large number of medications and forms of medications are used in the management of skin disorders. *Cortisone,* probably the most used and abused drug, comes in the form of pills, injections, salves, powders, and topical liquids. Its primary use is to control itching. While cortisone has antipruritic (anti-itch) and anti-inflammatory properties, it has some undesirable affects over the long term. Any corticosteroids taken either internally or applied topically to the skin can diminish the body's ability to fight infection. Its protein depletion effect on the body causes muscles to atrophy and the hair coat to become very sparse.

Some diseases do, in fact, require high doses of cortisone to control the effects of the disease. *Systemic lupus erythematosus* and the *pemphigus* class of skin conditions are examples. Use of cortisone for short-term seasonal allergy management is acceptable. However, repeated injections of potent corticosteroids to relieve an itchy dog create more risks than benefits.

Antibiotics are important drugs in skin disease treatment. If four to six weeks of routine antibiotic therapy does not eliminate an infection, *culture* and *sensitivity testing* should be considered to provide information on the most effective antibiotic on in vitro testing.

Medicated shampoos are necessary in the management of skin disease. Dogs with very sensitive skin do well with a hypoallergenic shampoo such as Allergroom® . The oxidizing agent, benzoyl peroxide, has a follicle flushing action in a type of medicated shampoo that is excellent in the management of folliculitis. Shampoos that help control excess scaling or *seborrhea* usually contain micronized tar, sulfur, and/or salicylic acid. The shampoos that contain tar are also antipruritic (anti-itch).

Hydrotherapy (soaking in water) is an excellent form of therapy for rehydrating dry skin. Combining a bactericidal liquid with warm water and adding a "whirlpool" action is very therapeutic for superficial skin disease.

Selenium sulfide, which is present in some shampoos, can be rather irritating even though it is a potent degreaser. Oils are sprayed on the coat or added to bath water to treat dry skin. While there are advantages to this form of therapy, if too much oil is used, it soon becomes evident around the house. Astringent liquids are used to dry up *acute moist dermatitis* (hot spots). A mixture of tannic acid, salicylic acid, and alcohol makes an excellent astringent for this purpose.

The complete coverage of the subject of treatment of skin disease is too complex for a text like this. A veterinarian who specializes in skin diseases can assist you further.

VITAMIN A DEFICIENCY SKIN DISEASE:

Two forms of vitamin A associated skin disease are observed in the dog. Although clinically they appear the same, in one an absolute *vitamin A deficiency* exists while in the other, no actual deficiency of vitamin A is found even though the affected dog responds to oral vitamin A. Vitamin A deficiency causes *hyperkeratosis* (an increased thickness to the layers of the skin and foot pads) in addition to generalized scaling with circular thick crusty lesions. Increased hair loss may be seen.

While vitamin A responsive dermatoses has not been reported in the Doberman Pinscher, they have been seen in Cocker Spaniels and Miniature Schnauzers. True vitamin A deficiency can occur in any breed. Today, however, with the availability of vitamin supplements and good dog foods, a true deficiency is unlikely because the liver is able to store adequate amounts of vitamin A.

WALKING DANDRUFF:

Refer to CHEYLETIELLA MANGE.

WARTS (PAPILLOMA):

Skin warts (cutaneous papillomas) are caused by a virus. These usually appear in young dogs. After growing rapidly for several months, they regress spontaneously with or without treatment. Clinically, they look like cauliflower growths affecting the head, feet, and mucous membranes of the mouth primarily. The form that affects older dogs does appear to affect males more frequently. These warts are usually singular in number. The treatment for warts is cryo-surgery, electrosurgery, wart vaccine usage, or "benign neglect" because most will spontaneously regress in two or three months.

ZINC RESPONSIVE SKIN DISEASE:

Two clinical syndromes that are zinc responsive occur in the Doberman Pinscher. Differentiating the signs is unimportant. In both cases, crusting plaques appear on the chin, ears, feet, foot pads, elbows, hocks, and other joints. These thickened, circular, inflamed lesions tightly adhere to the underlying skin. A generalized unthrifty coat appearance may also occur. Many of the affected puppies are sore and have fevers with swollen lymph nodes.

The disease is caused by either decreased absorption of zinc from the intestinal tract or a tying up of the zinc with phytates in plant protein found in dog food rather than from an actual deficiency of zinc in the diet. Over supplementation with *calcium* in growing puppies can also contribute to the syndromes.

Zinc responsive dermatoses are diagnosed by *biopsy* and lack of bacterial growth from a fresh lesion culture. Secondary infections may be observed if the lesion has been present for some time. Oral zinc supplementation is the treatment. A very rapid response is seen when zinc is given two times daily through the growth phase of life. After 14 months of age, an attempt should be made to stop zinc supplementation. While some Dobes do not need it as adults, others require zinc for life. The prognosis for normalcy is excellent with zinc supplementation and later without supplementation if the dog's system adjusts as an adult.

Chapter 12

UROGENITAL SYSTEM

Kidney, Reproductive Tract, Infertility

ABORTION:

The term abortion applies when the pregnancy ends early with the expulsion of one or more fetuses. Four conditions cause this uncommon problem. 1) Intrauterine infection may cause the death of the fetuses. As the tissues deteriorate, the dead fetuses and debris are discharged. 2) If the level of *progesterone* and its relationship with other hormones associated with pregnancy is not normal, a pregnancy may be terminated early. Usually all fetuses and tissues will be expelled. 3) The presence of a lethal gene which occurs from the combination of the sire's and dam's genetic pool may cause whelps to be born very prematurely so that life is not possible. 4) Most commonly, physiological crowding in the uterus causes an interruption in the viability of the placental attachment of some fetuses. In this case, some of the occupants of the uterus may be aborted while others can be carried to full term. On occasion, at normal parturition, a dead, partially formed puppy may be presented. Probably this is one that was crowded and expired earlier but could not be aborted due to its position in the uterus.

The treatment of a bitch to prevent future abortion requires a definitive diagnosis of the cause of the present abortion. Most important is to change the sire for the next litter. If a lethal genetic combination occurred, an unrelated sire should eliminate this possibility. Prebreeding *vaginal cultures* may assess the potential for intrauterine death from infection. A *canine brucellosis test* should be part of the prebreeding preparation. If a recurrence of the abortion happens after the above changes, the circulating *progesterone* levels should be measured on a weekly basis during a subsequent pregnancy. Under no circumstances should progesterone injections be given without knowing the physiologic level during all phases of pregnancy.

ADENOCARCINOMA:

Refer to *RENAL CANCERS.*

ANASARCA (WATER PUPPY):

Anasarca is a fetal abnormality most commonly seen in bulldog-type breeds. This can, however, occur in any breed. These puppies are totally filled with fluid, hence the common name *"water puppy."* The skin and all body tissues are engorged with fluid. Because of the dramatic increase in the size of the puppy, it usually cannot be delivered normally. Its presence is found on cesarean section. Not all puppies in a litter will appear as water puppies. Some of these puppies can be saved by using *furosemide,* a potent diuretic. Water puppies, if saved, should not be used for breeding purposes.

ANURIA:

Refer to *KIDNEY FAILURE.*

ARTIFICIAL INSEMINATION:

Artificial insemination (AI) may be performed for a variety of reasons. Some bitches are either temperamentally or physiologically incompatible with certain stud dogs. With the advances in *frozen semen* technology, bitches can be inseminated with semen from stud dogs that have died years ago or that live halfway around the world. Artificial insemination may also protect the stud or bitch from certain venereal diseases.

Most kennel clubs around the world have regulations to follow for artificial insemination procedures. These rules and regulations are directed primarily at the control and registration of litters derived from frozen semen. Before conducting an artificial insemination procedure, a letter to the American Kennel Club, 51 Madison Avenue, New York, NY 10010, requesting the current rules and regulations on artificial insemination is necessary. Most kennel clubs require the AI procedure to take place in the presence of or under the auspices of a veterinarian.

Several factors play a part in the effectiveness of artificial insemination in achieving conception. Because sperm are very easily killed, absolute asepsis is mandatory. All equipment must be sterilized by heat since chemical disinfectants kill sperm. Sperm are also very susceptible to many kinds of rubber or latex collection systems and insemination tubes. In addition, cold and heat can shock sperm to render them unviable.

BIOPSY, KIDNEY:

Kidney biopsies provide valuable information as to the degree of involvement and the prognosis of various kidney diseases. With biopsy information, exact treatment can be formulated. Because many kidney patients are gravely ill making them very poor anesthetic risks, the use of deep *sedation* and *local anesthesia* is most desirable in performing kidney biopsies. Uncontrolled hemorrhaging is a possible complication in the biopsy procedure. Because the surgeon is working through a small opening in the side, good visualization of the kidney being biopsied is impossible. Therefore, better than average surgical skill and special equipment are required for successful kidney biopsies.

BIOPSY, TESTICULAR:

Testicular biopsy can provide important information as to causes of infertility. Biopsies can be used for *chromosome infertility work* or for examination of the usual cell type present and maturation process. Testicular biopsy is usually done under general anesthesia. A small plug of testicular tissue is severed by a sharp, razor-like blade and immediately placed in fixative solution. For testicular biopsies, Bouin's fixative is recommended over the usual formalin. While some hemorrhage is associated with the surgical procedure, it usually is not a problem. Because of the manipulation of the testes, temporary sterility may be experienced. Barring unforeseen complications, any sterility initiated by the testicular biopsy is temporary.

BIRTH CONTROL METHODS:

Numerous methods for preventing unwanted litters of puppies exist. While some procedures are well established, some are still in the experimental stage. Both immunologic and irradiation methods of reproduction control are still very experimental.

Birth control methods are grouped into surgical and nonsurgical methods. The most common surgical procedure in the bitch is the **spay operation (ovariohysterectomy).** In this procedure, the bitch is given a general anesthesia. The uterus and both ovaries are then removed through an abdominal incision. Recovery from this major surgery is rapid. All normal activities can be resumed in 10 to 14 days when the sutures are removed. In the Doberman Pinscher, the ideal age for this surgery is just before the first heat period at six months of age. It can, however, be done at any age. Because of the prevalence of *Von Willebrand's disease* and *copper hepatitis,* your veterinarian may want to run some lab tests before undertaking this procedure. A rapid test for VWD and a *SGPT liver enzyme test* are desirable. Because blood clotting is not normal during an actual *heat period,* the only "bad" time to perform this operation is during this three week period.

Tubal ligation can be done in the bitch but is not routinely performed. The undesirable traits of the *heat period* such as the attraction of male dogs and the mess associated with blood spotting during *estrus* would still be present. Also, ovaries are not routinely left in place in the bitch because of the heat cycle and bloody discharge associated with them. Most spayed bitches do not suffer from *estrogen* shortages during their lives without the *estrus* cycle. However, in a few spayed bitches, a lack of bladder sphincter muscle control may occur with advanced years. This estrogen deficiency can be controlled nicely with *DES (diethylstilbestrol)* once a week.

Neutering (castration), is the most common surgical birth control method in the male dog. While under *general anesthesia,* both testicles are removed through one incision ahead of the scrotum. Postoperatively in dogs the size of the Doberman Pinscher, some swelling may occur but this usually dissipates without treatment in four to six days. A **vasectomy** can be done in place of *castration* in selected dogs. Because the procedure takes almost as long as the castration surgery, a vasectomy is generally reserved for dogs that are going to be shown but for some reason are rendered incapable of producing pups. Following a vasectomy, the testicles may undergo some minor degenerative changes making some conformation dog show judges suspicious.

The use of intravaginal devices is not common in the bitch. Over the years, several have been introduced with questionable effectiveness. Because of the great variation in size of bitches, an exact fit was difficult to find.

The other nonsurgical means of birth control is through drug administration. Currently, two pharmacological compounds are licensed for use in the United States to prevent reproduction in the bitch. **Cheque® drops** *(mibolerone),* manufactured by Upjohn Company as a liquid, is an anabolic and androgenic *steroid* compound. When given orally every day, it is 90% effective in keeping bitches out of heat. This drug should not be given before the first heat period. Usage should not exceed two consecutive years. The drops can be started again after 30 days or after the heat period is over if the estrus period begins after the drug has been stopped. *Cheque®* is well tolerated with all forms of *heartworm preventative medication.* It should not be used in bitches with a history of *liver* or *kidney disease.* Because the Doberman Pinscher is at higher risk for the development of *chronic active copper hepatitis,* this drug should be used with care. Liver enzyme levels should be checked two times a year. Over 40% of the bitches given *Cheque® drops* will show one or more of the following side effects. In order of decreasing frequency, clitoral enlargement which may even protrude through the vulvar lips, a sticky white vaginal discharge, increased tearing, increased body odor, and, least common, riding behavior. If the side effects are objectionable, the drug should be discontinued.

The compound *megestrol acetate* marketed by Schering Corporation as **Ovaban®** is the other form of oral birth control medication. This *progestational hormone* derivative is basically designed to postpone the heat cycle. It should not be used before the first heat cycle has been completed. Ovaban® is also contraindicated in pregnant bitches, in those with *breast tumors,* and in those with uterine diseases.

If *Ovaban®* treatment is started during the first three days of the heat period, a high eight day dosage is given to abbreviate the heat cycle. The signs of heat diminish quickly and attraction to male dogs should cease. If the tablets have been given for three consecutive days and a breeding should occur, conception should be prevented. If the treatment is started during *anestrus* (nonheat), a low 32-day dosage schedule is administered postponing the start of heat for two to nine months.

Certain situations indicate a need for the use of megestrol acetate (*Ovaban®*). Treatment is most useful in regulating an upcoming heat for show, vacation, or hunting season purposes. Good owner compliance is necessary for proper medication. The drug is expensive and may only be used for two consecutive dosage schedules.

Injectable progestational compounds like Depo-Provera® are sometimes used in the control of *estrus cycles*. These are not approved for this purpose for dogs and can be very dangerous. A much greater chance of development of *pyometra* is present after a progestational compound is injected. The drug may be long-acting resulting in bitches that will either no longer cycle normally or must be *spayed* because of an infected uterus.

A most effective form of birth control that is too seldom used properly is the **LEASH**. If a bitch in heat is on a leash and under the direct supervision of her owner, unwanted pregnancies will not occur.

BLOODY URINE:

Refer to *HEMATURIA*.

BREEDING (NORMAL AND ABNORMAL):

The act of breeding domesticated dogs can be a challenging adventure. In the wild, nature may eliminate two as a breeding pair because they are not physically or possibly psychologically compatible. Man, in his infinite wisdom, determines that two of the same breed should bear offspring and sets about the task of creating a litter of puppies. Our reasons for wanting puppies are many. Some genuinely desire to improve the breed. Others hope to make money selling the offspring. The desire to show children the "miracle of birth" may enter into the decision. Or, a mating of convenience may take place since we have a Dobe bitch and our neighbor has a Dobe male.

The only valid reason for bringing a litter of puppies into the world is in an attempt to improve on the genotype and phenotype of both parents. This goal requires planning and an expenditure of time and money to search out a complementary member of the opposite sex. One should never knowingly breed a dog with a serious genetically-linked medical problem. In some cases, a thorough prebreeding examination should be undertaken. Possible genetic conditions of concern in the Doberman Pinscher include *Von Willebrand's disease, wobbler syndrome, panosteitis, hypocortical kidney disease, cardiomyopathy, neutrophil bactericidal defect, chronic active copper hepatitis, narcolepsy,* and, of course, extreme variations in temperament. After a determination has been made that the Dobe bitch can be bred, a careful search for the most complimentary male is undertaken. The male should be strong in the areas where the bitch is weak, in both structural and mental properties. To breed two shy, fearful Doberman Pinschers is just as tragic as breeding two that are physically deficient in the same areas.

Elsewhere in this chapter and in Chapter 4 on HORMONES are topics of interest to those who aspire to raise puppies.

BREEDING FREQUENCY:

The frequency with which the dog and the bitch should be bred is open to conjecture. One breeding at the proper time is all that is necessary for fertilization to take place. If *smears* and *cervical glucose* are not used as criteria of *ovulation*, breeding the bitch every other day is the safest method of coordinating the meeting of sperm and ova.

In a normal *estrus cycle*, the bitch will first stand for the male dog on the ninth or tenth day after the first sign of a bloody discharge. Breeding on these days may be accompanied by some discomfort on the part of the bitch. A second breeding two days later usually does not cause any signs of discomfort in the bitch. If both partners are present, a third breeding should be consummated in 48 hours. While this spreads the due date over a six day period, you or your veterinarian can, by palpation, determine the twenty-eighth day from the successful breeding. Adding five weeks to the twenty-eighth day will accurately predict the parturition (whelping) date.

Some bitches are "breedable" for a two week period. The use of *vaginal smears* and *Tes-Tape®* to measure cervical glucose release are then necessary to determine the time of ovulation in the bitch. Many experienced stud dogs will not show interest in a bitch until the time she ovulates. The experienced stud dog may make lab tests obsolete.

BREEDING TIE:

The physical mechanics of the "tie" rely on the constrictor muscles of the bitch's vagina to hold the engorged male penis. The muscles constrict behind the enlarged bulb of the penis, preventing the stud from pulling away. The length of the tie can vary from five to fifty minutes. Older males frequently have longer ties. Their venous blood return is less efficient than that of a young male. A bitch should be tended to while the tie "is in progress." If she rolls on her back while tied, the male may be injured. A tie is not necessary for conception to take place. While a tie does not insure conception, it does assure that most of the semen will be deposited in the forward compartment of the vagina.

BRUCELLOSIS, CANINE:

Canine brucellosis is caused by the bacteria, *Brucella canis.* In 1966, it was found to be a disease separate from the other Brucella bacteria that infect cows, pigs, and goats. This disease affects the reproductive tracts in both the dog and the bitch. Stud dogs may show some lymph node swelling early in the disease. Swelling of the testes follows, then atrophy (shrinkage) from the inflammatory changes that occur. While most males are then sterile, some may still produce abnormal sperm contained in semen full of inflammatory cells.

The bitch most commonly is an inapparent carrier. She will have a history of not getting pregnant or of delivering a few dead or soon to die, weak puppies. Actual *abortions* are not uncommon between the 45th and 54th day. The vaginal discharge which follows lasts for a long time. This discharge is highly infective to any dog or person with whom it comes in contact. The disease is transmitted by breeding contact with an infected dog or contact with infected tissues or discharges following abortion or stillborn delivery. Since humans are susceptible to *canine brucellosis,* the disease has definite public health significance.

Elimination of the disease from a breeding kennel requires radical steps. All dogs in the kennel that test positive (1:200) on tube agglutination should be destroyed. If this is not possible, all of the infected bitches should be *spayed* and then placed on high levels of specific antibiotics for 60 days. They should then be tested monthly for six months to insure that they are no longer carriers. Since the organisms which isolate in the male *prostate* cannot be removed easily by surgery, all males should be destroyed. Long term high levels of appropriate antibiotics might eliminate the organism, but there is no guarantee.

All dogs must be tested to keep the infection out of an active breeding kennel. Each bitch coming in for stud service must be tested negative before service. All studs being breed to bitches should be tested before the breeding takes place. A rapid slide *brucellosis test* which is discussed next is an effective screening procedure performed in the veterinarian's office.

BRUCELLOSIS TESTING:

Almost every veterinarian can provide the rapid slide agglutination test for canine brucellosis. A small blood sample is required from which one drop of serum is mixed with a specific antigen tagged with a pink dye. A positive test sample is run at the same time to compare for results. If agglutination (clumping) occurs in two minutes, the test is considered positive. Since false positives do occur with some frequency, don't go out and immediately shoot the entire kennel!

Another blood sample should then be sent to the state diagnostic lab where a tube agglutination test will be performed. Sometimes blood cultures are requested. Only after these subsequent tests confirm the slide results should you be concerned. All positive tests should be confirmed by sending serum to Baker Institute, School of Veterinary Medicine, Cornell University, Ithaca, NY 14853.

Fortunately, virtually no false negative slide agglutination tests occur. A negative rapid test means the dog or bitch is clear. The rapid slide agglutination brucellosis test is available from Pitman-Moore Company, Washington Crossing, NJ 08560.

BUN TEST (BLOOD UREA NITROGEN):

The BUN (blood urea nitrogen) or *SUN (serum urea nitrogen)* test is a blood test commonly done to evaluate kidney function. A rough estimation of glomerular filtration within the kidneys is obtained. In all dogs, except the Dalmatian, the end product of protein metabolism is urea which is excreted by the kidneys. Even with adequate kidney function, *adrenal gland failure, congestive heart failure,* very high levels of protein ingestion, and dehydration and shock will elevate BUN levels. The normal levels are between 10 and 20 mg/dl. Serious clinical signs are observed at levels over 40 to 50 mg/dl. BUN tests should be repeated as therapy progresses to ascertain progress.

CANINE BRUCELLOSIS:

Refer to *BRUCELLOSIS, CANINE.*

CALCULI - RENAL, URETHRAL, BLADDER:

Calculi are mineral composition stones located somewhere that stones should not be found. In the urinary system, stones can be classified by their location in the system. Most commonly, single or multiple stones are found in the urinary bladder. The composition of calculi in the urinary bladder may be magnesium ammonium phosphate, calcium oxalate, ammonium urate, or cystine. While most stones are smooth, the oxalate calculi can be rough. Struvite is the crystal name of the magnesium ammonium phosphate. Calculi can also be located in the kidney pelvis, ureter, and urethra.

Difficulty in urinating and blood in the urine are the most common signs of urinary tract calculi. To determine the presence of "stones," various diagnostic aids may be needed. If the dog is thin and relaxed, some urinary bladder calculi can be *palpated* through the abdominal wall. *Urinalysis* and radiographs help with the determination of bladder stones. Special radiographic techniques like *intravenous pyelography* may be necessary to outline stones in the kidney pelvis or ureters.

Treatment of calculi is the surgical removal of the stones. Most veterinary practitioners can surgically remove stones from the urinary bladder and urethra. The level of surgical skill must be quite high to remove kidney and ureter calculi. Recently, a medical option to surgical removal of struvite-type stones has been brought forward. The patient is fed Prescription Diet® S/D and maintained on an appropriate antibiotic for approximately six weeks. The process is accelerated if a urease inhibitor is added to the treatment regimen. By keeping the pH of urine acid, struvite becomes much more soluble. Because of anatomical differences in the urinary tract of male and female dogs, this nonsurgical regimen is much more appropriate for bitches. Only when a single large calculus exists in the male dog urinary bladder should this form of therapy be considered for males. All dogs that have had urinary tract calculi removed either medically or surgically should be maintained on K/D Prescription Diet® for the remainder of their lives to prevent reformation of calculi.

CASTRATION:

Refer to *BIRTH CONTROL METHOD.*

CATHETERIZATION:

Refer to URINE SPECIMEN, COLLECTION OF.

CESAREAN SECTION:

Cesarean section (C-section) is the surgical delivery of puppies from the bitch through an incision in the abdominal wall. Many unnecessary C-sections are done for the convenience of the owner and/or the veterinarian. Because some bitches are very slow whelpers, due to the impatience of others, they are subjected to cesarean sections before being allowed to whelp the entire litter. The definite indications for cesarean section are *uterine inertia (primary or secondary),* history of broken pelvis in the pregnant bitch, radiographic evidence of a very large fetus, and the development of toxemia during pregnancy or delivery.

Whether or not a C-section should be done during parturition is a judge-ment call. With *dystocia* (difficult delivery), the bitch becomes a poorer surgical risk as time passes. To minimize chances of death to the bitch and/or the newborn whelps, early sections are most productive. Some of these, however, are not necessary. A good breeder-veterinarian team effort will know which bitch will need sectioning.

The dangers to the bitch in a C-section are from excessive hemorrhage, hypovolemic shock during or immediately after surgery, and, unfortunately, anesthesia accidents. Anesthesia is the veterinarian's preference. Some use *Innovar-Vet®* and a *local* block (freezing) along the midline to avoid fetal depression. Control of the bitch may be marginal. Some are able to use *sedatives* and *gaseous anesthesia* via mask and endotracheal tube with little fetal depression. Your veterinarian will use what works best for him to result in a live bitch and live puppies.

Most cesarean section incisions are made along the midline from the umbilical scar to the pelvis. Rare veterinarians make flank incisions separating muscles down to the pregnant uterus. An incision is then made in the upper or lower side of the body of the uterus. All pups are delivered through that one incision. After one last abdominal inspection, the uterus is closed with *cat gut suture.* The abdomen is flushed with antibiotic-saline solution and closed in several layers. One common postoperative problem is wound dehiscence (opening of the incision) because the puppies may nurse on the sutures or fetal fluids may have caused some abdominal infection. Because of this fact, the use of *stainless steel sutures* and antibiotic therapy post C-section may be indicated. All C-sections should be supported by intravenous fluid therapy during and for a short time following the surgery.

Once the bitch has recovered from the anesthesia, she should be sent home to be in her normal environment with her puppies. Unless postsurgical adhesions become too much of a problem, litters can be delivered yearly by cesarean section.

CHORIONIC GONADOTROPIN:

Chorionic gonadotropin (HCG) has a direct affect on follicular growth in the ovary and on interstitial cells of the testes in the male dog. Some forms of hormonal imbalance or insufficiency are treated with this substance. HCG has both *FSH* (follicle stimulating hormone) and *LH* (luteinizing hormone) activity. Chorionic gonadotropin is found in human pregnancy urine and in pregnant mare's serum.

CHROMOSOME COUNTING:

One form of infertility in the male dog is due to chromosomal abnormalities in which two or more X chromosomes exist in the male sex chromosome composition. This abnormality is called *Klinefelter's syndrome*. The only way to identify this syndrome is by *"karyotyping"* which grows cells from the suspected dog and identifies the sex chromatin bodies in the cell nuclei. This exacting procedure can only be done in a few laboratories. Contact Dr. Shirley Johnston at the University of Minnesota College of Veterinary Medicine, St. Paul, MN, for specifics on their capabilities.

CHRONIC INTERSTITIAL NEPHRITIS (CIN):

The end stage of kidney disease, if it occurs over a long period of time, is chronic scarring and inflammation of the kidneys. Many dogs by the age of eight or nine years will experience some deterioration in kidney function. The thousands of active functional units within the kidney called glomeruli, are tiny filters which are replaced by scar tissue as they wear out, reducing the size of the kidney.

In chronic kidney disease, generally an increase in water consumption becomes noticeable to the owner. As the kidney deficiency increases, the level of *uremia* in the blood stream also increases causing the dog to refuse food and to start to vomit. Unless the condition is treated and the level of uremia is decreased, the dog will develop severe electrolyte imbalances. The uremia will then become fatal.

This condition is diagnosed by a *urinalysis* specific gravity test. Affected dogs cannot concentrate urine making their specific gravity levels less than 1.030. The *BUN* and *creatinine* levels are also measured. Because of the chronic nature of the condition, a *nonregenerative anemia* is usually present.

The treatment for chronic interstitial nephritis includes free choice water, elimination of stress or hard work, supplementation with extra water soluble *B complex and C vitamins,* and the feeding of a restricted, high quality kind of protein diet. Adding sodium bicarbonate to the diet to alter the disturbed acid-base balance in the body may also be necessary. *Phosphate binders* like Amphojel® liquid (from Wyeth Laboratories) are useful in lowering high blood phosphorus levels associated with uremia. The kidney degenerative process cannot be cured. With proper care, however, a relatively normal life can be maintained. The protein restricted diets are not as palatable as normal menus. Heating the canned K/D or adding a small amount of chicken or turkey fat to the diet makes it more appealing. Dogs that require restricted protein diets are best fed three or four small meals daily instead of one big one!

"CLEAN OUT SHOT":

After a bitch has delivered her litter, an injection of oxytocin (POP-posterior oxytocic principle or PIT-Pituitrin®) is customary. There are many names for the same injection. The purpose of the injection is to stimulate milk letdown and to cause the uterus to contract, expelling any fluid or placentas still present. Giving an injection AFTER all of the puppies are whelped is good practice. Unfortunately, the practice is abused when owners attempt to speed up the delivery of puppies with oxytocin. While it may be successful some of the time, the shot can be dangerous since a violent drug-induced contraction can rupture the uterus. The "clean out shot" is best given by the veterinarian after an examination has shown the bitch is at the end of the delivery or only has one pup to go.

CREATININE TEST:

The creatinine test evaluates the kidney filtration function. Unlike the *BUN test,* the creatinine level is not affected by exercise, age, dietary protein intake, or protein breakdown. To prognosticate the outcome of a kidney disease, a series of creatinine tests are run as the treatment continues. Any creatinine level that stays at a high plane warrants a guarded prognosis.

CRYPTORCHIDISM:

Cryptorchidism is the failure of testes to descend normally into the scrotum. Affected dogs are more accurately identified as being unilateral cryptorchids if one testicle is not descended and as bilateral cryptorchids if both testes failed to descend properly. Whether or not a genetic component is responsible for this problem is debatable. The possibility that sibling litter mates may carry the genetic potential to produce cryptorchid offspring exists.

The American Kennel Club does not allow the showing of dogs that do not have two normal testicles properly descended in the scrotum. Also, while a unilateral cryptorchid male is usually capable of reproduction, breeding these individuals is discouraged. As a general rule, both testicles in the Doberman Pinscher should be descended and in the scrotum by 12 weeks of age. On occasion, one testicle may be slow in descending into the scrotum.

If one testicle is normally descended and the other can be found within one inch (2-1/2 cm) of the scrotum, the puppy should be observed up to nine months of age. If the testicle is not in place by that age, it generally will not descend.

Breeders and owners have used numerous methods to "encourage" an undescended testicle to move down into the scrotum. Most of these methods are therapy for the owners rather than the dog. The use of the male hormone, *testosterone,* is not effective and may actually be dangerous by producing a rebound sterility in the dog. Stroking and stretching a testicle that is almost down might be of some benefit. It certainly won't hurt. The surgical manipulation of a testicle can be construed as changing the normal appearance of the dog and would therefore be against American Kennel Club rules. The most realistic philosophy is, "If they descend, they descend. If they don't, they don't."

From a health standpoint, a much greater incidence of cancer is diagnosed in undescended testicles. Males with unilateral or bilateral cryptorchid problems should be *castrated* before five years of age. The undescended testicles should be removed even if they are abdominal and have not developed at all.

CYSTIC OVARIES:

Cystic ovaries are a cause of *infertility* in the bitch. In cases where the *estrus cycle* does not proceed past the point of vaginal bleeding and attraction of male dogs, cystic ovaries should be suspected. Bitches will cycle very frequently or appear to remain in heat continually. The term *nymphomania* is used when the *estrogen* levels remain at abnormally high planes and the bitch exhibits continual signs of *heat.*

Cystic ovaries contain multiple thin-walled cystic cavities filled with fluid. Some veterinarians advocate removing these cystic structures from the ovaries. Most others feel the only reasonable method of dealing with the problem is to *spay* the bitch. Hormone injections have been universally unproductive in correcting the cystic ovary condition.

CYSTITIS:

Cystitis refers to inflammation of the bladder which may be due to infection, *cancer, calculi,* or drugs. The signs of cystitis are frequent unproductive urination. The urine may contain blood and, on microscopic analysis, many cells from the bladder lining, bacteria, and white blood cells may be observed. Identifying the cause of cystitis is important. Radiography, *urinalysis,* and *urine cultures* may be required. Proper treatment can be initiated after the cause is determined. Some infections require months of medication to resolve.

CYSTOCENTESIS:

Refer to *URINE SPECIMEN, COLLECTION OF.*

DIALYSIS:

Kidney dialysis is not routinely done in veterinary medicine. However, a technique called *peritoneal dialysis* can achieve the same cleansing effect of the blood. Several recent advances have made peritoneal dialysis more realistic for the average veterinary practice. The new concept uses the peritoneal lining of the abdomen to diffuse toxic build-up products from the body into a special solution which is placed in the abdomen for a period of 45 to 50 minutes. The fluid is then removed, containing one-half of the amount of toxic waste levels present in the blood. Drawbacks to peritoneal dialysis are the possibility of peritonitis (infection) developing, abdominal trauma from the catheter, electrolyte imbalances, and cardiovascular problems resulting from the abdomen filling with dialyzing fluid too rapidly.

The Purdue column disc peritoneal dialysis catheter® , a specialized catheter that does not become blocked, was developed at Purdue University. This allows for continuous dialysis to occur once the catheter has been placed in the abdomen. This catheter can be ordered from Hemodialysis Laboratory, Purdue University, West Lafayette, IN 47907.

Dialysis is not the answer for every kidney disorder. If the trauma to the kidney is acute and recovery could be expected if the kidneys could rest, the dialysis system can be very effective. However, if the kidneys cannot regenerate or are totally scarred down, dialysis will only postpone for a short while death from kidney failure.

DIETS:

The special diets associated with dogs suffering from kidney disease are designed to provide restricted amounts of protein of a very high biological value. These diets are well described in Chapter 8 on NUTRITION. Also discussed in Chapter 8 are diets necessary for pregnant and lactating bitches which must provide higher levels of protein and fat.

DIFFICULT BIRTH:

Refer to *DYSTOCIA*.

DRUGS USED SAFELY DURING PREGNANCY:

None of the drugs in the following list cause birth defects when used during pregnancy.

Acetylcysteine	Chlorpheniramine	Diethylcarbamazine
Amoxicillin	Chymotrypsin	Digitoxin
Ampicillin	Clonazepam	Digoxin
Atropine	Codeine	Dimenhydrinate
Cephalexin	Dextromethorphan	Diphenhydramine
Chloramphenicol—	Dichlorvos	Disophenol
(last half of gestation)	Dicloxacillin	Doxapram

Doxylamine	Metaproterenol	Pyrantel
Enflurane	Methapyrrilene	Pyrilamine
Ephedrine	Methenamine	Salbutamol
Furosemide	Methohexital	Spironolactone
Glycopyrrolate	Miconazole	Sulfonamides —
Guaifenesin	Morphine	(Short-acting)
Halothane	Niclosamide	Tetracaine
Heparin	Nitrous oxide	Theophylline
Kanamycin	Oxytocin	Thiopental
Ketamine	Penicillin	Tiletamine
Lidocaine	Pilocarpine	Triamterene
Lincomycin	Piperazine	Urokinase
Mannitol	Pralidoxime	
Mebendazole	Procaine	

DRUGS THAT MAY BE USED WITH SOME RISK DURING PREGNANCY:

During pregnancy, drugs from the following list should be used after weighing the risk-benefit factors and then only with extreme caution. Some of the drugs listed have caused abnormalities in one species of lab animal. Other drugs are listed in this group because no information is available on their activity on the fetus during pregnancy.

Acepromazine	Iron dextran	Procainamide
Aminopentamide	Lenperone	Proparacaine
Arsenamide	Levamisole	Propiopromazine
Aspirin	Liothyronine	Pyrimethamine
Bunamidine	Methylprednisolone	Ronnel
Cimetidine	Methocarbamol	Spectinomycin
Cortisone	Methoxyflurane	Stanazolol
Cythioate	Neostigmine	Styrylpyridium
Dapsone	Nystatin	Thiabendazole
Dichlorophene	Phthalofyne	Thyroxin
Dithiazanine	Physostigmine	Toluene
Fentanyl-droperidol	Prazosin	Trichlorfon
Hydralazine	Prednisone	Xylazine
Hydrocortisone	Prednisolone	

DRUGS THAT SHOULD NOT BE USED DURING PREGNANCY:

All of the drugs listed below have adverse effects on the fetus, either causing fetal death or leading to the development of congenital anomalies (defects). In the case of *anticonvulsants,* it is better to risk hemorrhage or congenital anomalies in the newborn than to chance the development of *status epilepticus* as described in Chapter 7. Their usage should be continued with this in mind.

ALL anticancer drugs (azathioprine, cyclophosphamide)
ALL anticonvulsant drugs (phenobarbital, phenytoin, diazepam, primidone)
ALL anti-inflammatory drugs (aspirin, glucocorticoids, DMSO, phenylbutazone)

Amikacin	Gentocin®	Nitrofurantoin
Amphotericin B	Gold salts	Propranolol
Anticoagulants	Griseofulvin	Streptomycin
Chloramphenicol (early)	Isoproterenol	Sulfonamides —
Chlorpromazine	Male hormones	(long-acting)
Cholinesterase inhibitors	Meclizine	Tetracyclines
Erythromycin estolate	Mepivacaine	Trimethoprim
Female hormones (estrogen)	Metronidazole	Vitamins A, D, K

DRYING UP A LACTATING BITCH:

Drying up the milk supply from a lactating bitch can be painless to all involved if it is done in a sensible manner. The *weaning process* begins when the first food supplementation is given to three or four week old puppies. Any weaning process must be gradual. Remember, as the food provided for the weaning aged puppies is increased, the food for the lactating bitch must be decreased. If the changes are made over a 10 to 14 day period, the puppies can go from eating a milky gruel on a daily basis to consuming soaked dry-type puppy food four times a day. When four times daily puppy feeding is accomplished, the bitch should be fasted one day with only a small amount of water to drink. On the day the bitch is fasted, the puppies should be totally separated from her. This separation should continue for a minimum of 10 days following.

After the one day fast, the bitch is fed a small amount once daily. The amount is increased until she is back to her prepregnant food ration level. By allowing the bitch to have contact with the puppies up to eight weeks of age, some behavioral benefits may be observed.

DYSTOCIA (DIFFICULT BIRTH):

Dystocia may be the fault of the pregnant bitch or of the unpresented fetus. **Maternal dystocia** is caused by an abnormality in some part of the bitch's anatomy. These irregularities may be present from birth or acquired during pregnancy or later life.

The following anatomical abnormalities may cause labor and delivery to be difficult or impossible. The pelvic canal may be too small to accommodate a normal sized puppy. This is more of a problem in breeds like Bulldogs and Pugs which are a large-headed, small-waisted breed type. In some heavily pregnant bitches, a very acute angle has formed in the birth canal and the bony pelvis. The acute angle is very difficult to ascend causing labor to be unproductive and prolonged. This form of dystocia can be treated by using a towel to form a sling around the abdomen. The towel sling is raised as the bitch contracts making it possible to straighten the birth canal angle enough to deliver several pups in this manner. With less uterine weight, the bitch may be better able to complete the delivery process.

A broken pelvis may narrow the birth canal as it heals. Other scar tissue and adhesions make a *cesarean section* mandatory. The C-section can be planned for the 60th to 61st day of pregnancy. The bitch does not need to go into actual labor before the surgery.

Obstructions along the birth canal can cause dystocia. In unusual cases, tumors that can obstruct the delivery process may be present in the vaginal vault or in the cervical area. More commonly, juvenile vulvae may make delivery of the first pup too painful. If the vulva does not dilate as the pup is presented, an *episiotomy* (surgical enlarging of the vulvar opening) may be necessary.

All of the other maternal causes of dystocia are due to problems associated with the uterus. **Primary uterine inertia** occurs when the muscular wall of the uterus fails to contract. In primary uterine inertia, the usual signs seen with all stages of labor are missing. In many cases, the only sign that the due date has come and gone is a temperature decrease which has since returned to normal. If there is to be any hope of saving the whelps, bitches with primary uterine inertia should have a *cesarean section* when their temperature drops. Because a definite genetic relationship is seen in this condition, breeders are advised to cull affected bitches from their breeding programs in the future.

Secondary uterine inertia can occur after a long delivery of most of a large litter. In this situation, the last several pups are not delivered. The bitch may appear to rest and be finished with her delivery. This type of inertia is usually secondary and a short rest period (several hours) may be all that she needs before delivering the last whelps. Too frequently, a cesarean section is undertaken but is not actually necessary.

Two conditions involve the amount of fetal fluids present in the uterus. In the first instance, virtually no liquid is present around the fetus. After contractions start, an observer is impressed by how little fluid is found with contractions. Since most of these placentas fail to peel out of the uterine wall, a C-section will usually be needed with fair to poor pup livability.

The other extreme, *hydrops allantois*, is too much fluid associated with the puppies. Bitches with this problem will appear overly distended during late pregnancy. This extreme build-up of fluid can cause both respiratory and cardiac difficulty because of the abnormal distension of the abdomen. To further complicate matters, bitches with this condition have very poor uterine contractions because the uterine musculature and been stretched beyond its contractile abilities. While *cesarean sections* are often needed, beware of the more guarded prognosis with hydrops allantois. Sudden relief of the built-up abdominal pressure may cause irreversible cardiac shock. Puppies delivered from the excessive fluid compartments in the bitch generally show poor livability.

The causes of **dystocia due to the fetus** can be related to its size, the position of its delivery, and to rare fetal monsters. An oversized puppy may not be able to be delivered through a normal-sized birth canal. Puppies in one or two puppy litters are more apt to be too large. Puppies that are presented or positioned abnormally may be difficult to deliver in a normal manner. While 40% of all puppies are born in the breech position, two rear feet with toes pointing down and a tail should be found for a normal breech position. In the Doberman Pinscher, the size of the vaginal vault allows for some manipulation and repositioning in puppies that are not properly presented. While it is sometimes impossible to save the malpositioned pup, if it can be delivered, the remainder of the litter can be born normally without the aid of a C-section.

The most common fetal abnormalities are *anasarca (water puppies)*, *hydrocephalus*, and *Schistosoma reflexa*. All of these conditions may make a cesarean section necessary. In most cases, only one or two puppies in a litter will show fetal monstrosity signs. If the entire litter is affected, an infection or medication taken during pregnancy is probably the cause.

ECLAMPSIA (MILK FEVER):

Among the names that exist for eclampsia are *hypocalcemia, postparturient tetany,* and *milk fever.* This condition usually occurs during delivery or shortly after whelping but it may be seen during the last trimester of the pregnancy. A high strung Dobe that is nervous under normal circumstances is more likely to be affected than one that is not.

Extreme panting, nervousness, muscle twitching, and an elevated body temperature are the clinical signs associated with eclampsia. Fevers of 105° are not uncommon. Affected dogs should be treated promptly since the elevated temperature can reach life threatening levels. The classical treatment is an intravenous injection of a 10% calcium solution. *Calcium* can have a profound effect on the heart muscle. A nasty tissue slough may arise, however, if it is not administered intravenously. The injection should be slow using a solution with only 10% calcium for maximum safety. *Glucocorticoids* and intravenous sugar solutions are also used in the treatment of eclampsia. Response to treatment is almost immediate. As the temperature decreases, the panting and muscle twitching cease quickly, too. Since recurrences happen, the litter should be weaned immediately and raised as orphan pups.

ENDOMETRITIS:

Endometritis is defined as inflammation of the inner lining of the uterus. Classification is made in regard to when it occurs and whether it is acute or chronic in nature.

The most serious and life threatening form of endometritis occurs several weeks after the heat signs have ceased. Signs of serious discomfort occur very quickly. The temperature is very high. The abdomen is very tense. Increased water consumption and vomiting are observed. Little or no vaginal discharge is found but what is present will be thin and bloody in nature.

Although the prognosis is at best guarded, an *ovariohysterectomy* should be attempted as quickly as possible. On surgical exploration of the abdomen, a peritonitis (abdominal lining infection) and a very hard, friable uterus may be found. If the bitch can stand the stress of surgery, the condition will be over on recovery from the ovariohysterectomy.

A chronic form of endometritis also occurs several weeks after the signs of heat are gone in bitches that are about five years old. At that time, it is usually not life threatening and may go unnoticed for a while. The usual sign is one of a constant mucoid vaginal discharge. The condition is refractory to medical treatment but is responsive to *ovariohysterectomy* at the convenience of the owner.

Another class of endometritis occurs following *parturition (whelping)*. This acute form is accompanied by a dark bloody, foul smelling vaginal discharge. The temperature rapidly elevates. The bitch increases her water consumption but refuses food. A decrease in milk supply for the puppies may also occur. The treatment of choice is a broad spectrum antibiotic sometimes coupled with *oxytocin ("clean out shot")* to help the uterus expel any debris remaining from delivery.

A subacute or chronic form of endometritis can occur when the whelping process has taken a long time. Clinical signs are vague and may only be seen as poor mothering instinct. This condition also responds to appropriate antibiotics.

ESTROGEN HORMONE:

Estrogen is a hormone secreted by the ovaries during the *heat cycle* and is also produced in small amounts by the *adrenal glands.* Estrogen may be produced by a *Sertoli cell tumor* in the male testicle. This hormone is responsible for the signs associated with heat - bleeding, attraction of male dogs, and vulvar swelling.

When given shortly after breeding, estrogen hormones interrupt a pregnancy. The size of male *hyperplastic prostate glands* can be decreased with estrogen hormone. They also are effective in decreasing the size of *perianal adenoma tumors*. Extended usage of estrogen hormone may have a deleterious affect on the bone marrow causing fatal *aplastic anemia.*

ESTRUS CYCLE:

Refer to *HEAT CYCLE* in Chapter 4 and Chapter 12.

EXCRETORY UROGRAPHY:

Refer to *IV PYELOGRAM.*

FALSE PREGNANCY:

Pseudocyesis is the correct name for false pregnancy. After a bitch has ovulated, she goes through a luteal phase in which the hormone of pregnancy, *progesterone,* is secreted. If this hormone level peaks but does not decline, the bitch's body thinks she is pregnant. All of the signs associated with pregnancy, except an intrauterine fetus, may be present. Her abdomen enlarges. Her breasts develop and fill with milk. Her appetite increases. Her attitude becomes more sluggish and she craves for affection. In later false pregnancy, slight signs of uterine contractions and nesting will occur. The bitch may also "mother" inanimate objects and toys.

The abdominal distension which becomes very apparent between the 42nd and 49th day (earlier than in true pregnancy) will disappear just as suddenly as it occurred. Many breeders feel that when this phenomena occurs, the bitch has aborted or resorbed the litter. This is not true since the bitch was not pregnant in the first place.

No treatment is necessary for false pregnancies unless it becomes extreme. In most instances, removal of the toys that are being "mothered" and elimination of the nest are sufficient to cause the hormone levels to return to normal. Decreasing food and water intake may be necessary to "dry up" the mammary glands. In rare instances, the use of *Ovaban®*, *diethylstilbestrol,* or *testosterone* are used to reverse the affects of pseudocyesis. The use of hormones should be discouraged except in extreme instances.

Once a bitch has had a false pregnancy, others of varying intensity will occur. Only breeding the bitch will keep it from recurring. Of course, *ovariohysterectomy* will eliminate the condition. Spaying the bitch while she is producing milk is undesirable since milk production may continue for an indefinite time period even after the hormone source in the ovaries is removed.

FERTILITY LAB TESTS:

The tests listed here are helpful in the diagnosis of canine infertility. Each is discussed individually in the chapter.

Biopsy, testicular
Brucellosis test
Chromosome counting
  (Karyotyping)
Sex hormone assays

Sperm count
Tes-Tape®
Thyroid function tests
Vaginal cultures
Vaginal smears

FETAL MONSTROSITIES:

Hideous monstrosities may result from the administration of teratogenic (anomaly producing) drugs during the first five weeks of pregnancy. Refer to the listing of drugs to be avoided during pregnancy. The *dystocia* produced necessitates a *cesarean section.*

FOLLICLE STIMULATING HORMONE (FSH):

Follicle stimulating hormone (FSH) is a protein hormone substance produced in the anterior portion of the pituitary gland in the base of the brain. In the bitch, FSH plays a role in the development of the ovarian follicles. In males, the cells in the testes that will mature to produce sperm are affected. The purified form of the hormone may be used in the treatment of infertility in the bitch. Its usage can initiate a *heat period* which would then be treated with *luteinizing hormone (LH)*. *Chorionic gonadotropin (HCG)* is a commercially available hormone with both FSH and LH activity.

FROZEN SEMEN:

Since 1981, the American Kennel Club has allowed the use of frozen semen in the *artificial insemination* of dogs registered with the AKC. The advantages of this procedure include the fact that sires long dead can still have an impact on the breed, the spread of venereal diseases can be controlled, and the cost and stress of shipping bitches can be reduced.

Dogs participating in this program using frozen semen must use semen collected at one of the eight approved AKC frozen semen storage stations. The current guidelines require the semen producing dog be free from *canine brucellosis,* a copy of its AKC registration certificate is on file, and three color photographs (side and front views) for identification purposes be provided. Each frozen ampule of semen will provide from 100 to 300 million sperm for insemination. A list of approved frozen semen banks is available from The American Kennel Club, Department B, 51 Madison Avenue, New York, NY 10010.

GENITAL CANCER:

Tumors or cancer can develop in any part of the reproductive tract. Here each sex will be considered individually.

Tumors of the ovary are not uncommon. When these cancerous growths produce hormones, outward signs of heat, *nymphomania,* and usually hair coat changes are observed. If no hormones are produced and the mass grows large enough, the growth can be felt through the abdominal wall. Also, the bitch may exhibit some discomfort when she lies on her abdomen. Surgical removal, when possible, is the treatment of choice.

Uterine tumors, which are rare, are generally *leiomyomas* and not malignant. An *ovariohysterectomy* is curative. On the other hand, vaginal tumors are relatively common but are also usually benign. *Leiomyomas* and *fibromas* are most common. These tumors, while not malignant, can cause *dystocia* (difficult birth). If the breeding career is to be continued, surgical removal should be attempted.

An interesting tumor that affects both dogs and bitches is **transmissible venereal tumor (TVT).** This disease is spread only by coitus. Within seven days of transmission, evidence of tumor growth is seen. The vaginal wall and the penis are common sites for tumor growth whose tissue looks like cauliflower. About 60% of these tumors will regress and disappear spontaneously within 60 to 180 days. Only a very small percentage will spread to other areas of the body. This tumor is very x-ray responsive. Should metastasis (spreading) make surgical removal impossible, TVT is also sensitive to all of the usual anti-cancer drugs.

In male dogs, in addition to the *transmissible venereal tumor*, the two most common sites for genital cancers are the prostate gland and the testicles. **Prostatic cancer**, the same type that occurs in man - the *adenocarcinoma*, is uncommon. Being rather metastatic, it has usually spread by the time a diagnosis of prostate cancer is made. Surgical removal of the prostate may be successful in a small number of cases where the cancer has not yet spread to other organs. Removal of the prostate gland requires a high degree of surgical skill, usually resulting in a male dog that continually dribbles urine.

Testicular tumors are common in the dog. Three kinds of tumors occur in the testes. The least significant tumor, the *interstitial cell tumor*, does not secrete any hormones. Because it does not attain enough size to be noticed, finding is usually incidental on routine castration. Generally, testicular tumors do not metastasize.

The second type of testicular tumor, which is also benign and does not secrete any hormones, is the *seminoma*. This tumor can grow up to four or five inches (6 to 12 cm.) in diameter causing some general discomfort. Surgical removal is curative. Whether the remaining normal-sized testicle is removed during the surgery is up to the discretion of the surgeon.

The *Sertoli cell tumor*, the most significant testicular tumor, secretes female hormones. In undescended testicles, this type is the most common. While its presence in a descended testicle doesn't cause much increase in size, the tumorous undescended testicle can grow to rather large proportions in the abdomen or inguinal canal. Because of the female hormone influence, many changes occur such as a pendulous prepuce, an increased nipple size, an attraction of male dogs, and a *bilateral hair loss*. A small number of Sertoli cell tumors will metastasize late in the tumor's life. If the tumor is removed before spreading, the hair and skin changes will return to normal in two to three months. Additional discussion on SERTOLI CELL TUMORS is found in Chapter 4.

GLOMERULONEPHRITIS:

Glomerulonephritis is inflammation of the capillary loops of the glomeruli (functional units) within the kidneys. Generally, a bacterial infection or other changes causing deterioration of the kidney glomeruli bring about the problem. *Systemic lupus erythematosus (SLE), pyometra, endocarditis,* and *heartworm disease* may also cause this situation. Determining if the kidney changes are acute is important so that with adequate rest and therapy, recovery of normal function can be achieved. If the glomerular changes are causing permanent dysfunction, recovery is doubtful. A number of blood tests, *kidney biopsies,* and *urinalysis* results will need to be tabulated to determine the prognosis and best course of treatment.

HEAT CYCLE:

The heat cycle *(estrus cycle)* usually occurs for the first time after seven to ten months of age in the Doberman Pinscher. While most bitches will cycle two times a year, up to nine months between heat periods is not unusual. Four stages compose the cycle. *Anestrus,* the quiet period, has no outward sign of hormonal activity and may last for five months. *Proestrus* follows with vulvar swelling and bloody discharge for three to ten days. The end of the proestrus period occurs at the first acceptance of a male dog for breeding. During this period of acceptance *(estrus),* the bitch, on stimulation, shows signs of "flagging" her tail or moving it to the side as she lifts the vulva solidly planting her rear legs. Estrus may last from three to ten days. *Diestrus (metestrus)*\follows, lasting about two months. In many bitches, diestrus is not distinguishable from anestrus.

All of these phases of the heat cycle are influenced by different hormones. Several weeks before signs of proestrus are seen (swelling and discharge), the *estrogen hormones* increase and then peak during proestrus. A strong surge of *luteinizing hormone (LH)* occurs close to the start of estrus. Diestrus is marked by the influence of *progesterone hormone.* After either parturition, false pregnancy, or a decrease in the progesterone level, anestrus returns. Also refer to ESTRUS CYCLE in Chapter 4.

HEMATURIA:

Hematuria is the presence of blood cells in urine. Determining the origin and cause of the blood in the urine is important. Urinary bladder infections, trauma from *bladder or urethral stones,* trauma from accidents or injury, a side effect of the anticancer drug *Cytoxan®* , the presence of a urinary system tumor, a by-product of a blood *clotting defect,* or an incidental finding from a bitch in *heat* are some typical causes. Hematuria is a sign of disease and not a disease itself. Treatment and prognosis depend on the cause.

HERMAPHRODITE:

A hermaphrodite contains both male and female gonadal tissue. A differentiation between *pseudohermaphrodites* (males outwardly with ovaries internally or females outwardly containing testes internally) and the true hermaphrodite defined above exists. In either case, these dogs are infertile. There appears to be a hereditary basis for these conditions although the genetic mode of transmission has not been determined. Surgical elimination of gonadal tissue is desirable. A greater number of bilateral *cryptorchid* males are affected by this anomaly than other male dogs.

HERPES VIRUS:

Canine herpes virus (CHV) is a venereally transmitted viral disease that is particularly lethal to newborn pups up to two weeks of age. In adult males, no clinical signs are seen. In breeding bitches, history of stillborn pups, *abortion,* or *infertility* may be observed. Newborn pups are infected within the birth canal on delivery. Puppies that die of CHV have characteristic lesions on autopsy. The kidneys of these infected pups have petechial (pinpoint) hemorrhages over the surface beneath the capsule surrounding the kidney, typical of the disease.

Infected dogs and bitches in a *breeding kennel* should be eliminated from future breeding programs and isolated from other dogs. No treatment for the disease exists, but the virus can be killed with any common disinfectant. Canine herpes virus does not pose a public health hazard.

HYDROCEPHALUS:

Hydrocephalus is not common in the Doberman Pinscher but is seen more frequently in breeds of dogs that normally have round heads. This congenital anomaly occurs when the fluid-filled canals *(ventricles)* within the brain fill with enough fluid to cause the normal brain matter to atrophy. Affected puppies, if they survive birth, are very slow mentally and have a very appledomed head with bulging eyes. The diagnosis is made on the basis of clinical signs and radiographs of the skull. The enlarged head, if the condition is present at birth, will create dystocia which may create the need for a *C-section.*

HYDROPS ALLANTOIS:

Refer to *DYSTOCIA.*

HYPOCALCEMIA:

Refer to *ECLAMPSIA.*

HYPOCORTICAL RENAL FAILURE IN DOBERMANS:

A progressively fatal kidney disease of young Doberman Pinschers has been diagnosed. While there is no sex predisposition, males appear to be affected at a younger age. Most affected males are less than one year of age at the time the clinical signs become severe enough to require veterinary help. Bitches are slightly older.

The clinical signs are identical to those seen in any very severe kidney disease with a progressive *uremia.* Affected dogs have a poor appetite resulting in weight loss to the point of emaciation. They drink much water, vomit frequently, and are somewhat depressed. Increased urination leads to dehydration in spite of the increased water intake. Classical signs of uremic poisoning such as *anemia,* foul smelling breath from an ulcerative condition in the mouth, and even fluid accumulation in the abdomen leading to a potbellied look are seen. Because of a dysfunction in calcium metabolism associated with uremia, *fibrous osteodystrophy ("rubber jaw")* of the upper and lower jaw bones develops.

The usual tests for kidney disease will confirm severe renal failure and uremia. If the patient can tolerate a *kidney biopsy,* three types of renal lesions will be seen: cystic glomerular atrophy, glomerular hardening with scar tissue, and a combination of both atrophy and scar tissue buildup. The treatment is the same as for any severe uremic kidney condition. Refer to Chapter 8 for the NUTRITIONAL MANAGEMENT OF KIDNEY DISEASE. Unlimited fresh water, extra *water-soluble vitamins, phosphate binders* (Amphojel®), and possibly anabolic steroids to combat the *anemia* should be utilized. The prognosis for long-term survival is poor. Any dogs that achieve breeding age should not be used for breeding.

HYPOSPADIAS:

Hypospadias is the most common urethral congenital anomaly in the male dog. In this condition, the urethra opens on the bottom and behind its normal position at the tip of the penis. Because of the location of the opening, any semen would be deposited much posterior to the desired anterior section of the vagina making fertilization difficult to achieve. On occasion, surgical corrections may effectively change the opening to place it in a more normal location. The hereditary aspects of this condition are undetermined.

INCONTINENCE:

Incontinence, usually more common in bitches than in dogs, is the inability to control the elimination of urine. A number of factors cause urinary incontinence. In young dogs, a *patent urachus* (an embryonic remnant) or a mislocated (ectopic) ureter entering the urinary bladder can make house training appear to be impossible. In older bitches spayed before their first heat, a small percentage will develop a hormone responsive incontinence. The weekly use of *diethylstilbestrol (DES)* will control the problem. A *vaginitis* or a *urethritis* will cause frequent, difficult urination which may be construed as incontinence. The use of radiographs and other lab tests may be necessary to identify the cause of incontinence.

In some middle-aged Doberman Pinscher females, the observation has been made that incontinence with no infection which is unresponsive to female hormone therapy may be due to an abnormal location of the urinary bladder. All of these bitches had urinary bladders located in the pelvic canal. This location is more posterior than normal changing the normal bladder pressure gradients to cause a lack of control. Control of this type of urinary incontinence in Doberman Pinscher females can be gained with 50 mg. of ephedrine two to four times daily. No problems appear to be associated with long-term usage of this drug.

INERTIA, UTERINE (PRIMARY AND SECONDARY):

Primary and secondary uterine inertia are two causes of difficult birth. Uterine inertia is discussed more completely under *DYSTOCIA.*

INFERTILITY:

The topic of canine infertility is a very complex subject. Because both the sire and the dam are involved, the discussion is divided into causes of *male infertility* and causes of *female infertility.* Several obvious causes may affect both males and females.

Inadequate nutrition and proper vitamin and mineral intake can cause a physiologic infertility in females. Deficiencies in *either vitamin A or E* will cause reproductive failure. *Manganese deficiency* can cause *abortion* and impaired reproduction. A deficiency in the trace mineral, *iodine,* may be associated with fetal resorption and *abortion.* If *essential fatty acids* are not in adequate supply in the diet, reproduction is severely impaired.

Infectious diseases caused by bacteria, viruses, *mycoplasma,* and *rickettsia* may be associated with failures in the reproductive process. The most common diseases in dogs are the bacterial disease, *canine brucellosis,* and the viral disease, *canine herpes virus.* However, the presence of certain pathogenic bacteria in the genital tract of either the male or the female may cause failures in reproduction.

Disturbances in normal hormone levels in the body may alter normal reproductive function. The *thyroid gland* and its associated hormones are important in the normal metabolic processes in the body. Failure of the *pituitary gland* to secrete proper amounts of several different hormones will alter reproductive mechanisms in both males and females. Excesses or deficiencies of *adrenal gland hormones* have an effect on the reproductive process. Sex hormone problems specific to each sex will be mentioned under male and female related infertilities.

The other major cause of infertility in both sexes is psychological in nature. Attempting to breed a very subordinate, reserved male to an extremely dominant bitch can be a real adventure! This male is willing to take "no" for an answer. Raising a male in a home where he is not allowed to do male "things" is difficult for the dog that the owner then wants to breed. He can't lift his leg on the piano to mark territory. He can't mount the lady of the house when she has her menstrual period. He is not even allowed to ride someone's leg to masturbate because these activities are not usually acceptable traits for a house dog. Suddenly, at four years of age, the owner decides his dog should father a litter to insure the preservation of his wonderful traits. The owner who thinks that suddenly the "stud dog" will understand that it is okay to mount this bleeding bitch, when for the past four years the dog has gotten in serious trouble for attempting the same kind of activity is in for a surprise and disappointment. In most cases, the house rules and training over a period of years will keep the male dog from performing the normal breeding act.

Female related *infertility* causes can be divided into anatomical and hormonal. Fertility problems related to the genital anatomy can be present at birth. Others are acquired later such as the formation of a cancerous growth or adhesions after a litter or an accident. If congenital (present at birth) anomalies in the genital tract are suspected, a very complete surgical inspection of all of the related structures is necessary. General anesthesia and the use of dyes or stains to check on the patency of the fallopian tubes and uterine horns are required. *Uterine biopsies* may also be necessary. The term "breaking down a bitch" is used by some breeders to describe the digitally dilating and stretching of muscular rings present in the vaginal vault making a natural breeding impossible. Some of these can be relaxed with the drug *aminopropazine fumarate* (Jenotone® by Coopers Animal Health, Inc.) at the rate of 1 mg. per pound of weight given two or three hours before the breeding is attempted. Other strictures require surgical alteration. Still others require artificial insemination and may later require a cesarean section because of *dystocia* from the strictures in the vaginal vault.

Female hormonal causes of infertility are usually due to improper amounts of hormones at inappropriate times in the *estrus cycle.* As expertise in veterinary endocrinology progresses, the ability to assay (measure) these hormones at various times in the cycle improves. This information helps determine where the body is deficient in normal hormone levels.

Causes of *male infertility* may be related to anatomical blockages, environmental effects on the scrotum and testicles, and those of a hormonal nature. In young puppies, congenital abnormalities in the anatomy of the penis are usually apparent on careful inspection. Abnormalities involving the testicle and duct work are less obvious.

Transient infertility may be found in cases where testes have been exposed to high temperatures from the environment or from fevers. A curious type of infertility in the male involves the creation of antibodies against *sperm as an autoimmune reaction.* This usually results from an acute inflammatory response in the tubular duct work that transports sperm. Even if the initial reaction is only involving one testicle, the autoimmune response will be bilateral resulting in complete infertility.

Chromosome abnormalities are be another type of male infertility. In *Klinefelter's syndrome* in man, at least two X chromosomes in the male makeup exist. Only one X chromosome should be present. Refer to *CHROMOSOME COUNTING.*

The most common hormone abnormality in the male dog involves the *thyroid hormone.* Both libido and spermatogenesis (sperm formation) can be affected. Other hormone deficiencies or excesses will affect the fertility rate of the male dog.

Various drugs can affect fertility in both the dog and the bitch. If breeding the male is anticipated, your veterinarian should be consulted about the possibilities of stopping any medication several days before the anticipated stud service. This is not necessary with all medicines.

The identification of causes of infertility can require much testing and detective work on the part of the veterinarian. Most Colleges of Veterinary Medicine have specialists in theriogenology, the study of reproductive problems. These board certified specialists may be able to uncover the causes of infertility with equipment and testing not usually available to general veterinary practitioners.

IV PYELOGRAM:

The IV pyelogram is a technique also called *excretory urography*. An organic iodide compound is injected intravenously. As it is excreted through the kidney and ureters, radiographs are taken. While no information of renal function is obtained, visualizing the kidney looking for cysts, tumors, obstructions, *calculi,* and size variations in the kidney is possible.

To prepare a Dobe for an IV pyelogram, food is withheld for 18 hours. An enema is administered before taking the dog to the hospital for the procedure. The urinary bladder is emptied before the drug is injected. One or more radiographs are taken before the iodide injection. Radiographs are then taken at 1, 3, 5, 10, and 15 minutes post injection. The side effects from the iodide include sneezing, vomiting, and *hives.* In extremely rare cases, cardiac arrest and anaphylactic reactions have been seen. The procedure is considered safe. Only rare individuals will react adversely to the injected drug.

KARYOTYPING:

Refer to CHROMOSOME COUNTING.

KIDNEY FAILURE:

Kidney failure is classified as either acute or chronic in terms of the length of time in which the process has occurred. It is then further grouped into reversible and irreversible which is important from a prognostic standpoint.

Most of the signs of kidney disease are due to the rising level of urea (waste products) in the blood. Signs of *uremia* are depression, dehydration, vomiting, loss of appetite, and possible diarrhea. Long term affects cause *anemia.* Most acute kidney failures will produce smaller than normal amounts of urine or no urine at all *(anuria). Chronic kidney failure* usually causes increased dilute urine from increased water consumption. Some chronic cases, however, have lesser than normal urine output.

The causes of acute and chronic kidney failure are many and varied. Because acute renal failure may be treatable, tests are advisable to determine the feasibility of treating the condition. At best, chronic renal disease may be controlled, but the kidney damage is not reversible. Only removing urea from the blood will alleviate signs. The build-up of uremic waste products is continuous as the body burns calories doing work. Dietary management and fluid therapy will help keep uremia in check. Without the luxury of kidney transplants, management of kidney failure syndromes must be tied to the prospects for curing the condition or, at least, controlling the signs produced by uremia.

KIDNEY FUNCTION LAB TESTS:

The following list of kidney function lab tests are performed to diagnose kidney problems.

Biopsy, kidney   Plasma PSP test
BUN test   Urine PSP excretion test
Creatinine test   Urinalysis
IV pyelogram

KLINEFELTER'S SYNDROME:

Refer to *CHROMOSOME COUNTING.*

LABOR, SIGNS OF:

Labor is divided into three stages. No absolute, clear-cut lines separate one stage from another.

The first stage is the period of preparation and relaxation. This stage may vary in length from almost nothing to two days but probably averages 12 to 18 hours. The length of the first stage is somewhat influenced by the temperament of the expectant mother and the environment in which she has been placed to have her puppies. A mellow, laid back bitch has a shorter first stage than a neurotic house pet that isn't a dog any more. Placing the expectant mother in new surroundings like a whelping box may lengthen the first stage of labor.

The bitch experiences little pain as the cervix dilates. Clinical signs of **Stage I** are restlessness, nest making, and panting. No true contractions are occurring. During this period, the body temperature is dropping, possibly only for a short time. Taking a rectal temperature two times a day will usually catch this temperature decrease. The drop will be from between 100° to 101° down to 97° to 98°. Where one or two puppy litters are suspected, this temperature drop is very important. After a short drop, the temperature will edge up toward normal. If uterine contractions have not started, the bitch becomes a prime suspect for *primary uterine inertia necessitating a cesarean section.* As a rule, contractions producing puppies should begin within 24 hours of the temperature drop.

The **second stage of labor** initiates purposeful contractions. The bitch becomes more quiet and may lose various fluids at times during this stage. As contractions become more forceful, the bitch may arch her back as she delivers a newborn pup. The length of time to allow contractions is open to conjecture. Generally, the first pup may take up to two hours for full cervical dilation and birth canal dilation enabling delivery to take place. If the contractions occur for longer than six hours, placental separation will jeopardize the life of that pup. Subsequent pups usually come in groups of two or three over a 10 to 30 minute period. This flurry of activity is followed by a resting period of up to three or four hours. As long as the bitch rests between deliveries, concern over long whelping periods is not necessary.

The **third stage of labor** is the period when the fetal placentas and membranes are expelled. Placentas may come with each puppy delivery or they may be retained until later in the delivery process. Allowing the bitch to eat the placentas and membranes may provide some hormones that will stimulate uterine contraction and milk letdown. Consumption of one or two of these placentas is all that is necessary.

The whelping process is completed when the bitch relaxes and settles into the "nest" with her newborn. The new mother then usually falls asleep. If the whelping process was prolonged or if all of the placentas are not accounted for, your veterinarian should examine the new mother and give her a post partum injection.

The bitch's temperature after whelping may rise to 102.5° to 103°F. This is a physiological increase due to her activity and the initiation of lactation. Antibiotics are not required unless the temperature exceeds 103°F.

LUTEINIZING HORMONE (LH):

Luteinizing hormone is produced in the *pituitary gland* at the base of the brain. In the bitch, LH prepares the ovary for pregnancy by initiating a corpus luteum (the place on the ovary from which the egg is discharged). In the male, this hormone causes cells in the testes to secrete *testosterone hormone*. LH is sometimes injected into infertile bitches to stimulate follicle rupture and ovum release.

METRITIS:

Metritis is defined as inflammation of the uterus. Most metritis problems are actually *endometritis* involving the inside lining of the uterus and not the muscular wall or the serosal outer covering of the uterus. Inflammation of the muscular wall, inner lining, and outer covering can occur after surgery or after some natural form of trauma to the entire organ. Refer to ENDOMETRITIS as the same principles are true for metritis.

MIDSTREAM URINE SPECIMEN:

Refer to *URINE SPECIMEN, COLLECTION OF.*

MILK FEVER:

Refer to *ECLAMPSIA.*

MISMATE INJECTION:

Unwanted pregnancies are controlled by giving the bitch an injection of *estradiol cypionate (ECP)* within three days of the unplanned mating. Estradiol cypionate is not approved for mismate injections in dogs. Your veterinarian may ask you to sign a liability waiver before using the drug for this purpose.

Side effects from use of estradiol cypionate include an increased length to the estrus cycle with further attraction of male dogs and a greater incidence of *pyometra*. In fact, if the injection is given during *diestrus* (Refer to ESTRUS CYCLES in Chapter 4), the chance for the development of *pyometra* is up to 20% greater than normal.

The greatest danger from *estrogen* usage is to the *bone marrow*. Severe and even fatal bone marrow depression can occur from overzealous use of estrogen hormones. Under no circumstance should more than one injection of estradiol cypionate be given during any one heat cycle. *Prostaglandins* are occasionally used to cause abortion in dogs. Due to the side effects seen shortly after administration, they are not too popular. Prostaglandins are not currently licensed for use in dogs. Refer to PROSTAGLANDINS in this chapter.

MONORCHID:

Monorchid, which technically means only one testicle present, is a misused term. The presence of one testicle in the dog is very rare. In most cases, only one testicle has descended in the scrotum and the other testicle is in the inguinal canal or the abdominal cavity. A more correct description would be *unilateral cryptorchid*.

NEPHRITIS:

Inflammation of the kidneys is defined by nephritis. Usually adjectives are used to describe the type of nephritis and the duration and location of the inflammation. For instance, *"chronic interstitial nephritis"* is inflammation of a long-term nature occurring in the interstitial tissue of the kidney. Because the causes of nephritis are many and varied, the important kidney diseases are discussed individually within the chapter. Refer to CHRONIC INTERSTITIAL NEPHRITIS (CIN), GLOMERULONEPHRITIS, HYPOCORTICAL RENAL FAILURE IN DOBERMANS, KIDNEY FAILURE, and PYELONEPHRITIS.

NEPHROBLASTOMA:

Refer to *RENAL CANCERS.*

NEUTERING (CASTRATION):

Refer to *BIRTH CONTROL METHODS.*

OVARIOHYSTERECTOMY (SPAY):

Refer to *BIRTH CONTROL METHODS.*

PALPATION:

Palpation, a method of pregnancy diagnosis, is the act of feeling with the hand by applying the fingers with light pressure to the surface of the body for the purpose of making a physical diagnosis. The technique of palpating the abdomen to determine pregnancy must be developed with experience. For the novice, the best time to check for pregnancy is exactly 28 days from the conception date. Begin 28 days from the first breeding date, checking again 28 days from all breeding dates.

In the Doberman Pinscher, unless you have large hands, use both hands to palpate. The technique involves using both hands to feel and press against the abdomen, allowing the internal viscera (organs) to slide between your fingers while searching for the pregnant uterus. At 28 days of pregnancy, each fetus is enlarged to the size of a Ping-Pong® ball. Palpating multiple, round, firm masses is a positive pregnancy diagnosis.

The palpation technique has several shortcomings. Obese and very large bitches are extremely hard to palpate accurately. A tense, nervous bitch will usually not allow you to feel her abdomen deeply enough to feel the fetuses. Palpation earlier than 24 days or later than 30 days from the date of breeding is not possible with any degree of accuracy. The fertilized eggs do not implant in the uterine wall until the 20th day after a successful breeding. Even at 24 days, the uterine enlargement is "pea sized." By 30 days post breeding, the entire uterus is enlarged making it is difficult to distinguish a 30 day pregnant uterus from a colon full of stool.

PERITONEAL DIALYSIS:

Refer to *DIALYSIS.*

PLACENTAL SITES, SUBINVOLUTION OF:

Each fetal placenta is attached to a separate site in the endometrial wall of the uterus. After whelping, a raw zone is left where each placenta was attached. A thin bloody discharge is seen for up to six weeks as the placenta site scars. In some bitches, the placental site does not heal. While the bitch feels good, has no fever, and is eating well, she continues to have a bloody discharge for months following parturition (whelping).

Subinvolution of the placental sites is a self-limiting condition. No treatment is required unless the bleeding is considered very heavy. Healing will eventually occur if infection is not present. Treatments used for subinvolution of placental sites are antibiotics and ergotamine.

PLASMA PSP TEST:

This plasma test will show nonspecific kidney disease before the usual kidney tests (*BUN* and *creatinine*) are elevated. After a baseline heparinized blood sample is obtained, PSP (phenolsulfonphthalein) dye is injected intravenously. Exactly 60 minutes later, another heparinized blood sample is taken and examined for the amount of dye excreted during the 60 minute period. Values under 80 mg/100 ml are normal.

POSTPARTURIENT TETANY:

Refer to *ECLAMPSIA.*

POSTPARTUM HEMORRHAGE:

Vaginal bleeding after whelping is normal varying from slight to heavy. In bitches with *Von Willebrand's disease,* blood loss may be more severe. In these bitches, post partum injections of *oxytocin* may be very beneficial to contract the uterus. Normal post partum bleeding can last up to six weeks, becoming less and less frequent.

PREBREEDING EXAMINATION:

Both the dog and the bitch should have some prebreeding medical data. If the purpose for breeding the dogs is to improve the breed, it becomes necessary to assure ourselves that dogs with serious genetic defects are not being bred. All breeding stock should have radiographs on file showing normal hips. They should be free from *cervical spondylopathy (wobbler syndrome), Von Willebrand's disease, chronic copper hepatitis,* or any other suspected genetically linked disease.

A negative *canine brucellosis test* and possibly a clear *vaginal culture* before breeding are desirable. Both sexes should be current on all vaccinations and free from all parasites prior to breeding. If there is past history of irregular *heat cycles,* evidence of systemic illness, or other information that may jeopardize the pregnancy, competent veterinary help should be sought.

PREGNANCY DIAGNOSIS, METHODS OF:

Unlike other species of animals and man, no blood test assays in the bitch diagnose pregnancy. Early experimental work shows that testing urinary total *estrogen* levels at 21 days of pregnancy may show some promise. Also, decreases in serum gamma globulin (IgG) and serum *creatinine* levels are reported. A rapid, early blood test may be developed from these facts sometime in the future.

Radiography is of very limited use in pregnancy diagnosis because fetal skeletons are first seen on x-ray 21 days <u>before</u> delivery. In many instances, the fetal skeleton can not be seen on an abdominal radiograph before 16 to 18 days pre-delivery. Radiography is primarily used very near term to count numbers of fetuses and to determine *dystocia* possibilities. Always count fetal skulls not bodies or legs when determining numbers of fetuses.

The effectiveness of **ultrasound** equipment in the diagnosis of pregnancy is dependent on the type of ultrasound techniques used and the skill of the veterinarian. The light-weight, portable Doppler and A-mode ultrasound instrumentation are no more effective than palpation between 20 and 35 days of pregnancy. However, the more expensive sophisticated real-time equipment may demonstrate vesicle formation as early as 20 days. More experimentation is necessary to determine its use in clinical practice.

The limitations of **palpation** have been noted under *PALPATION.* Other signs of pregnancy are bright pink nipples and *anorexia* (lack of appetite) for four to seven days 21 days after breeding. These signs should only be used in conjunction with other clinical evidence of pregnancy.

PREGNANCY DURATION:

Almost all references refer to 63 days as the normal gestation period in the bitch. Considerable variation from this number is normal. Puppies can be born and survive as early as 55 days and as late as 70 days after breeding. Some confusion arises when multiple breedings have taken place but this can be settled by *palpation*. When the fetuses are palpated the size of a Ping-Pong® ball, a 28-day pregnancy is present. The breeding, if there were more than one, should be calculated to the date closest to the 28th day prior to palpation.

The *LH hormone* is important in the length of time considered to be normal gestation in the bitch. The 64-day time period is consistent from the preovulation LH peak to whelping. Ovulation occurs two days after the LH surge. The ovum matures for several days and may remain capable of being fertilized for four to five days after the luteinizing hormone peaks. The most reliable clinical signs of ovulation and LH peak are wrinkling of the vaginal wall and a loss of turgidity to the vulva.

PREPUTIAL INFECTION:

During their lifetime, most male dogs have a mucopurulent (pus colored) discharge from the preputial opening. If these infections are cultured, *Staph* and *Streptococcus* bacteria are discovered. The infection does not cause a febrile (fever) response and does not usually spread to the *prostate gland.*

Treating a preputial infection is a lesson in frustration. With appropriate antibiotics and preputial douches, the discharge can temporarily be eliminated. Usually, within two to four weeks of cessation of therapy, the discharge will return. This discharge should be eliminated before breeding a bitch. To keep "spotting" in the home to a minimum, an extremely heavy discharge should be treated. Continual douching is the only method of controlling the discharge in an ongoing basis.

PROGESTERONE HORMONE:

The progesterone hormone in the bitch, also called the hormone of pregnancy, is produced by the corpus luteum (where the follicle and ovum came from) on the ovary. When not pregnant, the bitch's levels of progesterone remain fairly constant for about 84 days before dropping off. During pregnancy, the level will rise for the first 30 days and then gradually decrease until reaching prepregnant levels one to two days before whelping. Progesterone is the only hormone necessary in the bitch to maintain pregnancy.

PROSTAGLANDINS:

Prostaglandins are naturally occurring, powerful, luteolytic drugs. The normal level of prostaglandins at whelping is high, playing a big role in the signs that the bitch shows in stage II of labor. Prostaglandin $F2_a$ (alpha) is used in the treatment of *metritis* and *pyometra*. Bitches given prostaglandins for medical problems exhibit signs of toxicity to the drug similar to those in Stage II labor - panting, scratching and shredding paper, vomiting, and nervousness. At the present time, prostaglandins are not licensed for use in dogs. Your veterinarian may require a release form for liability purposes.

PROSTATE GLAND:

The prostate gland is a muscular secreting accessory sex gland that surrounds the neck of the urinary bladder in the male dog. The function of the prostate is not clear. Its alkaline secretion neutralizes strongly acid urine in the urethra. It also flushes sperm down the urethra while acting as a transport medium.

PROSTATE HYPERPLASIA:

A common, usually asymptomatic condition of old male dogs is benign hyperplasia of the prostate gland. Because *castration* causes the enlarged gland to atrophy, hyperplasia is linked to the male hormone, *testosterone.* Sometimes, difficulty in passing stool is observed. The gland grows to such a size that it pushes against the rectum making the dog strain to pass stools. Those stools that are passed are sometimes termed "pencil stools" for obvious reasons.

The enlarged prostate can be treated by female hormone injections. Refer to *MISMATE INJECTION* for a discussion of the existing dangers. *Castration* remains the treatment of choice. The gland returns to normal size less than four weeks after surgery.

PROSTATITIS:

Prostatitis is the inflammation of the prostate gland. While not as common as benign hyperplasia, prostatitis is generally seen in younger male dogs. The affected dog will walk in a stilted manner, keeping his back arched. He will be off his feed and have a fever. Rectal palpation of the prostate gland is painful.

A *bacterial culture* and *sensitivity test* is recommended. However, *erythromycin* is very active in the prostate so is a good choice when a culture can not be obtained. On occasion, *corticosteroids* and *estrogens* are combined with the antibacterial therapy. Your veterinarian should reexamine these cases because chronic abscessation of the prostate is an undesirable sequelae. The prognosis is guarded to good.

PSEUDOCYESIS:

Refer to *FALSE PREGNANCY.*

PYELONEPHRITIS:

The inflammation of the kidney and kidney pelvis (cavity in the kidney for collecting urine) is defined as pyelonephritis. This problem is caused by many factors. Decreased urine flow will result from pyelonephritis. Elements in the urinary sediment of the *urinalysis* test are important in diagnosing pyelonephritis.

PYOMETRA:

Pyometra is a progesterone-mediated disease of the endometrial lining within the uterus. Usually occurring in *metestrus (diestrus)*, a bacterial infection in the uterus is usually present. "Open" or "closed" pyometra refers to whether or not the cervix allows drainage to be observed.

Most bitches that develop pyometra are at least five years of age. However, cases have been reported after the first *heat cycle*. Many of these bitches have histories of *false pregnancies* or never having had puppies. While considered a disease of the intact bitch, "stump" pyometra can occur in the remnant of the uterine body if some ovarian tissue is left in place following an *ovariohysterectomy (spay)*.

While the signs of pyometra vary, the most common clinical syndrome is depression, loss of appetite, vomiting, *polyuria* (increased urination), *polydipsia* (increased water consumption), and development of a pendulous abdomen. The body temperature varies from normal to three or four degrees above normal. Some bitches will appear lame probably due to the developing toxemia. If the cervix is open, a discharge varying from bloody to dark to thick or creamy in color is present. This may be continuous or intermittent. "Closed" pyometra has no discharge. The bitch also acts much sicker.

The disease complex is diagnosed from the history, *blood counts,* and *radiographs.* In rare instances, exploratory surgery is necessary to identify the enlarged uterus. In almost all cases of "closed pyometra," the white blood count is over 28,000. Some are as high as 75,000. A *blood urea nitrogen test (BUN)* is important in determining the degree of kidney involvement from the toxemia present. Some bitches have a concurrent *sugar diabetes* problem which complicates the recovery from surgery with a greater chance of infection and slower wound healing.

The treatment of choice in pyometra remains an *ovariohysterectomy.* When possible, the surgery should be delayed for a few days after initiating antibiotic therapy. This is not always possible. The surgical procedure is supported by intravenous fluids and the use of antibiotics both intravenously and within the abdominal cavity to minimize the chances of infection from the uterine "stump." Recovery is followed with oral antibiotics for seven to ten days. All of the clinical signs cease rapidly following successful surgery.

The surgical procedure is not without its dangers. *Anesthesia* is much riskier in the severely toxic patient. Many "closed" pyometras have a very thin-walled uterus that ruptures on the slightest manipulation during its surgical removal. The resulting contamination of the abdominal cavity makes additional procedures necessary to combat the resulting peritonitis. Placement of drain tubes, additional antibiotic therapy, and hospitalization may be needed.

In bitches used for breeding, the experimental use of natural *prostaglandins* may provide an alternative to *ovariohysterectomy* surgery. The use of prostaglandin F2$_a$ (PGF2$_a$) will cause the corpus luteum to lyse thereby lowering the progesterone level and reducing the endometrial lining growth. The uterine muscle contracts and is accompanied by some cervical relaxation. No clinical improvement is seen for 48 hours. The concurrent use of antibiotics is important. Serious side effects make hospitalization during treatment mandatory. *White blood cell counts* help monitor the improvement of the general condition. Bitches treated with this regimen should be bred the next heat period. Because this drug is not approved for use in dogs, your veterinarian may require a signed liability waiver. A higher incidence of pyometra may occur in families with an increased incidence of *primary uterine inertia.*

RENAL CANCERS:

Tumors of the kidney, ureter, urinary bladder, and urethra are uncommon to rare. The *adenocarcinoma,* the most common primary kidney tumor, is more frequent in older males than in females. Generally, the cancer spreads to the lungs but can also metastasize to other body organs. In dogs under one year of age, the *nephroblastoma (Wilms' tumor)* is observed, frequently spreading to the lungs. Metastatic tumors (those that have another primary site) are more commonly found in the kidneys than primary tumors. Various diagnostic tests may be necessary to identify the presence of renal tumors. These tests include *kidney biopsies, urinalysis, IV pyelography,* and possibly exploratory surgery.

Surgical removal of the involved kidney and ureter is the treatment of choice. Radiographs of the lungs should be taken before the surgery is undertaken. This surgical procedure requires a high level of skill. The use of other anticancer aids in primary kidney tumors is possible, but results are variable.

Ureteral and urethral tumors are extremely rare in the dog. Surgical treatment, when possible, would be the treatment of choice.

Transitional cell carcinoma, more common in females, is the most common urinary bladder tumor. The diagnosis is usually made following the observation of *bloody urine.* On occasion, tumor cells may appear in the urine on *urinalysis.* Abdominal radiographs may show the presence of a space-occupying lesion in the posterior portion of the abdomen. A partial surgical removal of part of the bladder wall is recommended. Catheterization for seven days keeps the healing bladder decompressed. Early diagnosis is important if a functional part of the bladder is to be saved. Prognosis on all renal cancers is guarded at best.

SCHISTOSOMA REFLEXA:

Schistosoma reflexa is a congenital anomaly. The presented fetus is generally doubled over with all or most of the abdominal viscera (organs) appearing outside of the abdominal cavity. Because of the transverse presentation, *dystocia* is usually present. The Schistosoma reflexa is found on the completion of a *cesarean section*. Fetal abnormalities of this nature are euthanized rather than attempting extensive abdominal wall reconstruction.

SEX HORMONE ASSAYS:

Currently, *testosterone, progesterone,* and *estrogen* levels can be measured from a serum sample. This sample must be shipped on ice. These tests are best run by Dr. Ray Nachreiner, Animal Health Diagnostic Laboratory, Endocrine Diagnostic Section, P.O. Box 30076, Lansing, MI 48909-7576.

SEX HORMONE INJECTIONS:

Each of the following sex hormones is discussed individually within the chapter.

Chorionic gonadotropin	Luteinizing hormone
Estrogen	Progesterone hormone
Follicle stimulating hormone	Testosterone

SILENT HEAT:

Some heat cycles are not obvious. No vulvar swelling or bleeding is apparent. Signs associated with heat ("flagging" the tail and vulvar lifting on stimulation) are very weak or unnoticed. This phenomenon is called a "silent heat." The cause is not known. These bitches are fertile so if they are bred at the appropriate time, they will bear puppies. Often *vaginal smears* are necessary at least three times a week to follow the cycle to find the time of greatest fertility.

SPAY (OVARIOHYSTERECTOMY):

Refer to *BIRTH CONTROL METHODS.*

SPERM COUNT:

Semen is collected by ejaculating the male dog in a quiet area, preferably after playing with a bitch in heat. The semen contains three fractions. The middle, thick, whitish fluid is the one containing the sperm. Sperm is evaluated for motility, numbers, and morphology (appearance). Minimal numbers for reproduction are 80% motile, at least 200 million sperm per ejaculate (500 million is average in a normal male), and less than 20% abnormal appearing sperm.

Semen must be collected carefully in a glass or Teflon® tube that has been warmed to body temperature to prevent shock to the sperm. The sperm containing fluid fraction varies from 0.5 ml. to over 3 ml. in volume. This portion is ejaculated within the first two minutes of fluid production.

SPLIT HEAT:

A "split heat" is most commonly observed at the time of a bitch's first heat period. Some vulvar swelling with four or five days of a bloody discharge which ends abruptly may occur. Four to five weeks later the bitch goes into true estrus starting with the *proestrus* stage. In 8 to 10 days, this leads into the standing fertile heat. The 'split heat' is related to the development of the ovarian follicles. In some bitches, follicular development causes enough *estradiol* increase to produce overt signs of heat. This follicular growth is about four to six weeks before actual proestrus begins.

If older bitches cycle every four months, they are not ovulating. Measuring the *estrogen* and *progesterone* levels in such a bitch will help pinpoint the phase of the cycle that is deficient.

TES-TAPE® :

Tes-Tape® is a paper tape that changes color in the presence of sugar. At the time of a bitch's ovulation, the cervical mucus contains *glucose.* Tes-Tape® is inserted into the vagina and moistened with vaginal secretions. If cervical mucus contains glucose, the change in tape color accurately indicates ovulation.

The presence of some types of *vaginitis* also cause glucose formation changing the color of the Tes-Tape® . A bitch with diabetes mellitus would also have glucose in vaginal secretions. The Tes-Tape® should be used with clinical signs of *estrus* and *vaginal smears* to determine the optimum time for breeding.

TESTICULAR BIOPSY:

Refer to *BIOPSY, TESTICULAR.*

TESTOSTERONE:

Testosterone is a male androgenic hormone produced by the Leydig cells in the testes. After these cells are stimulated by *luteinizing hormone (LH),* testosterone is produced within an hour. Much higher levels of testosterone are needed within the testes to maintain spermatogenesis (the formation of sperm) than are found in the circulating blood stream.

Testosterone hormone causes the male characteristics and actions - leg lifting, deep bark, territorial guarding, luxurious hair coat, and libido. Testosterone injections increase libido but may cause a temporary sterility. While the male will now mount and breed a bitch, he may have no active spermatozoa for about five to seven days after the hormone injection.

THYROID FUNCTION TESTS:

The three usual tests for thyroid function which are important in reproductive problems are the T_4 value, the T_3 value, and the TSH stimulation test. Additional discussion on these tests is found in Chapter 4. Many reproductive problems can be traced to poor thyroid function.

TUBAL LIGATION:

Refer to METHOD OF BIRTH CONTROL.

ULTRASOUND IN PREGNANCY DIAGNOSIS:

Refer to PREGNANCY DIAGNOSIS.

UNDESCENDED TESTICLE:

Refer to CRYPTORCHID.

URINALYSIS:

Much valuable information can be obtained from this relatively simple procedure. Any kidney or reproductive tract work-up should include this test.

URINE SPECIMEN, COLLECTION OF:

Three methods are utilized in the collection of a urine specimen. **Catheterization** can be accomplished with ease in the male and with some difficulty in the bitch. Some danger of introducing infection into the urinary bladder via the catheter exists. If the urethra is inflamed, the catheter may aggravate its sensitive lining.

The second method, **cystocentesis,** is a method of 'tapping' the urinary bladder by inserting a long needle through the abdominal wall into the bladder and withdrawing urine into a syringe. This requires a cooperative dog that will allow its front legs to be elevated and its abdomen to be manipulated so the urinary bladder can be restrained for needle penetration. Since this is a "blind" penetration, there is slight danger of internal organ damage and internal hemorrhage.

The third method, the collection of a **midstream urine specimen,** is suitable for many procedures. With a little practice, your dog will not mind the use of a flat, clean pie plate to enable you to collect an ounce of urine. Confine the Dobe overnight. Exercise it in the morning on a *leash.* Most dogs will urinate after overnight confinement even if they are not accustomed to leash restricted exercise. A bitch may raise up as you slip the flat pan under her. However, the urge to micturate is great enough that she will resume the squatting position and allow you to collect a specimen. The sample is then transferred to a clean glass or plastic container and transported to your veterinarian. Collected specimens should be transported within one hour of collection or refrigerated for up to three hours before analysis. Midstream urine specimens may not be acceptable for *bacterial cultures* of urinary tract infections.

URINE PSP EXCRETION TEST:

The urine PSP excretion test gives a good gauge of kidney tubular function. After a catheter is placed in the urinary bladder to remove all urine, phenolsulfonphthalein (PSP) is injected intravenously. All urine formed in 15 and 60 minutes is collected. The amount of PSP in each sample gives an assessment of kidney tubular function.

UTERINE HORN TORSION:

Uterine horn torsion is the complete twisting of a pregnant horn or of the entire uterus. The twisting effectively cuts off the blood supply to the affected part of the uterus causing profound shock to the bitch. While emergency exploratory surgery is necessary, most bitches are given a poor prognosis for survival.

A great amount of rolling or jumping behavior in a bitch with a heavily pregnant uterus is the reason for this rare condition. This activity causes the uterus to turn on itself. The only clinical signs present are profound shock and abdominal discomfort. Early surgery may slightly improve the prognosis.

UTERINE (PRIMARY AND SECONDARY) INERTIA:

Refer to *INERTIA, UTERINE (PRIMARY AND SECONDARY)*.

UTERINE PROLAPSE:

Uterine prolapses primarily occur after whelping is complete. Some however, do take place after one horn is empty and becomes evaginated with continued uterine contractions. These cases are diagnosed by the presence of abnormal "tissue" protruding from the vulvar lips. Manipulation and a surgical incision in the abdomen will replace the protruding tissue. Many replaced uteri will partially prolapse after subsequent *heat periods.* Most recurring uterine prolapses are treated with an *ovariohysterectomy (spay).*

VAGINAL CULTURES:

The use of vaginal cultures as an aid in fertility testing is controversial. The vaginal tract has a normal bacterial flora which includes *E. coli, Streptococcus canis, Staphylococcus aureus,* as well as a number of other bacteria considered to be pathogens (capable of producing disease). The amount and kind of bacteria in the forward area of the vagina near the cervix is the most important consideration in determining whether the bitch has a bacterial population deleterious to breeding.

Specialized instrumentation is necessary to culture the anterior vaginal compartment. With a Doberman Pinscher-sized bitch, at least a 10" guarded culture instrument is necessary. A comprehensive culture would include both aerobic (oxygen requiring bacteria) and anaerobic (bacteria that grow without oxygen) bacteria. The interpretation of *bacterial culture* results requires experience. If large numbers of bacteria are isolated from the anterior vaginal vault, they should be considered detrimental to the anticipated breeding. An *antibiotic sensitivity test* should be performed to determine the kind of antibiotic therapy to initiate.

Some bitches may be treated and bred during the same heat. Others should be treated, not bred, and recultured on the next heat. Under no circumstances should one assume that the bacterial flora will be identical from heat to heat. The techniques of vaginal culturing can aid in the management of infertility in the hands of an experienced veterinary clinician.

VAGINAL HYPERPLASIA:

Vaginal hyperplasia is caused by increased levels of *estrogen* and its effect on the tissues in the vaginal vestibule near the opening of the urethra. While most of these conditions occur in late *proestrus,* some are seen about the time of whelping when the estrogen levels again rise. This condition has a hereditary basis and continued breeding of affected bitches is questionable.

The prominent sign is a round, red, moist-appearing dome of tissue protruding through the vulvar lips. No pain or discomfort to the bitch is evident. This condition will resolve itself as the heat cycle proceeds and estrogen levels drop. Both breeding and whelping can usually occur naturally in spite of the presence of the soft mass of vaginal tissue.

To eliminate the passage of the genetic predisposition of vaginal hyperplasia, *ovariohysterectomy (spaying)* should be considered for affected bitches. Some surgeons recommend removal of the mass. This surgery causes much blood loss because of *estrus (heat).* Special care must also be taken to keep the urethral orifice open. Vaginal hyperplasia or prolapse can occur at subsequent heat periods even after surgical correction.

VAGINAL SMEARS:

The use of vaginal smears taken throughout a *heat cycle* can provide valuable information about ideal breeding times. While the technique is simple, the interpretation requires some experience. A sterile cotton swab is introduced into the vaginal vestibule and gently rubbed against the wall of the vagina. The swab is then rolled out on a clean glass slide and stained with any cytology stain.

Three cell types are observed: white blood cells, red blood cells, and epithelial cells. As hormone levels of *estrogen* increase, the shape of epithelial cells change. Normal epithelial cells in *anestrus* are circular with a large oval nucleus within the cell. As *proestrus* begins, the cells start to develop pointed corners. The nucleus shrinks in size, becoming darker. As the process continues, the cells become very pointed with a dark, pinpoint nucleus. This process is cell cornification. Full cornification reaches its maximum at the time the bitch stands for breeding during estrus. In *metestrus*, circular epithelial cells with large nuclei reappear and the cornified cells disintegrate.

While the epithelial cells are going through these changes, red blood cells are appearing and disappearing in the various stages of the heat cycle. White blood cells also disappear and reappear as the heat cycle progresses. The clinician observing serial smears will also note the presence or absence of cellular debris. As a rough, general rule, when the completely cornified cells make up 60% of the epithelial cell population, ovulation should occur. Emphasis is on the fact that this is a rough estimate. Using these smears in addition to the appearance of vaginal crenulation (wavy appearing vaginal lining) is the best means of pinpointing the *LH* peak. Ovulation occurs 48 hours after the LH peak.

VAGINITIS:

Vaginitis is the inflammation of the vagina characterized by discomfort. In some cases, a mucopurulent (pussy) discharge is present. Other cases are asymptomatic. *Juvenile vaginitis* is not uncommon in puppies after 10 weeks of age. They may show some increase in urinary frequency and a sticky yellow discharge. Many of these infections are rather resistant to antibiotics. However, the onset of the first *heat period* is curative.

Most vaginitis problems are due to superficial infections of the vaginal epithelium. These infections can play a role in infertility. Appropriate antibiotic therapy and in some instances, therapeutic douches are necessary to restore normal fertility.

WATER PUPPY:

Refer to *ANASARCA.*

WEANING PROCESS:

Refer to DRYING UP A LACTATING BITCH

WILMS' TUMOR:

Refer to *RENAL CANCERS.*

BIBLIOGRAPHY

CHAPTER 1

Physicians' Desk Reference, 40th Ed, Medical Economics Co, Oradell, NJ, 1986.
Short, CE, *Practical Use of the Ultrashort-acting Barbiturates,* Veterinary Learning Systems Co, Princeton Junction, NJ, 1983.
Swaim, S, *Surgery of Traumatized Skin,* WB Saunders, Philadelphia, PA, 1980.
Veterinary Pharmaceuticals and Biologicals - 1985/1986 Ed, Veterinary Medicine Publishing Co, Lenexa, KS, 1986.

CHAPTER 2

Degen, MA, Canine and Feline Immunodeficiency - Part I, *Comp on Cont Educ,* 8, May 1986, pp 314-316.
Dodds, WJ, Von Willebrand's Disease in Dogs, *MVP,* 65, Sept 1984, pp 681-686.
Hamilton, H, et al, Von Willebrand's Disease Manifested by Hemorrhage From the Reproductive Tract, *JAAHA,* 21, 1985, pp 637-641.

CHAPTER 3

Calvert, CA, Cardiomyopathy in the Doberman Pinscher Dog, *Cal Vet,* 38, Dec 1984.
Calvert, CA, Dilated Congestive Cardiomyopathy in Doberman Pinschers, *Comp on Cont Educ,* 8, May 1986, pp 417-429.
Lombard, CW, Echocardiographic and Clinical Signs of Canine Dilated Cardiomyopathy, *JSm AnPrac,* 25, Feb 1984.

CHAPTER 4

Feldman, EC, editor, Symposium on Endocrinology, *Vet Clin No Amer,* 7, 3, Aug 1977.
Peterson, ME, editor, Symposium on Endocrinology, *Vet Clin No Amer,* 14, 4, July 1984.
Rosychuk, R, Management of Hypothyroidism, in Kirk RW (ed), *Current Veterinary Therapy VIII,* WB Saunders, Philadelphia, PA 1983, pp 869-876.

CHAPTER 5

Brunner, CJ, et al, Canine Parvovirus Infection: Effects on the Immune System and Factors that Predispose to Severe Disease, *Comp on Cont Educ* 7, Dec 1985.
Crawford, MA, et al, Chronic Active Hepatitis in 26 Doberman Pinschers, *JAVMA,* 187, 12, Dec 15, 1985.
Dillon, AR, editor, Symposium on Gastroenterology, *Vet Clin No Amer,* 13, 3, Aug 1983.
Leib, MS, et al, Acute Gastric Dilatation in the Dog: Various Clinical Presentations, *Comp on Cont Educ,* 6,8, Aug 1984.
Palminteri, A, editor, Symposium on Gastrointestinal Medicine and Surgery, *Vet Clin No Amer,* 2,1, Jan 1972.

Skrentny, TT, Dog Teeth for Dog Lovers, *DPCA Educational Materials*, Set 4.

Thornburg, LP, et al, The Diagnosis and Treatment of Copper Toxicosis in Dogs, *Can Prac*, 11, 4, Sept-Oct 1984.

Thornburg, LP, et al, High Liver Copper Levels in Two Doberman Pinschers with Subacute Hepatitis, *JAAHA*, 20, Nov-Dec 1984, pp 1003-1005.

Thornburg, LP, et al, Copper Toxicosis in Dogs - Part 2, *Can Prac*, 12, 5, Sept-Oct 1985.

Twedt, DC, editor, Symposium on Liver Diseases, *Vet Clin No Amer*, 15, 1, Jan 1985.

Zawie, DA, Chronic Hepatitis in Doberman Pinschers, in Kirk RW (ed), *Current Veterinary Therapy IX*, WB Saunders, Philadelphia, PA, 1986, pp 937-938.

CHAPTER 6

Alexander, JW and Roberts, RE, editors, Symposium on Orthopedic Diseases, *Vet Clin No Amer*, 13, 1, Feb 1983.

Shores, A, Canine Cervical Vertebral Malformation/Malarticulation Syndrome, *Comp on Cont Educ*, 6, 4, Apr 1984.

Trotter, EJ, Canine Wobbler Syndrome, in Kirk RW (ed), *Current Veterinary Therapy IX*, WB Saunders, Philadelphia, PA, 1986, pp 806-809.

Watson, AD, et al, Craniomandibular Osteopathy in Doberman Pinschers, *JSm Anim Pract*, 16, 1, 1975.

CHAPTER 7

Baker, TL, et al, Diagnosis and Treatment of Narcolepsy in Animals, in Kirk RW (ed), *Current Veterinary Therapy VIII*, WB Saunders, Philadelphia, PA, 1983, pp 755-759.

Chrisman, CL, editor, Symposium on Advances in Veterinary Neurology, *Vet Clin No Amer*, 10, 1, Feb 1980.

Chrisman, CL, *Problems in Small Animal Neurology*, Lea and Febiger, Philadelphia, PA, 1982.

CHAPTER 8

Alpo Pet Center, *Canine Nutrition and Feeding Management*, Alpo Pet Center, Allentown, PA, 1984.

Lewis, LD and Morris, ML Jr, *Small Animal Clinical Nutrition*, Mark Morris Associates, Topeka, KS, 1984.

CHAPTER 9

Kirk, RW, and Bistner, S, *Handbook of Veterinary Procedures and Emergency Treatment*, WB Saunders, Philadelphia, PA, 1981.

Oehme, FW, editor, Clinical Toxicology for the Small Animal Practitioner, *Vet Clin No Amer*, 5, 4, Nov 1975.

Oehme, FW, consulting editor in Kirk RW (ed), *Current Veterinary Therapy VIII*, WB Saunders, Philadelphia, PA, 1983.

Osweiler, GD, consulting editor in Kirk RW (ed), *Current Veterinary Therapy IX*, WB Saunders, Philadelphia, PA, 1986.

CHAPTER 10

Aguirre, G, editor, Symposium on Ophthalmology, *Vet Clin No Amer*, 3, 3, September 1973.

Muller, G, et al, *Small Animal Dermatology,* WB Saunders, Philadelphia, PA, 1983.

Peiffer, RL Jr, editor, Symposium on Ophthalmology, *Vet Clin No Amer,* 10, 2, May 1980.

Stades, FC, Persistent Hyperplastic Tunica Vasculosa Lentis and Persistent Hyperplastic Primary Vitreous (PHTVL/PHPV) in 90 Closely Related Doberman Pinschers: Clinical Aspects, *JAAHA,* 16, 1980, p 739.

CHAPTER 11

Johnston, DE, editor, *Small Animal Dermatology in Practice,* Veterinary Learning Systems, Lawrenceville, NJ, 1985.

Muller, G, et al, *Small Animal Dermatology,* WB Saunders, Philadelphia, PA, 1983.

CHAPTER 12

Chew, DJ and DiBartola, SP, Familial Renal Disease in Doberman Pinscher Dogs, in Kirk RW (ed), *Current Veterinary Therapy VIII,* WB Saunders, Philadelphia, 1983, pp 975-976.

Johnson, CA, editor, Reproduction and Periparturient Care, *Vet Clin No Amer,* 16, 3, May 1986.

Jones, DE and Joshua, JO, *Reproductive Clinical Problems in the Dog,* Wright, PSG, London, 1982.

Osborne, CA and Klausner, JS, editors, Symposium on Urinary Tract Infections, *Vet Clin No Amer,* 9, 4, Nov 1979.

Osborne, CA, Canine Urolithiasis I and II, *Vet Clin No Amer,* 16, 1 and 2, Jan and Mar 1986.

Rhoades, JD, editor, Symposium on Reproductive Problems, *Vet Clin No Amer,* 7, 4, Nov 1977.

INDEX

BOLD PRINT refers to major topics and definitions.

Dear Doberman Owner,

Thank you for your interest in THE DOBERMAN OWNERS' MEDICAL MANUAL. The objective of the author and the publisher is to provide you with a helpful reference book. Your suggestions regarding its contents and ease for use would be greatly appreciated. Please include your name and address with your suggestion in order that we can include it in the acknowledgment section of the next edition.

Of particular interest to the future contents of this book are any medical situations which you may have encountered regarding Dobermans that are not found in this edition. Your contributions are very valuable. In addition to acknowledging your input, you will receive a complimentary copy of the next edition.

SUGGESTIONS:

PLEASE SEND YOUR SUGGESTIONS TO:

EDITOR—
BREED MANUAL PUBLICATIONS
3370 JACKSON DRIVE (BOX DP)
JACKSON, WI 53037

THANK YOU FOR YOUR CONTRIBUTION.

ORDER BLANK

SEND ORDER TO: **BREED MANUAL PUBLICATIONS**
3370 JACKSON DRIVE (BOX DP)
JACKSON, WI 53037

Please send me _____ copy(ies) of THE DOBERMAN OWNERS' MEDICAL MANUAL for $13.95 each plus $1.05 postage per book. (For delivery in Wisconsin add $.70 sales tax. Foreign orders add $3.00 postage per book.)

☐ Check or Money   Please charge to my ☐ MasterCard   ☐ VISA account:
   Order enclosed   CARD # _____ Exp. Date___/___

X _____
SIGNATURE (as shown on Credit Card)

NAME: _____

ADDRESS: _____

CITY: _____ STATE:_____ ZIP CODE:_____

PHONE NUMBER: AREA CODE (_____) _____

☐ THIS IS A GIFT, PLEASE SEND IT TO:

NAME: _____

ADDRESS: _____

CITY: _____ STATE:_____ ZIP CODE:_____

GIFT CARD MESSAGE: _____

FROM: _____

NUMBER OF BOOKS ORDERED......... _____ x $13.95 = $_____

WISCONSIN DELIVERY ADD
$.70 SALES TAX PER BOOK ...._____ x $ 0.70 = $_____

POSTAGE PER BOOK
(UNITED STATES & U.S. TERRITORIES) _____ x $ 1.05 = $_____

FOREIGN ORDERS ADD
$3.00 PER BOOK .... _____ x $ 3.00 = $_____

TOTAL FOR THIS ORDER $_____

THANK YOU! © BREED MANUAL PUBLICATIONS
(All orders are shipped A.S.A.P.)

Dear Doberman Owner,

   Thank you for your interest in THE DOBERMAN OWNERS' MEDICAL MANUAL. The objective of the author and the publisher is to provide you with a helpful reference book. Your suggestions regarding its contents and ease for use would be greatly appreciated. Please include your name and address with your suggestion in order that we can include it in the acknowledgment section of the next edition.

   Of particular interest to the future contents of this book are any medical situations which you may have encountered regarding Dobermans that are not found in this edition. Your contributions are very valuable. In addition to acknowledging your input, you will receive a complimentary copy of the next edition.

SUGGESTIONS:

PLEASE SEND YOUR SUGGESTIONS TO:

    EDITOR—
    BREED MANUAL PUBLICATIONS
    3370 JACKSON DRIVE (BOX DP)
    JACKSON, WI 53037

THANK YOU FOR YOUR CONTRIBUTION.

ORDER BLANK

SEND ORDER TO: **BREED MANUAL PUBLICATIONS**
3370 JACKSON DRIVE (BOX DP)
JACKSON, WI 53037

Please send me _____ copy(ies) of THE DOBERMAN OWNERS' MEDICAL MANUAL for $13.95 each plus $1.05 postage per book. (For delivery in Wisconsin add $.70 sales tax. Foreign orders add $3.00 postage per book.)

☐ Check or Money   Please charge to my ☐ MasterCard   ☐ VISA account:
    Order enclosed   CARD # _____ Exp. Date____/____

X _____
        SIGNATURE (as shown on Credit Card)

NAME: _____

ADDRESS: _____

CITY: _____ STATE:_____ ZIP CODE:_____

    PHONE NUMBER: AREA CODE (_____) _____

☐ THIS IS A GIFT, PLEASE SEND IT TO:

NAME: _____

ADDRESS: _____

CITY: _____ STATE:_____ ZIP CODE:_____

GIFT CARD MESSAGE: _____

    FROM: _____

NUMBER OF BOOKS ORDERED......... _____ x $13.95 = $_____

WISCONSIN DELIVERY ADD
  $.70 SALES TAX PER BOOK ...._____ x $ 0.70 = $_____

POSTAGE PER BOOK
  (UNITED STATES & U.S. TERRITORIES) _____ x $ 1.05 = $_____

FOREIGN ORDERS ADD
  $3.00 PER BOOK .... _____ x $ 3.00 = $_____

                  TOTAL FOR THIS ORDER $_____

THANK YOU! © BREED MANUAL PUBLICATIONS
(All orders are shipped A.S.A.P.)